The Citizen and the Administrator in a Developing Democracy

An empirical study in Delhi State, India, 1964
A study completed under the auspices of
The Indian Institute of Public Administration, New Delhi

SAMUEL J. ELDERSVELD, *The University of Michigan, Ann Arbor*

V. JAGANNADHAM, *The Indian Institute of Public Administration, New Delhi*

A. P. BARNABAS, *The Indian Institute of Public Administration, New Delhi*

Scott, Foresman and Company

To V. K. N. Menon

Library of Congress Catalog Card No. 67-19691
Copyright © 1968 Scott, Foresman and Company
Glenview, Illinois 60025
All rights reserved
Printed in the United States of America
Regional offices of Scott, Foresman and Company are
located in Atlanta, Dallas, Glenview, Palo Alto, and
Oakland, N.J.

Foreword

In January 1950, India launched upon its career as a free democratic republic. One of the features of the Indian democracy is the exercise of adult franchise by millions of people who are relatively new to representative government and who do not have the benefit of a high level of literacy. More than a decade of experience of the working of Indian democracy in the above context makes a fascinating study.

Secondly, India is committed to achieve a rapid rate of development through democratic process with the initiative and enterprise of administration at different levels. Students of Political Science and Administration are naturally attracted to a study of the citizen-administrator relationships and interactions in a developing democracy like India to observe and verify the conventional hypotheses about democracy in the older democratic countries and also to examine the adaptation of democratic institutions and procedures to the developmental needs and requirements.

The immediate impetus to this study was provided by a similar study in Detroit, U. S. A., by Janowitz and his team. Professor S. J. Eldersveld of the University of Michigan, who was impressed by the above study called "Public Administration and the Public—Perspectives Toward Government in a Metropolitan Community," suggested to Professor V. K. N. Menon, the then Director of The Indian Institute of Public Administration, to undertake a similar study on a pilot basis in and around Delhi. Professor Menon took the initiative to secure financial aid for the project and persuaded Professor Eldersveld to undertake the study on a scientific sample survey basis. With him were associated Professor V. Jagannadham and Dr. A. P. Barnabas as coauthors. Professor R. D. Singh also participated in the study in the early stages of its formulation. The Institute is grateful to the authors of the study. The Institute is also happy to note that the study has provided an opportunity for employing and training its alumni, Sarvashri: Subhas C. Mehta, T. S. Shahi, T. Venkaiah, M. V. Narayana Murthy, Kumari Shanta Kohli, B. B. Kumar, S. Satyamurthi, and Mrs. Mehta. The authors and the investigating staff have worked as a team and prepared questionnaires both in English and Hindi and carried out the survey notwithstanding many inconveniences and discomforts.

This is a pilot study of the mutual images of citizens and administrators in a developing democracy. I hope that the publication of this study by Scott, Foresman in the United States and by our Institute in India will encourage further studies of a similar nature in other parts of India and in other developing countries so as to extend the frontiers of knowledge about the working of democracy and democratic administration processes in the developing countries.

J. N. Khosla, Director
The Indian Institute of Public Administration
New Delhi
March 1967

Preface

This study is in a sense an implementation of a research interest articulated at The Indian Institute of Public Administration several years ago. It was strongly supported by Indian government officials who serve in an advisory capacity to the Institute.

The attitudes of Indian citizens toward the officials and agencies of their government—national, state, and local—have been the subject of much speculation for years. The press, public administration scholars, and governmental officials, to say nothing of the citizens themselves, have discussed and debated at length the performance of government as measured by objective criteria or by the evidence, unsystematically collected, of the level of public approval and cooperation. In August 1961 an annual conference was held under the auspices of The Indian Institute of Public Administration, on the subject of "Administration and the Citizen." Mr. V. T. Krishnamachari, Chairman of the Institute's Executive Council, in opening the session emphasized the concepts of "active citizenship" and "self-help" on which he felt the success of Indian administrative relationships with the citizen rested. He then stated: "The Institute should study this subject in great detail in the coming year and make arrangements to publish the results of its studies so that they might be of practical value to the Central and State Governments."[1] Under the encouragement of Professor V. K. N. Menon, until recently Director of the Institute, and Dr. J. N. Khosla, the present Director, and with the continuous support and aid of Dr. Howard K. Hyde, Chief Management Advisor of the USAID, as well as top officials in the Indian Government, notably Mr. L. P. Singh, Special Secretary in the Ministry of Home Affairs, the Institute pressed ahead in January 1964 with the study. This is the first major report of the findings of that study. It is a study which seeks to generalize the public perspectives and attitudes toward government and administration in the urban and rural sections of Delhi State on the basis of scientifically selected samples of the population and administrators, and on the basis of interviews personally conducted in the field. We hope the results as presented here will have both theoretical value and practical utility.

We are grateful for the support which we received from the Indian government, particularly from the major officials in the five agencies on which our investigation focused. The financial assistance received from USAID was indeed critical. And we cannot forget the host of administrators and village leaders who believed in the value of our work and took innumerable pains to see that it would succeed. Finally, the loyal research assistants and interviewers at The Indian Institute of Public Administration and The Indian Institute of Public Opinion, who worked indefatigably in the face of a demanding operational schedule, were indispensable to this achievement. We only hope that our results will eventually justify this confidence and support.

---

[1]See the report, "Administration and the Citizen," The Indian Institute of Public Administration, p. 4.

Samuel J. Eldersveld
V. Jagannadham
A. P. Barnabas

Contents

The citizen
and the administrator
in India:
Theoretical concerns

chapter 1

The achievement of social and political change in developing societies like India is heavily dependent on the qualitative performance
of the administrative system. "Administration" is a set of critical
structures and processes serving as intermediaries between citizens
and leaders, between consumer-producers and planners. In this
dual capacity, administration is involved, in one sense, with the utilization, management, allocation, and development of human and
material resources. However, it is not only involved with the satisfaction of material needs. It will not succeed unless it modifies public
attitudes and beliefs, and redirects public and official behavior.

In modern, developed societies today we are more than ever
inclined to emphasize the importance and complexity of the roles of
administrators. In developing societies these roles are preëminent,
particularly in societies dedicated to massive programs of social
innovation. In such developing societies the communication of
welfare-state goals, the education of the populace, the mobilization
of citizen support, and the translation of this support into new
patterns of action make administrative structures and personnel
centrally important. The roles of others, such as the politician, the
intellectual, the entrepreneur, are important, but the administrator

is a vital cog in the achievement of social planning. Public servants in the new, developing society must adapt to new, challenging responsibilities. A basic requirement for them is "commitment" — to the larger goals of the welfare society, to the norms of the new bureaucracy, to the function of administration as the agent of change. Above all, whatever the "democratic" orientations of the new system, the new bureaucrats need to be identified, recognized, and supported as the "public's administrators."

The growing technicalities and complexities in the administrative organization of modernized societies stagger the imagination. In a developing society, administration is equally complex and perhaps more demanding because of the rapid movement from colonial traditions to modern demands and pressures. It is so also because of the scarcity of resources and the necessity for administrators to husband these resources while pointing toward egalitarian objectives. It is so, finally, because of the great and inevitable gulf between the social status and cultural orientations of the governors and the governed in a developing society. The problem of administration in the developing society is to accommodate the past with the modern present, to economize resources in the face of mounting and cumulating crises, and to elicit intelligent and meaningful cooperation from a public thus far ignorant and indifferent in its orientations towards the distant government. This is the central, bewildering problem of administration in India. It is the problem which, in a limited and exploratory fashion, this study seeks to analyze.

Concepts and criteria for effective and democratic administration: some excerpts from the literature

In the twentieth century an impressive and constantly increasing body of literature has concentrated attention on the problems of administration in modern and developing nation-states.[1] There has been, however, much less empirical study of the problems posed in this literature. Theories have been advanced and models of the administrative process have been formulated. The absence of reliable data, however, leads to confusion if not skepticism on the part of governmental leaders, who hope for pragmatic insights, and on the part of social scientists, who seriously search for answers to significant theoretical questions about the administrative process.

The relationship between administrators and citizens has proved

---

[1] For one review of this literature see Ferrel Heady, *Public Administration: A Comparative Perspective* (Englewood Cliffs, N.J.: Prentice-Hall, 1966).

particularly intriguing and crucial to many theorists. This is so particularly in Western societies because of the assumption that the nature and quality of citizen-administrative interactions vitally affect the pattern and prospects for the achievement of democracy. One may well argue the importance and relevance of democratic criteria for evaluating administrative performance in a developing society. Nevertheless, in a country like India, democratic perspectives are important, because of the assumption that the achievement of developmental goals hinges in large part on the extent to which public involvement and cooperation can be mobilized by the bureaucracy.

In some of the recent literature the emphasis is on the subtlety of the relationship between citizen and official. The nineteenth century conflict between the state and the citizen as stated in simplistic theory is no longer perceived as exclusively important, if important at all, primarily because it is an obscurantist formulation. The relationship is not clearly conflictual nor dichotomous: all citizens versus all officials. As one student has put it: "The central administration is not isolated from the community, but entangled in it everywhere, in office hours and out of them." A gradient of relationships exists, from elite bureaucrats to secondary officers and divisional heads, to that administrative cadre most closely in day-to-day contact with the citizenry. And the public in turn is not one "mass," but is also distinguishable in terms of differential patterns of social status and administrative contact, ranging from those who are frequent clients of administrative agencies to those who are completely isolated from the administrative process. It is this image of the citizen-administrative subsystem of the society which must be borne in mind in any study of the functioning of bureaucracy in modern societies.

Underlying the concern for a democratic or effective public administration is, first, a belief that public administration must be based on public consent or support. The actions of public agencies and officials should reflect the aspirations, interests, demands, and support potential of the public it serves and directs. Official action should be responsible as well as rational, and, above all, must command the respect and cooperation of citizens. Second is the concept of administration as a "circular process," from the initial formulation of policy, to its implementation, to the modification of policy subsequent to its evaluation in the process of implementation, including feedback from the public at various steps in this process. This is a continuous, dynamic set of interactions. It conceives of citizens in a double role, as producers and consumers of goods and services, or as policymakers and subjects. From both analytical and value premises, therefore, has come the emphasis on democratic responsiveness by officials and responsible citizen involvement as preconditions for an effective administrative process in the modern polity.

But what specific conditions or criteria for the achievement of a democratic and functional set of relationships in administration can one specify? Professor William A. Robson, who is read by many in India, has said much on this subject. He suggests the following bureaucratic maladies as relevant: "an excessive sense of self-importance on the part of officials"; "an indifference towards the feeling or the convenience of individual citizens"; "an obsession with the binding and inflexible authority of departmental decisions, precedents, arrangements or forms"; "an inability to consider the government as a whole"; "a failure to recognize the relations between the governors and the governed as an essential part of the democratic process."[2] On the other hand, he emphasizes the role of the citizen:

> The achievement of good relations between the government and the public is a matter which does not by any means depend solely on the conduct of civil servants and politicians. It depends equally on the attitude of citizens, groups, corporations, associations of all kinds and indeed of all unofficial bodies to public authorities. If we want public servants to behave well towards us, we must behave well towards them. Moreover, we must normally assume that they for their part will behave well . . . . If politicians and civil servants are held in low esteem, if their work is derided, if abuse and invective is poured on them continuously, if loose and unsubstantial allegations are made about their incompetence, dishonesty, laziness and indifference to the public interest, it is unlikely that officials will develop or display qualities of integrity, industry and public spirit.

The Report of the Committee on the Training of Civil Servants has also commented on those faults which impede a democratic pattern of administration: "The faults most frequently enumerated are over-devotion to precedent, remoteness from the rest of the community, inaccessibility and faulty handling of the general public, lack of initiative and imagination, ineffective organization and

---

[2]*The Civil Service in Britain and France*, ed. William A. Robson (London: The Hogarth Press, 1956), p. 13.

waste of manpower, procrastination and unwillingness to take responsibility or to give decisions." These tendencies, if true, lead to expectations concerning the mental image which the common man has of the bureaucrat. C. R. Hensman has summarized these aptly:

> He is at various times: — a) a perverse God who must be propitiated; b) a recalcitrant ass that must be driven; c) a privileged snob, impossible to get the better of; d) a lazy hound, impossible to bring to book; and e) (occasionally) a hard-worked, underpaid and harassed officer doing his best under difficult circumstances. This last is likely to be a judgment by, and of, upperclass layers and no doubt often coincides with the self-image of the high ranking public servant.[3]

The best attempt to conceptualize the citizen-administrator relationship in democratic terms was probably that of Morris Janowitz, in his unique empirical study in 1958 of public attitudes toward administration in Detroit, Michigan. Janowitz was primarily concerned with the democratic components of the citizen's relationships to the bureaucracy. "A bureaucracy is in imbalance," he says, "when it fails to operate on the basis of democratic consent. . . . Bureaucratic imbalance may be either *despotic* or *subservient*. *Despotic* implies that the bureaucracy is too much the master while *subservient* implies that it is too much the servant." He then proceeds to specify four types of requirements for the achievement of a democratic balance:

> 1. Knowledge. The public must have an adequate level of knowledge about the operations of the public bureaucracy. . . .
> 2. Self-interest. The public must consider that its self-interest is being served by the public bureaucracy. As a check on the disruptive consequences of self-interested demands on the bureaucracy, the public must be aware simultaneously of the bureaucracy's capacity to act as a neutral and impartial agent in resolving social conflicts.
> 3. Principle-mindedness. The public must be of the general opinion that the public bureaucracy is guided in its actions by a set of principles guaranteeing equal and impersonal treatment. Administrative routines, however, must be sufficiently

---

[3]C. R. Hensman, "The Public Servant—A Self-Portrait and a Self-Criticism," *Community*, No. 3, (1963), p. 44.

flexible to cope with individual differences in order to insure adequate dealings with clients.

4. Prestige. Public perspectives toward the public bureaucracy must include adequate prestige value toward public employment as compared with other types of careers. Very low and very high prestige values would interfere with the bureaucracy's ability to operate on the basis of democratic consent.[4]

These operationalizations were heavily relied upon in our study of citizen-administrative relationships in India.

The focus for analysis

These are but a few of many attempts to identify the critical requirements for the development and maintenance of a democratic and effective pattern of relationships between the citizen and the official. These formulations are concerned with attitudes, perceptions, and/or evaluations which relate to both the citizen and the official. Thus, the content of the administrator's *self-image* is involved, as well as *his* image of the public; on the other hand, the content of the citizen's image of *his* own place in the system is involved, as well as *his* image of the administrator, the agency, and its programs and procedures. Implicit in any complete analysis, therefore, is a comparison of at least two different levels — a comparison of the official's view of his own performance and role with the public's view of that performance and role; and a comparison of the official's view of the public's role with the public's view or orientation toward that role. An additional type of comparison is also useful — the administrator's *predictions* of what the content of public perspectives toward administrators is compared to the *actual* content of the public's perspectives. Since the behavior of leaders and citizens in any society is based on expectations, understandings, or predictions of the attitudes and behavior of other actors in the system, this type of analysis may be vital. It may lead us to clues about the premises, perhaps empirically unsubstantiated, on which actions of both administrators and citizens rest.

In any analysis where both the administrator and the citizen are the objects of observation and interview, we are basically concerned, then, with the need for different types of data and analysis. First, we need a *description* of the content of public and official attitudes or perspectives toward the administrative process. Second, we need

---

[4]Morris Janowitz, Deil Wright, and William Delany, *Public Administration and the Public: Perspectives Toward Government in a Metropolitan Community* (Ann Arbor, Michigan: Institute of Public Administration, University of Michigan, 1958), pp. 6–8.

an *explanation* of the differential attitude patterns for subpopulations in terms of independent variables such as social status, group identifications, geographical residence, political affiliation, or psychological predispositions. Third, we must be interested also in the extent of *congruence* or difference in the perceptions, attitudes, and orientations of officials, on the one hand, and citizens, on the other. Fourth, if the function of the bureaucracy is to be properly examined, we must examine the nature of communicative and contact patterns between officials and citizens, with the particular goal of determining the relevance of bureaucratic contact for citizen perceptions, attitudes, and orientations. The problem posed particularly in a developing society is that of analyzing how administrative action is and can be translated into citizen action functional to developmental goals.

The historical and contemporary context: Indian bureaucracy in transition

In adapting the concerns of various writers on the subject to the Indian context, we were preoccupied with several primary convictions. It is important to remember that the theory and practice of the Indian administrative system is still to a certain extent a blend of the steel frame of the British administrative system and the concepts and directions of the indigenous system established since Independence. The formalism, impersonality, and deferential character of the old regime, its emphasis on security and lack of bureaucratic initiative, have naturally left an imprint, a legacy, with which the new leaders of India have had to cope in establishing and motivating a development bureaucracy. In contrast to the British period, certain key values in the post-Independence theory of administration are crucial to bear in mind. First, within the framework of central direction from Delhi, it was based on the theory of considerable decentralization of structure and function, with much autonomy and initiative vested in the states and local units of government. Second, it was welfare-state oriented, with the explicit goals of egalitarianism in role and services replacing older colonial and capitalistic norms. Third, administrative structure and practices were viewed as functional to the vital objective of integrative nation-building, involving both communication of administrators with the most isolated sectors of the society and the development of a commitment and identification by both administrators and citizens to the broad goals of the total society. Finally, it emphasized a public not parasitic in its relationship to the administrative system, but participant, a public which accepted duties as well as made demands, a public confident in the administrative hierarchy and motivated to share in the responsibilities of development.

The transformation of the old bureaucracy into a new order has not been simple. Administrators do not change their backgrounds, normative orientations, or behavioral practices overnight. Nor can the public be expected to understand the system and adapt to it quickly. Penetration of the new ethic is a slow process, especially in a democratic society in which indecision, deliberation, debate, and conflict attended the movement towards new structures and new norms. It is a credit to India that the pace of political and social progress since Independence has been so great despite the strains and tensions of releasing a nation from the administrative influence of the former occupying power.

The key problem in India is the training, socializing, and directing of a cadre of administrators who can and will adapt to public needs and sensitivities. Although this is so for all branches of public administration, it is particularly vital for the Community Development program. Reinhard Bendix has described the problem and context well:

> The Community Development Movement of the Indian Government is an attempt to bridge the gap between the ruling elite and the masses of the Indian people. . . . At the level of the village the development officials have the delicate task of enlisting cooperation with projects of whose soundness and desirability the villagers must first be convinced. To do this officials must strike a balance between making suggestions and listening to demands, taking advantage of modern knowledge but also adapting it to the local situation.[5]

Bureaucratic impersonality, compulsive professionalism, and rigidity must give way to pragmatism, populism, and perhaps even personalism if the system is to succeed.

At the Administrative Reforms Conference held at The Indian Institute of Public Administration in August 1963, the term "cutting edge" was used to refer to "the level at which a counter clerk deals with a common citizen in a public office." In reviewing the state of Indian public administration it was contended that "under cover of hierarchy, decentralization, and delegation, the task of administration at the level of its 'cutting edge' comes to be dealt with by low

---

[5]Reinhard Bendix, "Public Authority in a Developing Political Community: The Case of India," *Archives Européennes de Sociologie*, No. 1, IV (1963), 61–63.

level functionaries, ill-equipped and ill-trained for the point of physical contact between the administration and the citizen . . . as one descends down the hierarchial ladder, generally speaking, competence decreases, there is less resilience in administration, less wisdom in using judgment or discretion within the law or regulation, more rigidity, and a tendency to be 'authoritative.'" The working paper of the Conference posed the key question: "What then are the principal lines along which administrative reform . . . should be pursued so as to make the cutting edge of administration more efficient, more resilient and more responsive to the common citizen whom it seeks to serve?" Both as an indictment and as a conception of the problem of administration in India today, this statement sets the stage for our empirical study of the citizen and the bureaucrat in Delhi State.

Our theory and objectives

Certain critical, system relevant, theoretical concerns motivated our research. In a general sense we were preoccupied with communication patterns between the elite sector and the citizen mass. These patterns can be conceived of as instrumental to the elite in achieving its support-mobilization objectives, its recruitment of personnel, and its aims for the maintenance and development of consensus, or its transformation. The intelligence function of such interactions cannot be understated — the elite needs constant contact with and evaluation of the ever-changing content of citizen demands. Only then can it determine the cooperation and the alienation potentials of significant sectors of society. From the viewpoint of the citizen, such communicative relationships can resolve his doubts about elite objectives and motivate him to share in government programs.

In a developing society like India elite-citizen contacts and interactions are more than ordinarily significant. First, of course, are the post-Independence aims of national integration and unity, explicitly recognized in the Constitution as major goals, which today, eighteen years after Independence, seem far from achievement. This is not merely because of linguistic or geographic provincialism. It is a question of the identification of the rural peasant and urban resident with larger social collectives than the immediate village or caste or religious group in which he is born and lives. It is also a matter of the extensiveness of the average citizen's knowledge of, and commitment to, the goals of the larger society and political order.

A second problem in a developing society like India is that of the involvement of the citizen with the developing, more modern, social and political institutions and secondary, or intermediary associations in the society. As the traditional associations are modified and adapted to the processes of modernization, the question is whether the ordinary peasant or urban resident will perceive these institutions as meaningful agencies for action, or will see them as alien and ineffectual for him. A new development bureaucracy, a new party system, new interest groups come into existence, while old caste and religious associations are changed, wittingly or unwittingly, to conform to the requirements for organized action in the new order. For the ordinary citizen, still illiterate and clinging to the traditional forms, involvement in these new or modified forms of social and political action is necessary if the new elite is not to become hopelessly distant from the old society. Under what conditions does he come to trust this new bureaucracy, this new party system, these new agencies for action? How does he arrive at cognition of these agencies as useful avenues for political action, as agencies through which he can communicate with, support, or take reprisal action against the elite—how utilize such institutions for legitimate political-action objectives? The process by which those committed to the traditional order come to accept and participate in these westernized and secular institutions for action is critical for the development of a country like India.

A third problem concerns the citizen's involvement in economic and social development programs. The extent of his participation is not only critical for the immediate aims of these programs, it is also highly relevant for the development of a modern, truly national, state. Such participation in economic and social planning is essentially again a matter of good communication, in the broadest sense. It requires a citizenry which is informed about these goals, supports them, has social and economic aspirations and perspectives which mesh with such goals and which are realistically achievement oriented, and, finally, has aspirations which, as the result of contacts with the elite, or despite such contacts, result in certain specific citizen actions which are congruent with and do indeed implement developmental goals. The requirement, then, is an aspiration pattern and action pattern which is utilitarian, pragmatic, and consistent with elite aspirations and actions. If in India today certain programs, such as that of agricultural production, fail, it may be traceable in part to a failure of the elite to commit the peasantry to action through the party system, through caste leadership, through more modernized interest groups, or through bureaucratic contacts with the public.

The study of the administrative-citizen relationship in India today must bear in mind these contextual theoretical and historical conditions. Above all, the special field conditions within which the Indian administrator works cannot be ignored. Cognizant of such conditions and working with this theoretical perspective, in the research reported here we concentrated on specific dimensions of official and citizen behavior and orientation relevant to the Indian context. We asked repeatedly two types of questions:

1. What evidence is there that citizens and officials perceive, understand, and accept the norms of the new administration; what conditions and factors impede the acceptance of these new norms, and in what subpopulations; in what respects are there incompatible images of the administrative process, incompatibilities which signify the breakdown in the communication process and which may lead to dissent, if not alienation?

2. What is the evidence that a *participant* orientation toward the administrative process has developed in India on the part of both officials and citizens; is there a movement in the direction of citizen confidence in the system which is translated into realistic achievement perspectives, public cooperation with the new bureaucracy, and positive action leading to social and economic change?

These two leading questions focus attention on two problems and needs. One basic need in India is for unity, integration, *consensus*; the second basic need in India is for *achievement*. The two needs are intertwined. Is the new "development bureaucracy" one which the Indian citizen accepts or rejects or is indifferent to; and, if he accepts it, is it a bureaucracy which he can and will work with or one which he merely tolerates?

The major components of the citizen-bureaucrat relationship on which we focused in our study were similar to those identified by others. We applied them specifically to the Indian setting. Our theory specified the following prerequisites for an effective, functional, and democratic administrative system in India:

— adequate citizen and official knowledge of administrative norms, practices, and structure;
— genuine support for the goals, policies, and programs of the government;

—positive evaluations of the job performance of governmental officials;

—perceptions of the administrative system as sensitive and responsive to the public, rather than inflexible and remote;

—belief in the integrity and honesty of the administrative cadre, rather than a tendency to view it as corrupt or corruptible;

—a high prestige status for public employment;

—perception of administrators as committed to egalitarian goals and practices, rather than to favoritism or political advantage;

—feelings of efficacy and optimism about citizen action in the political system generally, and in the administrative subsystem particularly;

—motivational orientations emphasizing cooperative action with administrative officials in the implementation of developmental goals.

These theoretical concerns indicate the range of our research perspectives. They apply, though in different ways, to the administrative cadre as well as to the citizen public. We are convinced that these areas must be the major focus of any study of citizen-administrative relationships in India. Although all are, in our opinion, relevant elements of the problem, we are inclined to feel that the emergence of a functional and democratic system of relationships in India is probably highly contingent on the spread of greater knowledge of administrative structure and norms, on the mobilization of support for developmental programs, on convictions that the bureaucracy is egalitarian, accountable and sensitive to public interests and on feelings of citizen competence, confidence, and optimism. But certainly, prestige perceptions, positive public evaluations of job performance by officials, and officials perceived as principle-minded are theoretically significant, and possibly crucial.

Since this is an exploratory analysis, we intend to examine and describe these components of public and administrative behavior. After description, we were interested in looking at the factors which might explain the differential patterns of their incidence.

Many factors in the Indian society, as in any society, have to be examined if one is to understand elite and public behavior. In this study we have focused on the phenomena of public knowledge and support of the Indian administrative system, narrowly conceived, and the "expansion of the polity," democratic integration, and the public's role in social and economic development, broadly conceived. A complex set of social and individual forces converge to facilitate or obstruct such specific or general societal goals. We have attempted to isolate such factors as social status, conditions of village life, and exposure to mass communication. In addition, we have looked at individual orientations toward authority, toward administrators and the political system, and toward the modernization process itself. But, above all, we have attempted to investigate carefully the relevance and impact of bureaucratic structures and personnel — their social characteristics, internal training and socialization processes, and their contacts with the public — for the achievement of administrative support by the public. Hopefully, then, we will secure evidence related to the larger theoretical concerns of political and socioeconomic development. These relationships are set forth in the accompanying diagram.

The public, as well as the new bureaucrats, in the developing Indian society, as the diagram suggests, is in a conflict-laden, transitional, crisis period. On one hand, certain social conditions predispose it to individual political orientations which theoretically could induce either apathy and isolation, or involvement and participation. These social preconditions also may have limiting effects on the contacts citizens have with political and administrative officials. On the other hand, a counterpressure is supplied by the perspectives and actions of the new bureaucrats, dependent in turn on the structural, social, and psychological stimuli acting on these officials. The effects of these stimuli on administrators will vary considerably, some being socialized to democratic job perspectives, others reflecting bureaucratic perspectives. Citizen contacts with administrators will also vary in frequency and content, according to citizen opportunities and interest, as well as the varying job perspectives of administrators and the action commitments of their agencies. The basic test, then, for political development in our research is the relative strength and direction of the societal environmental factors and individual predispositions, on one hand, and the stimulus resulting from bureaucratic contacts, on the other hand. Our theory suggests that administrative contacts can move the public toward greater knowledge of the system, greater optimism about the public's role in the system, greater attitudinal support for the system, and greater cooperation with the goals of the system. This depends, however, on the strength and nonfacilitative nature of the traditional social and individual orientations as well as the extent and nature of their bureaucratic contacts.

In a very real sense in our study we are concerned with the "stages in the modernization process" as manifested at one point in time. We are studying citizens and bureaucrats with different caste

Framework for our analysis: Major variables and critical relationships

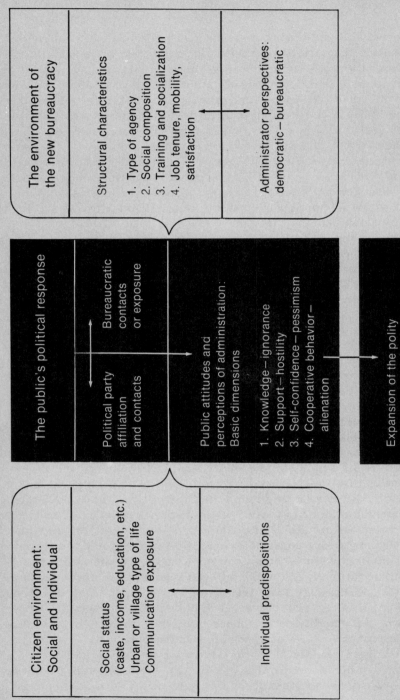

The environment of
the new bureaucracy

Structural characteristics

1. Type of agency
2. Social composition
3. Training and socialization
4. Job tenure, mobility,
   satisfaction

Administrator perspectives:
democratic – bureaucratic

The public's political response

Bureaucratic
contacts
or exposure

Political party
affiliation
and contacts

Public attitudes and
perceptions of administration:
Basic dimensions

1. Knowledge – ignorance
2. Support – hostility
3. Self-confidence – pessimism
4. Cooperative behavior –
   alienation

Expansion of the polity
Democratic integration
Social and economic change

Citizen environment:
Social and individual

Social status
(caste, income, education, etc.)
Urban or village type of life
Communication exposure

Individual predispositions

statuses, economic position, educational levels, and individual orientations, living in different types of urban areas and villages, villages which are both geographically and traditionally isolated as well as villages which are modernizing. These citizens are exposed in varying degrees to mass media, political communications, and administrative contacts. Thus the citizens in our study are arranged along one traditional-modernism continuum; our bureaucrats are arranged along another. The major question is: Does the interaction of the two change the position of the individual on the continuum, in functional terms, toward more involvement or less, toward democratic commitments or away from them, toward support for the system or alienation, toward new or old forms of social, economic, and political behavior? One central question which confronts a developing society like India is: Can and does the bureaucracy facilitate the achievement of developmental goals and aspirations?

The sample design

The data for this exploratory study were obtained in a series of interviews with citizens and administrators in Delhi State from January to May 1964. Delhi State, according to the last census, had a population of 2,659,000, of which almost 300,000 were found in the 256 villages in the state. We drew a random probability sample of 400 adults from the rural area and a second sample of 400 from the urban area. In constructing our rural sample we stratified the villages by population size and by objective measures of their degree of traditionalism or modernization. We selected eight villages from the strata so devised, in which we did our interviewing.[6] The objectives of the study were defined by the project staff of the IIPA, the questionnaire was prepared and pretested by the staff and research assistants of the IIPA, and the final interviewing was done jointly by these research assistants and the field staff of The Indian Institute of Public Opinion. In designing our questionnaire we relied heavily on the only other similar study, that completed by Morris Janowitz in the Detroit area in 1954. Many of our questions were adapted from his schedule. In addition to interviewing a cross section of adults, we drew a sample of about 220 administrators from the five basic agencies or departments in the area on which we concentrated most of our attention. These five agencies were: Health, Police, Postal, Community Development (CD), and the Delhi Transport Undertaking (DTU). The administrators we inter-

---

[6]See the Appendix for a more detailed description of the sample selection process, the questionnaires, and the indices used.

viewed were presumably in fairly close and constant interaction with the public — village level workers (VLW), Panchayat secretaries, block development officers, constables, postal workers, bus inspectors, doctors, and compounders. This permitted us to study administrative contacts with the public from both the viewpoint of the administrator and the citizen. It must be emphasized that this was a demonstration or pilot project. Its findings are strictly applicable only to Delhi State. It is hoped that with modification it can be used to study the same problem in other regions of India.

Public perceptions
and evaluations of
the administrative system:
Basic patterns

 chapter **2**

In a developing society one might well expect that the prerequisites for effective administrative relationships with the public would be only minimally met. The public's limited experience with the new development bureaucracy, the brief opportunity for the new agencies to establish contact with the public and to demonstrate their utility would suggest limited public knowledge of administration, partial penetration, and marginal commitment. In this chapter we seek to explore the general pattern of public perspectives about Indian public administration. After presenting this overall survey we will analyze more specifically the factors related to public attitudes, and the role of administrative behavior in inducing these attitudes.

Evaluations of governmental performance

The Indian public's estimate of the job being done at various governmental levels reveals a considerable range in approval for different types of officials. If one looks at the proportions of our sample populations who feel that governmental officials are doing a poor job, one notices that rural adults seem relatively more satisfied than the residents of the city of Delhi. Thus 15% of the rural sample felt

that village officials were doing a poor job, while 36% of the urban
sample felt that the Municipal Corporation officials were performing poorly (Table 2.1). Again, 12% of rural adults were dissatisfied
with the central government's record while 21% of urban adults
considered its performance to be poor. With 20% or less of the
public being ordinarily dissatisfied (with the exception of the
evaluation of the Delhi Municipal Corporation), one cannot claim
that the public is unduly disillusioned. This does not mean that they
are extremely enthusiastic, since less than 6% considered the performance at any governmental level as "very good." Rather there is
a grudging agreement by the vast majority of the public that their
government is middling, tolerable, and reasonably satisfactory.

Greater variations can be found in the reactions to the job performance of individual agencies (Table 2.2). Only 5% to 6% feel the
postal service is poor. About 20% are overtly critical of health and
Community Development agencies. But, in urban Delhi particularly,
there is greater disapproval of the police and the Delhi Transport
Undertaking. Over 35% of the urban adults feel the police are doing
a poor job, while 47% are dissatisfied with the bus service provided
by DTU.

A comparison of these levels of approval-disapproval with the
1954 study in Detroit suggests higher proportions of rejection or
dissatisfaction in India (Table 2.3). At both the state and municipal
levels the performance of officials is criticized more frequently by
the Delhi sample than in Detroit. Public transportation, interesting-
ly enough, evokes the greatest criticism in both studies. For all

2·1 General evaluations of governmental performance

*What do you think of the job the governmental officials are doing in village, state,
and the central government?*

	Poor job	Fair job	Good job	Very good job	Don't know
Village officials	15%	12%	63%	4%	7%
Delhi Corporation officials	36	22	25	1	16
Delhi State officials					
Rural sample	12	7	46	3	32
Urban sample	23	27	23	1	27
Central government officials					
Rural sample	12	8	51	4	24
Urban sample	21	26	34	3	17
Block officials	17	12	53	6	13

2•2   Comparative levels of public disapproval of certain administrative agencies

	"dissatisfied," "disapprove," or "doing a poor job"
POSTAL	
Urban sample	6%
Rural sample	6
HEALTH	
Urban sample	19
Rural sample	21
COMMUNITY DEVELOPMENT	
Rural sample	20
POLICE	
Urban sample	36
Rural sample	24
DELHI TRANSPORT UNDERTAKING	
Urban sample	47

agencies and levels, then, the range of criticism and the amount of dissatisfaction is greater in Delhi — as low as 6% dissatisfaction with postal officials and mounting to 47% who were dissatisfied with bus services. It is significant in this connection to note comparative results also on another question: "In general, would you say that your dealings with public employees were — poor, fair, good, or very good?" In Detroit 28% of the sample said their relationships were

2•3   Comparisons of extent of public dissatisfaction with administrative agencies or officials — Detroit and Delhi

	1954 Detroit	1964 Delhi
Municipal officials — "doing a poor job"	6%	36%
State officials — "doing a poor job"	4	23
Police — "doing a poor job"	6	36
Municipal transportation*		
— critical and dissatisfied	24	48

*For comparative purposes, these percentages are based on those who had contact with or used transportation facilities.

"poor" or only "fair"; in Delhi 60% responded the same way (Table 2.4).[1] Our Indian urban sample, thus, is more critical of officials and agencies as well as more aware that their own relationships with officials are relatively poor. Yet, in both urban and rural Indian samples less than 20% feel their dealings with governmental employees are "poor." There is no evidence here of widespread and majority discontent.

Evaluations of the worth of governmental activity

The worthwhileness of governmental activities, an important dimension of citizen relationships with the government in a democracy, is clearly endorsed by Indian citizens (Table 2.5). When asked if they feel that health services should be provided by the government, only a small fragment of less than 3% dissent. Although a larger proportion have uncertainties about the Community Development program (22% are not sure or have no opinion), 67% are convinced of the worthwhileness of this program. And as Table 2.6 indicates, only 12% of the rural population oppose the Community Development program. Not only do individuals when queried about their own degree of support for these programs indicate overwhelming approval of them, but they also sense that the majority of people do not stand in opposition.

Another measure of evaluations of the worthwhileness of governmental activity concerns attitudes towards taxes. When we asked

2•4 General perception by public of relations with governmental employees

In general, would you say that your dealings with public employees are poor, fair, good, or very good?

| | DELHI STATE, 1964 | | DETROIT AREA, 1954 |
	Urban	Rural	
Poor	19%	16%	6%
Fair	41	16	22
Good	24	57	48
Very good	3	3	17
Don't know	13	9	7

[1] For the Indian rural sample the comparable percentage was 32%.

2·5 Public acceptance of the worthwhileness of health and Community Development programs

Do you think it is necessary for the government to provide these health services?

	Rural	Urban
Yes	96%	91%
No	1	3
No opinion	4	6

Do you think the Community Development program is worth while or do you think the government should stop this program?

Is worth while	67%
Should be stopped	8
Uncertain, no opinion	22
Not ascertained	2

2·6 Public awareness of opposition or support for Community Development (rural sample)

Who are the people here who are opposed to Community Development? And who are the people in favor of it?

No one is opposed	47%
Many are opposed	4
Some, or a few, are opposed	8
Don't know if there is opposition	41

our respondents how they felt about paying taxes, we found 39% of the rural sample and 48% of the urban sample responding that they were paying more taxes than they should. On the identical question in the Detroit study 41% felt that taxes were too high. Another similar question was asked seeking to probe evaluations concerning the relative balance between "what the government gives the public" and "what the government gets back from the public." Of our urban respondents 53% and of our rural respondents 39% felt the government got back from the public more than it gave. These findings indicate that while government programs are generally accepted as worthwhile, large numbers of respondents feel taxes are too high, and fail to see sufficiently tangible results from governmental programs for themselves to warrant the taxes they paid. For

many there is obviously no close link between the worth of governmental programs and services, and personal taxes.

Public knowledge of governmental programs

Although these findings concerning the levels of generalized public
discontent may be at least partially gratifying, the lack of public
knowledge about public administration and governmental programs may be greater cause for worry. Throughout our study the
inadequacies of general and specific information about government
was very apparent. In the health and Community Development
fields this is particularly clear. Over 50% of the rural sample have no
knowledge of the goals of Community Development, and about the
same proportion do not know any Community Development officials at any level in the rural areas (Tables 2.7–2.8). And for the
agricultural program, less than 20% know precisely what the government expects them to do (Table 2.9). Responses to very specific
informational questions often reveal considerable ignorance. When
asked what the sources of income for the government were, over
50% of both the urban and rural samples did not know or gave
vague and incorrect replies. Perhaps more relevant is the ignorance
revealed when our respondents were asked where the nearest
Family Planning Center is located—60% of the urban sample and
77% of the rural sample said they did not know. One must, of
course, proceed cautiously in interpreting these findings. But one
might argue that if the government is to secure the cooperation of
the public in the implementations of its social welfare programs this
level of public knowledge may not be high enough. It appears that
although Indian citizens are generally satisfied with the performance record of officials, their inadequate knowledge of this government and its programs raises questions as to the meaningfulness of
this generalized support.

2·7 Public knowledge of goals of Community Development
(rural sample)

*What would you say are the most important purposes, goals, or activities of
the Community Development program here?*

Has considerable knowledge	5%
Has some knowledge	40
Has poor knowledge	26
No knowledge	30

2·8 Public knowledge of Community Development officials in the area or block (rural sample)

Who are the officials in the Community Development program in this area?	
Knows none or can mention none	48%
Mentions one	33
Mentions more than one	18
Mentions one or more officials *and* says he has seen him frequently in the past month	— 26

2·9 Public awareness of governmental programs and expectations for increasing agricultural production (rural sample)

In what ways has the government been trying to increase agricultural production?		*What does the government want you to do to increase agricultural production?*	
Mention nothing	29%	Nothing or don't know	30%
Mention one or two ways	24	General response only (as "work	
Mention three or four ways	35	hard") and irrelevant response	55
		Specific and relevant response	15
Mention more than four ways	12		

We do not mean to imply here that the Indian public is *comparatively* more ignorant of governmental programs than the public in other countries, even Western countries. Indeed, though comparisons with the Detroit study in this connection are difficult and probably misleading, Indian citizens may be as well informed as those in the United States.[2] But for a developing society which has staked much of its plans on programs requiring public information, instrumental knowledge, and understanding of its goals, our findings on the level of public knowledge are disillusioning. Our data suggest a serious communication gap between the planners and a majority of the Indian rural, and probably the urban, public.

---

[2]Janowitz, *op. cit.*, pp. 17–21.

Citizen perceptions of the accessibility of officials

While a system which is structured so that leaders are too accessible may be subverted to particular interests at the cost of the broader goals of governmental policy, a system in which citizens see their government as inapproachable or approachable only through devious pressure may be a system where manipulation may replace service. The question we posed throughout our study was: Does the Indian citizen perceive his government officials as accessible, approachable, and sensitive to public needs and demands, and oriented toward the public interest rather than toward narrow, particular, and special interests? Where does the balance lie in India?

To begin with, we asked our samples whether, if they had to go to a governmental department for action on a problem, they would act by themselves or get help from others. Our respondents indicated clearly that the probabilities of success if they worked by themselves were limited (Table 2.10). Thus, almost 65% of those in rural areas, and 50% in urban areas (with another 25% having no opinion) felt they should get help from other persons or organizations. The rural public felt more helpless in such a situation than did the urban population. This may be construed as a high level of pessimism or futility for individual action; if so, it applies equally to Detroit, as Table 2.10 indicates.

In pressing this matter further, we asked the same question in India, which had been used in the United States study, concerning

2·10 Perceived need for assistance from others in contacting governmental officials

In general, if you had a problem to take up with a governmental department or municipal office, would you do it yourself, or do you think you would be better off if you got the help of some person or organization?

	DELHI, 1964		DETROIT, 1954
	Rural	Urban	
Do it myself	23%	25%	16%
Get help	64	50	67
It depends	7	1	11
No opinion	5	25	—

2•11 Perceived importance of political pull in public contact with administrative officials

In your opinion does political pull — knowing the right person — play an important part in whether the government will help a private person with some problem he has?

	DELHI		DETROIT
	Rural	Urban	
Yes — pull is important	70%	54%	41%
Yes — pull sometimes is important	5	6	28
It depends	2	3	4
No — pull hardly matters	11	7	15
No opinion	12	30	13

the need for political pull or knowing the right person. We asked the respondent whether he thought this "played an important part in whether the government will help a private person with some problem he has." The levels of public agreement to the need for political pull are somewhat higher than in the Detroit study (Table 2.11). At least 70% of the rural public agree (plus an additional 7% who feel it may be important). In urban areas the affirmative response was 54% (plus an additional 9%). This contrasts with 41% who saw it as important in the American study (although an additional 28% said it played some part). This is, then, a high level of public cynicism (or realism) so far as the nature of successful citizen-administrator interrelationships are concerned.

It is interesting to note that most of those who see political pull as important are individuals who admit that they have not had any personal experience with this phenomenon. Only 19% of our rural sample and 17% of the urban sample claimed to have had such a personal experience. Janowitz notes the same findings in the American study. It seems that in democratic societies, developed or developing, the expectation is that the way to get proper and satisfactory administration is through the utilization of influence. This is the norm which is accepted.

There is an added note of futility, however, in the Indian data which may be more alarming. The great majority of Indians do not feel that the ordinary citizen can do much if administrative officials do not perform their jobs properly. And at least 30% to 40% *do* feel that administrators do not treat all citizens alike. The question we asked on this matter was used at several places throughout the questionnaire. The findings vary for different agencies. For health, as an example, we found that only 38% of the urban sample felt that "all are treated fairly and are given the same treatment" while the comparable percentage for the rural sample was 58%. Large numbers feel that the wealthy, the elite, or politicians are given favorable treatment (Table 2.12). This nonegalitarian perception of public

2•12 Egalitarianism in administration as perceived by the public

Do you think that all people are treated fairly and are given the same treatment by the health officials, or isn't the treatment equal and fair?

	Rural	Urban
Yes—all are treated equally and fairly	58%	38%
No—some people are favored (the wealthy, influential, etc.)	30	40
Don't know	11	22

administration is compounded by feelings of inadequacy so far as appealing or reporting improper behavior by officials is concerned (Table 2.13). Over 33% say bluntly that "nothing could be done" if a health official was not performing his job properly, while only 21% of the urban sample indicated he knew that *he could* complain and *to whom* he could complain. In rural areas approximately 40% were self-confident about their right to complain, and the efficacy of such action.

2•13 Sense of personal confidence or efficacy in contacting governmental officials

Suppose you found that a health official was not performing his job properly, could you do anything about it? If yes, what could you do?

	Rural	Urban
Could complain to higher officials or other leaders	41%	21%
Don't know if could complain or to whom	23	39
Nothing	33	39

There appears to be a complex attitudinal and perceptual set of expectations about the citizen's relationship with administrators. The components of this syndrome are: lack of self-confidence on the part of the ordinary citizen in dealing directly with officials; a feeling that the best way to deal with administrators is by enlisting the support of others, particularly individuals with the right contacts and political pull; that administrators do not and will not treat all people equally; and that these administrative actions are final, complaints availing very little or being difficult to process. In one sense this view represents a type of realism about political life. But though these attitudes do not find a reflection in general images of the task performance of administrative officials, they can hardly be expected to lead to great enthusiasm for and cooperation with governmental personnel or programs. The mixture of cynicism and realism here may both reflect and contribute to an unhealthy orientation towards democratic involvement.

Prestige perceptions of public service

The prestige levels of public service in India are sensationally high. We asked the same general question which has been used in studies in other countries: "If the pay were the same would you prefer to work for the government or for a private firm?" In urban Delhi 76% of our respondents said they would prefer governmental employment; in rural Delhi 89% gave the same response (Tables 2.14 and 2.15). This compares with a 56% prestige level in the U.S. in 1954, a 44% level in an Australia study in 1948, and a 36% level in Canada in a study in 1948.[3] In addition, as was done in the United

2•14 The prestige level of Indian government service

If the pay were the same, would you prefer to work for the government or for a private firm?

	Urban	Rural
Government preferred	76%	89%
Private firm preferred	9	3
Don't know	14	7
Not ascertained	1	1
Number of cases	*347*	*337*

[3]See Janowitz, *op. cit.,* pp. 61–62.

States, we asked our samples to indicate their preference for public or private employment for specific types of occupations. Thus, we asked them to tell us "if the jobs were the same in kind of work, pay, and so forth," whether they would prefer a clerk's position in a private firm or in a municipal government office; the same comparisons were made for a night watchman, and a doctor. The level of prestige remained very high, although only 53% of the urban respondents would prefer a doctor's position in government, compared to 77% who thought that a clerk's position in government would be preferable. In the rural areas 87% thought more of a doctor's position in government as compared to a private practitioner's position.

2•15 Prestige of selected occupations in government and private employment

If the jobs were the same in kind of work, pay, and so forth, which has the most prestige — that is, which do you think the most of?

	OCCUPATION		
	Clerk	Night watchman	Doctor
PREFER PRIVATE			
Urban	7%	8%	30%
Rural	2	3	5
PREFER GOVERNMENT			
Urban	77	76	53
Rural	90	90	87
DON'T KNOW			
Urban	16	16	17
Rural	6	6	6
NOT ASCERTAINED			
Urban	.3	.3	.3
Rural	2	2	3

Note: Each percentage is a proportion of the urban or rural sample which indicated a particular preference.

These data document the tremendously high status of government employment in India. They indicate that in terms of status perceptions private employment has been demeaned in the public's eye. Without going into the reasons for this high prestige value of

2.16 Perceptions of corruption in the public service

How many of the government officials would you say are probably corrupt — many of them, just a few, or none at all?

| | DELHI | | DETROIT |
	Urban	Rural	
Majority are corrupt	42%	48% >	13%
About half	17	9	
Just a few	19	16	71
None at all	7	12	7
Don't know	14	15 >	9
Not ascertained	1	1	
Number of cases	*347*	*337*	*764*

government positions, one might argue that this indicates an unbalanced and unhealthy relationship. When prestige for governmental employment is at such a high level, it may be difficult for administrative behavior to be based on consent and if the system seeks to function through the cooperation and effective management of the private sector of society, such prestige levels may prove a hindrance. The danger always exists in a society with such high prestige for the public service, useful as it may be for governmental goals, that administrative behavior may be arbitrary and not adequately public-service oriented. Admittedly, however, where practically automatic public compliance with administrative actions is desired, such prestige levels may be in one sense exceedingly functional. But what may appear to be superficially functional to governmental programs may not be functional to the development of healthy democratic relationships between administrators and the public.

The public's image of official corruption

The irony of these attitudinal patterns emerges when we look at responses concerning corruption among governmental officials, both general and in specific departments. We asked, "How many of the government officials would you say are probably corrupt — many of them, just a few, or none at all?" For our urban sample we found that almost 60% felt that at least half of the government officials were corrupt, with 19% saying "just a few," and only 7% saying "none at all" (Table 2.16). When asked about individual departments the percentages vary, as our subsequent analysis will show. The contrast with the findings of the Detroit Study are striking. Only 13% of the Detroit sample said "many are corrupt," compared to 57% of our rural sample and 60% of our urban sample. The expectation of dishonesty and corruption in government is high in India and, paradoxically, for the same people who see government service as prestigeful. Government service is apparently seen in two separate images, from two distinct value positions. It is both corrupt and prestigeful!

Conclusions: Indices of public support and self-confidence

In assessing the meaning of these general findings concerning public perspectives one is struck by the seemingly contradictory patterns which emerge. The Indian public in Delhi State is inclined to feel that officials are doing a good job and supports developmental programs as worth while. On the other hand there is evidence that this public is not convinced that officials treat citizens equally, nor is a majority certain that action can be taken against officials who do not perform their jobs properly. There are cynical overtones to responses about the integrity of officials. Yet, the great majority look on governmental positions as highly valued.

Any citizen has a host of impressions and perceptions about administrators, not all necessarily consistent from the viewpoint of the outside observer. Together these may be conceived as contributing to a general orientation or potential for cooperation, influence, or democratic involvement. To establish a composite image of the Indian citizen's potential for such involvement we have developed two indices for each of our respondents. One is an index of attitudinal support for governmental officials and programs.[4] The second index is that of citizen self-confidence in his relationships with governmental officials.[5] Five items were used in developing the

---

[4]Based on the questions we asked as to the kind of jobs officials were doing, whether governmental programs were necessary, whether officials were egalitarian, and whether they were corrupt.

[5]Based on our questions about the citizen's dealings with officials, whether he felt he could act if he had a problem to process with administrators, as well as his general reactions to two statements we presented to him at the end of the interview, and to which we asked him to indicate his agreement or disagreement:

"People like me don't have any say about what the government does."

"Public officials really care quite a lot about what people like me think."

support index; four items were used in the self-confidence index. Together these two indices give us a basis for generalizing what the general pattern of support and potential for administrative involvement is.[6]

If we look at the general distributions emerging from these indices there may be greater cause for optimism concerning the potential for involvement, particularly in the rural sector (Table 2.17). The rural population is inclined to be more supportive and also more self-confident than the urban sample. This is particularly apparent when one compares those highly supportive as well as highly self-confident for both samples — 20% or more of the rural sample rank high; only 3% to 8% of the urban sample do. In sum, from 20% to 33% of the population reveals a pattern of negativism and pessimism in their attitudes toward the bureaucracy.

When we combine the two indices, five types of patterns emerge, as follows:

	Rural	Urban
High support — high self-confidence	9%	1%
Moderate support — moderate or high self-confidence	57	47
Moderate or high support — low or no self-confidence	13	16
Low or no support — high self-confidence	14	17
Low or no support — low or no self-confidence	8	19

Very few, less than 10%, of our samples combine both high support for governmental programs and officials with high self-confidence in dealing with such officials. Close to 30% rank high on one or the other, but not on both. A large minority in these samples do not meet both criteria for involvement, while 8% to 19% seem completely withdrawn or alienated. In the urban sector, therefore, less than 50% of the population approximate needed levels of potential for involvement, while the figure is close to 66% in the rural areas.

There is strong evidence that these two attitudinal sets, or orientations toward administration, are linked, though not perfectly, as the above data indicates. Table 2.18 reveals that as support for governmental officials and programs declines and as people become more critical, there is less self-confidence in the citizen's relationships with officials. Thus, in rural areas, 44% of those who are highly

---

[6]The maximum score possible on the first index was 10; on the second index it was 8.

2·17 Summary indices of attitudes toward government and administration

	Rural	Urban
Index of attitudinal support for officials and programs		
Very supportive	20%	8%
Moderately supportive	59	57
Moderately critical	20	33
Very critical	2	3
Index of self-confidence about own status and relationships with governmental officials		
High self-confidence	22%	3%
Moderate self-confidence	57	62
Limited self-confidence	18	29
No self-confidence	3	6
Number of cases	*332*	*347*

2·18 Patterns of correlation between attitudes toward governmental officials, and attitudes of self-confidence in citizen relationships toward governmental officials

	Levels of support for government		
Levels of self-confidence	High support	Moderate support	Low or no support
RURAL			
High self-confidence	45%	22%	6%
Low or no self-confidence	9	19	36
URBAN			
High self-confidence	11	3	2
Low or no self-confidence	11	28	52

Note: Each per cent is a proportion of the support group with a particular level of self-confidence.

supportive are also highly self-confident, but only 5% of those who are critical of officials are highly self-confident—a percentage difference of 40. And, while only 9% have low self-confidence if they are very supportive, 36% have low self-confidence if they are critical of governmental officials and programs. The urban sample reveals a similar direction of relationships. This suggests that an identification of those factors which lead to more support for, and less criticism of, governmental administration and programs may be important if one is interested in maximizing citizen attitudes of cooperation, optimism, and self-confidence in relationships to officials. It is the total pattern of citizen perspectives and their consequences for citizen action, rather than inaction and withdrawal, which must be the focus of attention in any program of development in a society which is participant-oriented.

Social and political influences on public attitudes concerning Indian administration

chapter 3

The social distinctions and distances in Indian society lead one to expect clear patterns of social conformities and divergencies in attitudes toward governmental authority, generally, and administrative behavior, specifically. Caste and religious communities persist, educational stratification is admittedly steep, age differences seem significant, income differences are considerable. One is inclined to hypothesize that these social differences will be reflected in the varying patterns of public attitudes toward officials, and, indeed, may help explain them. The existence of status hierarchies and distinctive social groups suggests that some groups are on the periphery of the political system while others are more proximately involved. This assumption plus the expectation of mutual exchange and reënforcement of attitudes by relatively self-contained groups, i.e., patterns of insulation as well as isolation, combine to lead one to a theory of the importance of social group status and membership for knowledge about the system, communicative involvement with it, and support for it.

To what extent this theoretical position is valid is the focus of this chapter. We are concerned with two simple questions: to what extent are there significant differences in public attitudes toward the bureaucracy in caste, educational, income, and social categories and groups; in what social sectors does one find the major pockets of public criticism, ignorance, and alienation concerning bureaucratic programs and efforts?

That social group attitudinal variations exist in India can be seen from the data on most of the individual questions we asked in our study. For example, we asked all respondents what type of job they thought the officials in the central government in Delhi were doing. As Table 3.1 reveals, the group differences are sometimes large. The high caste groups are more critical of official performance than low caste groups in both urban and rural areas. But more significant probably is the much greater criticism of government in urban caste groups. There is more than a 20 percentage point differential for the same caste levels — thus, only 21% of rural *high* caste members are critical but 49% of urban high caste members are critical (among the *low* caste members the comparable figures are 15% rural, 38% urban).

3•1 Social group differences in public evaluation of the job of central government officials: Caste and education

	Doing a poor or fair job		Doing a good or very good job		Don't know	
	Rural	Urban	Rural	Urban	Rural	Urban
CASTE GROUPS						
High caste	21%	49%	59%	37%	21%	15%
Middle	24	—	48	—	27	—
Low	15	38	62	45	21	16
EDUCATION GROUPS						
Illiterate	22	30	47	43	29	27
Primary	15	47	62	28	23	25
Middle	19	48	70	34	11	18
Highest	23	56	73	41	4	3

Note: Each percentage is a proportion of the social category giving a particular response.

Among educational groups the same general picture emerges, although rural persons do not vary greatly by educational level. The rural and urban illiterates and those with a little education are much less able to evaluate the job being done by governmental officials than are those with more than a primary school education. But generally only 20% of rural groups are overtly critical of official

performance despite educational level. In the urban sample, however, the criticism is greater *and* it varies much more by educational
level. Thus, while 30% of urban illiterates are critical of government,
over 50% of those who have a good education are critical. This
suggests both more rural social homogeneity or conformity in
attitude distributions, as well as more general support for government in rural areas.

The lowest income groups are the least critical of the government
in both urban and rural areas. Among the higher income groups,
however, as Table 3.2 reveals, there is much more criticism in the
urban sample. Among those in the highest income bracket in the
city, 60% tend to have low evaluations of governmental officials.
Our breakdown by age groups indicates a similar antiofficial
pattern of attitudes in the city, although there is no significant
difference by age within the urban and rural samples separately.

3.2 Social group differences in public evaluations of the job of central government officials: Income and age groups

	Doing a poor or fair job		Doing a good or very good job		Don't know	
	Rural	Urban	Rural	Urban	Rural	Urban
INCOME GROUPS*						
Under 50 rupees	20%	16%	50%	62%	29%	23%
51–100	21	40	55	35	22	24
101–200	15	43	63	39	22	18
201–300	19	47	57	43	24	10
Over 300	30	60	61	33	9	7
AGE GROUPS						
Below 25	20	45	55	36	23	18
26–35	19	49	60	35	18	17
36–45	22	43	57	36	20	21
46–55	22	42	57	46	19	12
Above 55	16	49	47	37	38	15

*Based on monthly family income

Four types of findings are suggested from such data: (1) lower
status groups (in urban areas particularly) are inclined to be more
supportive and less critical than are high status groups; (2) lower
status groups are more in doubt as to their attitudes, or more reluc-

tant to make an evaluation of official performance; (3) rural groups are more homogeneous and like-minded in their attitude patterns than are urban respondents; (4) rural support in all social groups is higher, and usually much higher, than in the same groups in urban areas.

The same general patterns emerge if we look at responses to the question concerning the job that local officials in the village or in Delhi Corporation are doing (Table 3.3). The criticisms of Delhi municipal officials was relatively very high. But again, except for the caste group differentials, low status groups were less critical. In the villages we find only a minority who evaluate official performance negatively, with no consistent variation by social categories. In Delhi City from 30% to 70% have negative impressions, depending on the social group concerned.

3.3   Social group differences in evaluation of job of local officials (city, village)

	Percentage saying poor or fair	
	Rural	Urban
CASTE GROUPS		
Low	22%	60%
Middle	30	—
High	24	62
INCOME GROUPS		
Under 50 rupees	23	31
51 – 100	35	52
101 – 200	16	59
201 – 300	29	52
Over 300	30	72
EDUCATION GROUPS		
Illiterate	28	48
Primary	24	52
Middle	16	55
High and above	35	70

Another type of question was designed to determine citizen attitudes toward the worth of governmental activity in relation to the burden of taxation. Almost half, 48%, of our urban sample felt

3.4 Social group differences in citizen attitudes toward taxation

Percentage who say they are paying more taxes than they should in terms of the services rendered by government

	Rural	Urban
CASTE GROUPS		
Low	41%	35%
Middle	39	—
High	36	52
INCOME GROUPS		
Under 50 rupees	31	42
51 – 100	41	34
101 – 200	35	51
201 – 300	35	59
Above 300	39	53
EDUCATION GROUPS		
Illiterate	40	31
Primary	39	41
Middle	36	56
High and above	36	61

that taxes were too high, while 39% of the rural sample felt that way. Again, when we look at the percentages of antitaxation sentiment by social groups we find no discernible pattern among rural groups, with the variations among rural groups being small (Table 3.4). In Delhi City, however, there is a pattern. The high status groups are much more antagonistic than low status groups. Thus, among urban illiterates 31% feel taxes are too high, while 61% of those with the most advanced education are critical. There is corroboration in these data again, therefore, for the finding that social status is related to perceptions and attitudes toward government in urban Delhi.

The extent of citizen knowledge about governmental activities shows striking contrasts between the urban and rural populations (Table 3.5). To test the state of instrumental knowledge we used a series of questions about the type of health services available and their cost to the citizen. The data reveal that whereas only 21% of our rural sample was ignorant of the nature of these services, 65% of our urban sample was uninformed. This ignorance pervaded all

urban social groups—high status groups in the city were not significantly better informed. In rural Delhi State all social groups were
much more knowledgeable, with some evidence that those with
advanced education and higher incomes were the best informed.
Thus 28% of the rural illiterates were uninformed about these health
services while only 4% of those with a high, intermediate, or advanced education were uninformed. The most significant fact,
however, is the low level of instrumental knowledge in the city,
coupled with our previous findings of a relatively greater criticism
of governmental activities and officials in the urban population.
From our data, the rural population seems better informed on this
particular question, more homogeneous in their attitudes toward
government, less hostile, and less alienated.[1]

A variety of questions were used in our study to determine the
extent of self-confidence or efficacy people have in dealing with
administrative officials. For example, we asked them whether they
could do anything if the officials of a particular agency were not
performing their jobs satisfactorily. The pattern of responses by

3.5 Differential levels of knowledge about health services
(Percentage who have no knowledge of health services)

	Rural	Urban
INCOME GROUPS		
Under 50 rupees	25%	69%
51–100	21	68
101–200	16	65
201–300	19	60
Above 300	4	65
EDUCATIONAL GROUPS		
Illiterate	28	67
Primary	15	70
Middle	8	70
High and above	4	59
CASTE GROUPS		
Low	19	61
Middle	23	—
High	19	65

[1]The probability exists, of course, that services such as these were indeed more available to
rural citizens, and perceived as more vital to them.

social groupings for one type of officials, the health officials, is given in Table 3.6. The differences in self-confidence between the urban and rural population are striking again. For every one of these social categories the total proportion who either do not know whether they can take action against officials, or do not know what channels to use, is higher in Delhi City than in Delhi villages. For illiterates it is 71% in the villages, 84% in the city; for low caste members it is 60% in the villages, 88% in the city; for those with the lowest incomes it is 54% in the villages, 84% in the city. In comparison with these low status groups, high status groups have more confidence in approaching officials. The differential is not great among caste groups. But only 31% of those with considerable education in rural areas feel inadequate—a 40 percentage point differential. In urban Delhi the difference between high and low status groups exists also but is much smaller.

From these data it seems that the majority of residents of both urban and rural areas have no conception at all of how to take action against ineffective or delinquent officials, and that this sense of inadequacy may be related to social status. There is much less pessimism or ignorance (or both) in the rural population, which may be linked in turn to the generally higher level of administrative support, greater knowledge of administrative officials and programs, and closer contact with the bureaucracy in rural areas.

We developed two indices (of support for administrative officials and programs, and of citizen self-confidence in relation to administration), which were described in Chapter 2. We found urban respondents less supportive (36% at the lowest score levels, compared to 21% for rural respondents,) as well as having less self-confidence (35% at the lowest score levels, compared to 21% of the rural sample). If we now look at the scores by these indices for caste and educational groups we can see the differential importance of social factors (Table 3.7). On the support index our findings suggest that caste and education are relevant in both urban and rural areas. It is interesting that the lowest level of criticism is found in rural areas among low caste members with some education; in urban Delhi the lowest level of criticism is found among illiterates who are low caste. The high caste illiterates, however, are much more critical in the city. Among all groups the range in support is considerable —from 9% to 16% of rural low caste members are critical, but from 29% to 53% of the urban low caste and high caste members are critical. The urban environment seems a very consistent factor, perhaps more important than either caste or educational status. The government has the greatest support in the villages, and particularly among the low caste members in the villages.

3.6 Social group differences in sense of efficacy of citizens in relation to administrators

If health officials are not performing their jobs properly is there anything you can do? What can you do?

	RURAL			URBAN		
	Can do nothing	Don't know channels	TOTAL– Low sense of efficacy	Can do nothing	Don't know channels	TOTAL– Low sense of efficacy
CASTE GROUPS						
Low	30%	30%	60%	46%	42%	88%
Middle	35	24	59	–	–	–
High	35	22	57	38	37	75
EDUCATION GROUPS						
Illiterates	42	29	71	38	46	84
Primary	33	23	56	46	40	86
Middle	3	24	27	44	44	88
High and above	12	19	31	35	33	68
INCOME GROUPS						
Under 50 rupees	27	27	54	38	46	84
51–100 rupees	40	22	62	45	44	89
101–200 rupees	30	30	60	41	43	84
201–300 rupees	38	19	57	38	31	69
Over 300 rupees	22	17	39	35	31	66

3·7 The relationship of caste and education to public levels of support and self-confidence

	HIGH CASTE		LOW CASTE	
	Some education	Illiterates	Some education	Illiterates
INDEX OF SUPPORT FOR ADMINISTRATION Per cent at the lowest levels of support (score 0–3)				
Rural	24%	24%	9%	16%
Urban	32	43	53	29
INDEX OF SELF-CONFIDENCE Per cent at the lowest levels of self-confidence (score 0–2)				
Rural	15	38	9	20
Urban	27	59	28	35

On the self-confidence index (based on several items designed to identify the extent to which the citizen feels he can act effectively in the political-administrative system and has an important role in that system) the rural population again has a much better set of scores for caste and educational groups. The urban high caste illiterates are the least self-confident (59% feeling alienated), while the rural low caste educated are the most confident (9% feeling alienated).

Both caste status and educational status seem important in rural areas — it is high caste plus illiteracy which is related to low self-confidence. In urban Delhi illiteracy seems to be the chief factor, although again, high caste illiterates have the largest proportion of alienated among illiterates. This convergence of high caste status and illiteracy seems then to be linked to lack of political *self-confidence*, while these factors are much less clearly relevant to the variations in political *support*.

The influence of village environment

Having discovered and demonstrated that there is more support for administrative officials and programs in rural areas, as well as more optimism in the role of the citizen in the system, the question can now be raised whether the type of village the citizen lives in is related to these supportive and self-confident perspectives. We did our interviewing in this study in eight villages, selected at random but in such a manner that they included small villages (under 1000 population), medium-sized (population 1000 to 2000), and large villages (from 2000 to 5000 population). They were also selected to include villages which could be objectively described[2] as traditional and isolated, as well as more modernized and in closer proximity to Delhi. This permitted us to analyze our data by village type, differentiating between the two factors of size and modernization status.

Our data reveal that it is not the small or most traditional villages, on the basis of our index, which are the least supportive and most out of touch with the administrative system (Table 3.8). Rather, one finds two different patterns, one for small and one for large villages. The greatest support and political self-confidence is actually found in the smallest villages which are most modernized. Among small villages the support of government ranges from 38% to 13%, being highest in the small village which was most modernized. The same was true for self-confidence, dropping from 46% to 21%. In the larger villages the amount of criticism of the government, and pessimism about the individual's role, tends to be higher than in the small villages, and increases as the village becomes more modernized. Thus, two of our larger villages which scored high on our modernization index revealed the greatest criticism or lack of support of the government—at the 46% level of criticism—and the lowest percentage of self-confidence—less than 5%. But a caution must be injected into the analysis, because our most modernized large village had relatively high levels of support and self-confidence, not as high as the most modernized *small* village, but higher than was the norm for larger villages.

What is suggested here is that modernization tendencies in small villages reduce governmental criticism and personal pessimism about government drastically. As larger villages go through the transitional-modernizing process, however, the contacts of citizens with government become more negative, and criticism increases. And also, in the most modernized village, one in which a great deal of investment of resources and personnel by the government takes place, citizens' perceptions of government and of their role in the administrative pattern of relationships change. In such large villages it is possible that a sense of citizen involvement and support for governmental programs and administrative action develops. In any

---

[2]As explained in the Preface and Appendix notes on methodology.

3·8 Village differences in levels of public support and confidence

	SMALL VILLAGES			MEDIUM AND LARGE VILLAGES				
	Most modernized		Most traditional	Least modernized	Transitional	Modernized		Most modernized
Low on administration support index	3%	11%	21%	21%	19%	46%	46%	11%
Low on self-confidence index	5	7	13	17	21	37	40	17
High on administration support	38	17	13	14	26	0	17	25
High on self-confidence index	46	33	21	21	24	2	4	28

Note: The interviews were conducted in eight villages—three small and five medium to large.

46

event, in our study the greatest citizen alienation is not found in small villages, but in traditional, small villages *and* in larger villages where the modernization process is incomplete. In these latter villages the problem of developing citizen identifications and acceptance of the system may be most critical.

Role of the newspaper

The relevance of newspaper readership for public perceptions of the bureaucracy and its programs is a subject on which there is little information. The high percentage of illiteracy and the small percentage of the population which has developed the daily newspaper habit go hand-in-hand to some extent, and limit the newspaper's potential role. In our study we found that only 24% of our rural sample read a newspaper regularly, while 60% in urban Delhi claimed they were regular newspaper readers. Despite such levels of relatively low exposure, it is important to analyze to what extent such exposure is associated with differential levels of public support for government.

Generally, we find that the regular readers tend to be more supportive (Table 3.9). Again, rural and urban samples differ considerably. In rural areas readership seems to reduce citizen criticism of the government, and personal defeatism in dealing with officials to a minimum. The difference is not as great, though in the same direction, in urban Delhi. It is significant that our rural respondents who *do not* read were more supportive and self-confident than our urban respondents who *do* read. Living in urban Delhi seems related to more criticism of the government and more personal alienation than

3.9 Newspaper readership and public support for the bureaucracy

	RURAL		URBAN	
	Readers	Non-readers	Readers	Non-readers
Low level of support for governmental programs and leaders	12%	26%	33%	38%
Low level of self-confidence in relationship to the bureaucracy	11	23	30	40
Number of cases	*76*	*237*	*199*	*130*

| 3.10 | The importance of caste and newspaper readership in explaining citizen perspectives toward administrators |

	HIGH CASTE		MIDDLE CASTE		LOW CASTE	
	Readers	Non-readers	Readers	Non-readers	Readers	Non-readers
Low level of support						
Rural	15%	31%	8%	35%	14%	13%
Urban	34	33	—	—	54	34
Low level of self-confidence						
Rural	8	36	17	21	0	20
Urban	30	38	—	—	30	36

Note: Each percentage is a proportion of each readership group who ranked low on each index.

in rural villages, irrespective of greater exposure to what is going on through the newspaper medium.

However, it is important, to control for newspaper readership within social groups, to see whether social group status eliminates the importance of exposure to newspapers, and, conversely, whether newspaper readership makes social distinctions unimportant in this analysis. Caste differences in newspaper readership are, of course, great. In our study we found that in the villages only 13% of the low caste respondents read the newspaper, while 43% of the high caste members did. In urban Delhi, 18% of the low caste members were regular readers, compared to 71% of the high caste members. In Table 3.10 we have presented the data for caste groups and newspaper readership, using our indices of political support and self-confidence.

Both caste status and newspaper readership seem to be relevant factors explaining some of the differences in citizen attitudes. But the findings are somewhat peculiar, and not consistent. In rural areas it is clear that low caste status is still important — for example, among the rural "Non-readers" the low caste members have the lowest criticism scores (13% low caste, 31% and 35%, high and middle caste). Readership is a discriminating factor in the rural middle and upper caste groups; it is less relevant in the low castes, although among rural low caste members who read the newspaper, none were in self-confidence. (One must remember, of course, that only 13% of our rural low caste sample do regularly read a newspaper!)

In urban Delhi the role of caste and newspaper readership is strange, and it is difficult to see any consistent meaning in the data. As was to be expected there is much more criticism and less support in all urban subgroups. The relevance of caste status differences in urban Delhi seems to be washed out when we divide caste groups into those who read a newspaper and those who do not. The one exception is the 54% of the urban low caste readers who are very critical of the government (coinciding with the educated low caste members in Table 3.7). Readership makes some difference in self-confidence scores in urban Delhi; but the factor of illiteracy, as pointed out previously, is probably much more important than newspaper readership. In short, our data suggest again that in rural Delhi newspaper readership is an important variable, except for low caste members' political support levels, which are high despite readership. Our data suggest also that in urban Delhi readership may have some relevance, but that reading a newspaper does not necessarily lead to greater support of the government. In urban Delhi newspaper readership may be relatively unimportant in the mobilization of public support and in the generation of political-administrative self-confidence in the citizen's relationship to the bureaucracy. His educational status may be more important, although even here the pattern is not completely consistent in urban Delhi.

The relevance of party contact

An interesting query which should be posed for a developing society with democratic political group structures is: To what extent is contact with party organization and leadership associated with support for administrative programs and officials? In India the party struggle has a long history even though well-developed party structures have come into existence only in the past two decades. Today there are many parties besides the dominant Congress party. In the Delhi area one finds the Jan Sangh as a primary opposition party, as well as the Swatantra, Socialist, and Communist parties, with varying degrees of organizational articulation and strength. The question is to what extent is exposure to, or contact with, these party leaders functional for the generation of attitudes supportive of administrative behavior?

We asked the citizens in our sample whether they felt party leaders would be helpful in problems requiring governmental action, as well as whether they had ever sought the help of party leaders. The distributions are shown in Table 3.11. The data suggest a considerably higher confidence in party leaders in rural Delhi than in the city—40% compared to 19% feeling party leaders would be helpful. A large proportion of urban respondents (45%) were uncertain on this matter. Not quite 20% of both urban and rural samples had gone to party leaders for assistance. This is probably a higher proportion than in developed societies such as the U.S. in recent years.[3] It suggests the potential role which the party might play in mobilizing citizen support, or in communicating public demands, in India.

The social characteristics of those who had sought the help of party leaders are interesting. The middle and upper income groups in rural areas were more likely to go to the party leaders than the lower income groups. The illiterates in both urban and rural Delhi did not seek out the party for help to the extent that those with a middle and high school education did. Among the castes, the Harijans and lower caste members in urban Delhi were more actively in contact with party leaders, while it was the Jats and other middle caste and high caste members who were more likely to approach party leaders in the rural areas. Generally, with the exception of the urban Harijans, those with lower social status do not approach party leaders as much, due either to their lack of knowledge of these leaders, a feeling that they are not accessible, or feelings that such action would be improper or not efficacious.

3.11 Citizen perceptions and contacts with party leaders in the context of personal assistance on administrative problems

	Urban	Rural
A. *Would party leaders be helpful?*		
Yes	19%	40%
No	35	34
Don't know	45	22
B. *Have you sought the help of party leaders?*		
Yes	16	18
No	76	77
Don't know	8	4

Does party contact seem related to increased or decreased support for the administration and to feelings of self-confidence in the citizen's perceived role in relationship to the administrator? If we

---

[3]In a study which we made in 1956 in the Detroit area less than 1% of the adults in the sample said they had gone to party leaders for action on personal or governmental problems.

3.12 Relationship of personal experience with party leaders to administration support levels and personal self-confidence

	RURAL		URBAN	
	Had an experience	No experience	Had an experience	No experience
Levels of administration support				
High	20%	20%	0%	9%
Moderate	51	59	65	55
Low	29	18	29	34
No support	0	3	6	2
Levels of personal self-confidence				
High	24	22	0	4
Moderate	62	59	63	62
Low	14	19	35	27
No self-confidence	0	3	2	7
Number of cases	*59*	*270*	*54*	*293*

identify those who have gone for help to party leaders and look at the level of their support and self-confidence (as measured by our two indices) we find virtually no relationship in rural areas and a slight inverse relationship in urban Delhi (Table 3.12). About 20% of our rural respondents were highly supportive irrespective of their experiences in contacting party leaders. Similarly, from 22% to 24% had self-confident perspectives whether or not they had contacted party leaders. For our urban sample one can observe that, first, they had lower levels of support and self-confidence than rural citizens, and, second, that they were less likely to be highly supportive if they had contacts with party leaders. The percentage differences are small and exist only at the high support levels. Nevertheless, the finding may be significant for urban residents. Contact with urban party leaders certainly does not seem functional to the mobilization of public support or feelings of confidence and optimism in dealing with administrative officials.[4]

We tested these findings by using other indications of contact with party leaders, particularly whether the respondent knew party

---

[4]We hasten to add that this is only a preliminary, and therefore tentative, exploration of this crucial matter. We are in the process of analyzing the functional consequences of party activity and leadership in a separate study.

leaders personally. An index of personalized party contact was calculated for each respondent based on three responses in which he might have manifested personal contact with or personal knowledge of party leaders. The same patterns emerged (Table 3.13). The urban-rural differentials are again striking at the high score levels. There is virtually no urban high support despite party contacts, while over 20% of rural respondents are supportive and self-confident. Further, urban respondents with the least party contact are more highly supportive — 11% of those with "low" party contact are highly supportive while none of those in urban Delhi with "high" or "medium" contact are highly supportive. It seems, therefore, that on the basis of our data, party contact may be relatively unimportant for the mobilization of citizen administrative support and self-confidence.

A final point of interest is the relationship of party affiliation to citizen attitudes toward administration. It is significant that we found this to have no explanatory power in our study. Among our rural respondents we found that 20% of the Congress followers were highly supportive; but 20% of those who voted for the opposition parties were also highly supportive. At the other extreme, 22% of the Congress followers were highly critical and nonsupportive,

3.13 Relationship of personal party contact and the indices of political support and personal self-confidence

| | PARTY CONTACT SCORES: | | | | | |
| | Rural | | | Urban | | |
INDICES	High	Medium	Low	High	Medium	Low
Political support						
High	25%	18%	19%	0%	0%	11%
Moderate	50	55	61	56	70	53
Low	25	25	17	40	26	34
No support	0	2	3	4	4	2
Political self-confidence						
High	23	22	22	2	2	4
Moderate	59	53	59	55	70	62
Low	18	22	16	41	28	25
No confidence	0	3	3	2	0	9
Number of cases	*55*	*63*	*211*	*45*	*57*	*244*

while 20% of those voting for opposition parties were nonsupportive. The same basic percentages obtained on our self-confidence index, with no discernible difference for Congress and opposition followers. From this very preliminary analysis, then, it appears that identification with the Congress party does not seem to be related to citizen attitudes toward the administrative system. Congress followers are no more supportive of, nor alienated from, the bureaucracy than those who identify with other parties.

Conclusions

This exploration of the social bases of public attitudes toward the Indian bureaucracy suggests several important findings. The rural public in our study was consistently more supportive than the urban public, less alienated, more confident about how to act in relationship to officials, possessed of more "instrumental knowledge" about the administrative process. However, social status differentials exist in both urban and rural areas. High status groups tended to be more critical of government, more skeptical of the worthwhileness of government, and to some extent more self-confident about their relationships with bureaucrats. Those with the most education tended to score highest on our self-confidence index in both urban and rural samples. This was not true for the administration support index, however. The low caste illiterates in rural areas had the least criticism of government officials and programs.

Within the rural sample we found that the greatest support for the bureaucracy was located in the rather small village which is not completely isolated or traditional, and in those larger villages scoring very high on our modernization index. However, even our most traditional small villages had better support and self-confidence scores than larger villages which appeared to be in a transitional stage of change. The most modernized, large village had high support and self-confidence scores. Both village size and developmental status seem, therefore, to be related to attitudes toward governmental administration.

Newspaper readership is clearly related to public attitudes supportive of public administration in rural areas, particularly in middle and upper caste groups. Among low caste members the relationship is dubious. In the urban areas, readership is slightly associated with self-confidence perspectives, but not with administration support perspectives.

The greatest pockets of actual, or potential, discontent or alienation seem to be in certain social categories of the urban populace and among residents in the large villages, which are undergoing a modernization process. In urban Delhi both the high caste illiterates and the low caste members with some education are critical of governmental programs and performance. The high caste illiterates in the urban population may be a particularly significant factor, since three-fifths of them have defeatist and negative perspectives about their roles in relationship to the new bureaucracy. This group of high caste illiterates, constituting over 10% of our urban sample, represents considerable "frustration potential" in the Indian society. It is this category, plus the residents of middle-sized and large villages moving from a traditional to a modernizing status which appears only *minimally* committed to, identified with, knowledgeable about, and supportive of the administrative process in modern India.

Patterns
and sources
of personal hostility
toward
administration

chapter 4

In the preceding chapters we have dealt primarily with the ordinary Indian citizen's cognitive and perceptual orientations toward the Indian bureaucracy as a system or subsystem. We have been concerned with his answers to questions probing his evaluations of the job the governmental officials are doing, whether he feels governmental programs and services are worth while, the extent to which he knows and accepts the purposes of these programs, his perceptions of official corruption, and what he would do if he had a problem to take up with governmental officials. These questions elicit *general* reactions or evaluations by the public. We have utilized the responses as information concerning the levels of support or lack of support, of citizen confidence or lack of confidence, regarding the administrative system. Throughout this analysis, despite relatively high levels of public support in response to certain questions, there has been considerable evidence also of personal hostility toward administration. It is obvious that citizens may be supportive of governmental programs and actions generally, while also being personally hostile to officials, as the result of personal experiences with them or in a stereotypic sense. The purpose of this chapter is to analyze specifically the extent and nature of this hostility, some of its probable sources, and its relationship to the levels of public support.

A variety of questions used in our study can be used to suggest the range of personal antagonism toward administrators (Table 4.1). The vast majority of respondents reveal some degree of hostility toward the police, when asked about police treatment if they "got involved in some trouble with the police." Almost 90% of our rural sample and 67% of the urban sample felt they would be mistreated. This is the extreme incidence of hostility. No doubt other questions concerning the behavior of policemen produced hostile reactions from a much smaller proportion of the public. Thus, less than 50% feel the police are discourteous, only 6% (urban) and 9% (rural) feel that the police would not be helpful in time of personal need, and only about 10% (of each sample population) say they would not go to the police for help. There are different kinds of questions, then, which reveal hostility to the police. And only a small minority are consistently critical and bitter in their responses.

The same observation is true when we look at the components and extent of hostility to other types of officials. A sizeable minority are antagonistic towards health officials—less than a third at the most in rural Delhi, slightly higher, at least on certain questions, in urban Delhi. Postal officials' behavior evokes very little hostility, while the behavior of the inspectors on the DTU buses evokes considerable antagonism. Although some people are consistently hostile toward one agency, there is no doubt a latent, cumulative pattern of hostility toward administrative officials which could interfere with the development process in India.

4.1 Evidence of personal hostility toward administrators

Types of Hostility Responses	Rural	Urban
Police would mistreat citizens	89%	67%
Police are rude or discourteous	28	43
Health officials favor the wealthy, upper classes, or politicians	30	40
Health officials are rude or discourteous	20	24
Has had specific unsatisfactory contacts with postal officials	6	6
Critical of Delhi Transport Undertaking (urban only)	—	47

We constructed an "Index of personal hostility to administrators" based on responses to twelve questions used in our study, probing the personal contacts and experiences of citizens with different types of officials. Each hostile response was scored separately, with a maximum score possible of 12. The distributions for our respondents are found in Table 4.2. From this, one can see that the frequency of hostility responses is much greater in the urban area. Roughly, for every three urban respondents who reveal personal antagonism there are two rural respondents. From 30% to 45% of urban respondents indicate some repetition of hostility in their responses, compared with 20% to 30% of rural adults who are chronic complainers. Only 16% of our urban adults manifest no hostility at all, while 35% of our rural adults do not seem to be hostile. A minority of 20% seem to have personal antagonisms only against one agency or one type of official included in our survey.[1]

For these citizens who do reveal hostile attitudes toward administrators a majority are hostile toward more than one agency. The hostiles who complain only against one agency are divided as follows:

| | HOSTILE ONLY TOWARD: | | | |
	Police officials	Health officials	DTU officials	Postal officials
Urban	10%	10%	7%	.4%
Rural	16	20	—	.4

Thus, certain officials, notably the police and health officials, are the only targets of hostility for certain segments of the population.[2] But over 50% of the rural hostiles and over 70% of the urban hostiles do not concentrate their antagonisms. They are inclined to be hostile toward more than one category of officials, and usually this includes officials at more than one level of governmental authority.

Analysis of the socioeconomic correlates of hostility reveals that the phenomenon pervades all levels of the social stratification hierarchy in India (Table 4.3). But we found less hostility among

---

[1] Actually, the hostility level would be higher for both samples if we had included the responses to the question concerning mistreating and physical beating by the police. Since this type of stereotypic hostility included 89% of the rural and 67% of the urban populations, and was at a much higher level than other hostilities, and therefore probably not discriminating as a test of hostility, we excluded it from our index.

[2] There were no respondents who were hostile only against Community Development officials.

low status groups than in the upper social strata, particularly in the rural areas. For example, 30% of the urban illiterates have a zero score (no hostility) while only 5% of those with the most education have zero scores. (The differentials are in the same direction, but smaller for the various rural subgroups.) Conversely, if one looks at those with relatively high hostility scores (five or more) one finds the high status groups more hostile. For example, 23% of the urban high income groups reveal chronic hostility, while only 7% of the lowest income groups are very hostile. The greatest hostility is found, in both the city and the villages, among those with considerable education.

4.2 Distributions of citizens on an index of personal hostility to administrators

SCORES	INDEX I (Based on 12 items)		INDEX II* (Based on 11 common items for both samples)	
	Urban	Rural	Urban	Rural
Highest = 5 plus	18%	9%	13%	8%
4	12	10	9	8
3	15	10	14	12
2	21	13	18	13
1	19	22	25	23
Lowest = 0	16	35	22	37

*The responses to Panchayati Raj and the Delhi Transport Undertaking are eliminated from this index since they were relevant in *either* the urban *or* rural areas, but not in both.

The suggestion implicit in these findings is that improvement in social status is accompanied by increased hostility toward the administrative system, that there is a greater tendency to criticize public authority as a person moves from his traditional and depressed social status towards more enlightenment, higher income, and more exposure to modernization influences. Although it is difficult with our data to test here the "trend hypothesis of movement," it is possible, and perhaps instructive, to test the proposition that the more traditional a person's orientation toward the system is, the more inclined he is to accept authority and to mute his personal antagonism toward administrative officials.

We asked each respondent to react to two statements which may tap his traditional or modernizing attidudinal orientations:

Item #1: "If something grows up over a long time, there is bound to be much wisdom in it."

Item #2: "The way the government runs things today is better than the way things were run in the past."

Although "traditionalism" stands for a complex set of perspectives and attitudes, agreement or disagreement with these statements suggests the direction of a person's thinking—whether he has a retrospective or prospective cast of thought, whether he prefers the political past to the political present. By combining these two measures we can begin to classify citizens in a country like India. Actually our respondents were inclined to support both statements (which admittedly may indicate a tendency to agree, or to be discriminating in their responses to these statements): 78% of the rural sample (54% of the urban) agreed with the first statement, but only 15% of the rural sample (29% of the urban) disagreed with the second statement. Thus, although there is a latent retrospective traditionalism in the sense of respect for the past, only a minority

4.3   Social status and hostility toward administrators

SOCIAL FACTORS		INDEX OF HOSTILITY SCORES:					
		5+	4	3 and 2	1	0	N*
A. CASTE							
Low	Urban	18%	10%	27%	20%	24%	49
	Rural	4	9	23	25	39	108
High	U	19	12	37	18	13	206
	R	10	11	22	24	33	63
B. EDUCATION							
Illiterates	U	10	4	33	24	30	84
	R	8	11	25	24	33	207
Well educated	U	27	17	36	15	5	125
	R	12	12	12	35	31	26
C. INCOME							
Low	U	7	7	47	20	20	15
	R	15	0	19	17	48	52
High	U	23	15	39	15	8	124
	R	9	20	14	14	43	44

*N = number of cases.

4.4 Citizen hostility toward administrators in relation to latent traditionalism

Generalized preference for the wisdom of the past: *If something grows up over a long time, there is bound to be much wisdom in it.*

	HOSTILITY SCORES:						
	High 5+	4	3	2	1	Low 0	N*
AGREE							
Rural	10%	10%	8%	13%	22%	37%	260
Urban	15	10	17	22	19	17	187
DISAGREE							
Rural	10	15	20	12	17	26	41
Urban	35	14	14	20	14	2	84

*N = number of cases.

translated this into a preference for government officials and programs of the past.

Using these two measures and relating them to patterns of citizen hostility toward administrators, interesting findings emerge (Table 4.4). The hypothesis seems confirmed that in a developing society the more traditional one's orientations the greater one's acceptance of authority, and, thus, the less one's hostility toward authority figures such as administrators. Those with nostalgia for the past (in response to item #1) revealed much lower hostility—70% of our traditional rural respondents were at the low end of our hostility scale, while 60% of our traditional urban respondents revealed low hostility toward administrators.

The second test (using item #2 also) suggests that such findings are not supportable.[3] For, when we look at the hard-core traditionalists (those who not only are generally nostalgic but also specifically prefer the government of the past), we find much more hostility toward administrators (Table 4.5). Almost 50% of the hardcore and confused traditionalists score high on our hostility index, while less than 20% of our modernizing traditionalists do so. It seems from these data that those Indian citizens who rigidly adhere to nostalgia for the past are in a minority, but this rigid traditionalism is re-

[3]We are here making a distinction between "modernizing traditionalists" and "hard-core traditionalists." The former are conceptualized as having a nostalgia for the past but accepting the government of the present. The latter not only have a nostalgia for the past but specifically prefer the government of the past.

flected in considerable antipathy to present-day administrative officials. From 50% to 65% are revealing modernized attitudes toward public authority, perhaps reluctantly recognizing that the administrative process today is superior to the past. Along with such modernizing attitudes comes less bitterness and antagonism for governmental officials. Admittedly this is only one test of the traditional-modern hypothesis as reflected in citizen attitudes toward government. As such it is highly suggestive.

Are hostility feelings a consequence of contact with officials or does this phenomenon appear to be a stereotype, unrelated to bureaucratic contact? Our data suggest that *some* contact seems to be definitely a factor in explaining hostility (Table 4.6). Thus, we find that in rural Delhi those with no bureaucratic contact are much less likely to be hostile toward administrators.[4] Only 8% are very hostile compared to about 20% of those who have come into frequent contact with administrators. In urban Delhi, where the proportion who have had contact is higher, we again find that those

4.5 A typology of traditionalism-modernism in relation to citizen hostility toward administration*

	HOSTILITY SCORES:							
	Rural sample				Urban sample			
Group	High	Medium	Low	N**	High	Medium	Low	N**
I. Hard-core traditionalists	48%	30%	22%	33	46%	44%	10%	39
II. Modernizing traditionalists	14	19	67	213	20	38	42	143
III. Confused traditionalists	45	21	34	29	51	29	20	69
IV. Consistent modernists	22	39	39	23	29	45	26	31

*Each group was classified on the basis of the following responses to the two statements used:

Group	Item #1	Item #2
I	Agree	Disagree
II	Agree	Agree
III	Disagree	Disagree
	No opinion	Disagree
	Agree	No opinion
IV	Disagree	Agree

**N = number of cases

[4] The technique employed for scoring each respondent in terms of contact with administrators is explained in detail in Chapter 4.

4.6   The consequence of bureaucratic contact for citizen hostility toward administrators

Bureaucratic contact score:	HOSTILITY SCORE:							
	Rural				Urban			
	High	Medium	Low	N*	High	Medium	Low	N*
Very high (score 7+)	18%	26%	56%	66	37%	39%	24%	132
High (score 5-6)	19	24	57	63	35	38	27	85
Medium (score 3-4)	22	21	56	95	25	31	44	75
Low (score 1-2)	22	26	52	86	9	26	65	55**
Zero (no contact)	8	22	70	27	—	—	—	***

*N = number of cases.
**Includes six cases with "zero" contact scores.
***Too few cases for analysis.

with no (or little) contact are less likely to be very hostile — 9% compared to 25%, and 37% with a high frequency of contact.

This is a paradoxical finding for the Indian government from a practical standpoint, for it suggests that expansion of the bureaucracy and the policy of involving citizens with developmental programs through more contact with officials also has its risks. It may produce hostility and alienation from the administrative subsystem which could be dysfunctional to integrative goals.

To assess further the conditions under which bureaucratic contact was functionally related to hostility we attempted to determine the relevance of a variety of factors. For those individuals with a high frequency of contact, we looked at the social characteristics of those who were hostile and not hostile, and found that such characteristics were not significantly different. Illiteracy, for example, was not a discriminating factor. Two other factors did seem related however: whether the respondent had a personal experience with the police, and whether the respondent had a personal acquaintance with administrators. We found the following differences in rural Delhi:

Among those with a high bureaucratic contact score:	Had police contact	Had considerable personalized contact with officials	Number of cases
Those very hostile	59%	93%	29
Those not hostile	37	63	27

Thus, police contact seems related to hostility to administrators, as does the personalized nature of bureaucratic contact. In our urban sample we found the same type of differences. This suggests, *first*, that bureaucratic contact does not necessarily lead to hostility — the nature and character of the contact is important. *Second*, a certain

amount of hostility to administrators is stereotypic, since 30% or more of our respondents with little or no contact with administrators are hostile. Contact with administrators of certain types does seem conducive to hostility reactions. But contact by itself does not lead to hostility necessarily. It is significant that 35% of our rural sample had high frequency of contact with administrators, and 55% of these had little or no hostility. The corresponding urban percentages were 60% and 25%.

The final question in this analysis is: What are the consequences of personal hostility for public support and self-confidence in relation to the administrative system? Our measures of support reflect the individual's cognition and evaluation of administrative policies, programs, and the job performance of officials. Similarly, our measures of self-confidence reflect the individual's assessment of his own competence and efficacy in the system. The question now is whether personal hostility (as a separate measure) is related, as might be expected, to lower support and less self-confidence.

As can be seen from Table 4.7 there is some relationship between intensity or amount of hostility and degree of support, in both urban and rural populations. As personal hostility increases, support declines, indicating that these two responses, the one affective and the other cognitive, are functionally related. But it is only at the highest hostility levels that support for the administrative system declines to a significant, or dangerous, point. Two thirds of those with high hostility scores are not supportive of administrative programs and officials; those at the three lower levels of hostility have percentages of 74% to 94% who are either very supportive or moderately supportive of the system. Thus, though hostility inhib-

4.7 The consequence of personal hostility for public support of administrative programs and officials

ADMINISTRATIVE SUPPORT SCORES:

Personal hostility index	High 7+		Moderate 4-6		Low 1-3		Zero		Number of cases	
	R*	U**	R	U	R	U	R	U	R	U
High (5+)	3%	0%	29%	31%	65%	64%	3%	5%	31	61
Moderate	5	6	67	63	27	27	1	3	112	164
Low	20	15	61	58	14	26	5	0	74	65
Zero	37	12	57	58	5	26	1	4	118	57

*R = Rural
**U = Urban

4.8 The consequence of personal hostility for self-confidence concerning the role of the individual in the system

SELF-CONFIDENCE SCORES:

Personal hostility index	High R*	U**	Moderate R	U	Low R	U	Zero R	U	Number of cases R	U
High (5+)	3%	2%	55%	54%	42%	42%	0%	2%	31	61
Moderate	15	3	63	68	20	25	2	4	111	164
Low	20	6	57	65	16	23	7	6	74	65
Zero	36	2	52	52	10	29	2	18	117	56

*R = Rural
**U = Urban

its support, since less than 20% are very hostile in both urban and rural areas, the magnitude of the problem is not alarming. Further, it is significant for Indian society that 29% to 31% of those who have a high hostility score are still moderately supportive of the system.

Personal hostility also seems to be somewhat related to individual feelings concerning one's role in the system (Table 4.8). In rural areas much more than in urban Delhi, high self-confidence and feelings of efficacy about participation are linked to relatively low levels of personal hostility against administrators. Thus, while only 3% of the very hostile rural respondents were very self-confident, 36% of the non-hostile rural respondents were very self-confident. This relationship does not appear among our urban respondents. Their level of self-confidence can be as high if they are hostile as it is when there is low hostility. In fact the highest incidence of zero self-confidence (18%) is found among those urban respondents with no apparent hostility. These may be the withdrawn, apathetic, or alienated urban respondents, who may be more resigned than hostile. Although there is no significant relationship for urban respondents in these data, the fact that a lessening of rural hostility is related to higher rural self-confidence is a finding of no little importance for the developmental process in rural India.

Conclusions

This exploration of patterns of citizen hostility toward administrators indicates that the incidence of this phenomenon varies by type of agency, by the fact of urban or rural residence, to some extent by socioeconomic status, by traditional attitudinal orientation, and by frequency of contact with administrative officials. We found from 8% to 13% of our respondents very hostile; from 22% to 37% not hostile at all. We found that for most hostile people their antagonism is not directed at one agency alone, although contact with the police is probably most functionally related to hostility. It seems that hard-core traditionalists are most likely to have hostile reactions, often stereotypic reactions, towards authority figures such as administrators. The extent and nature of bureaucratic contact can apparently intensify such latent hostility feelings, although bureaucratic contact is not necessarily a contributing factor. It is perhaps to be expected in a transitional society such as India that bitterness and hostility toward administrators emerge as the administrative system assumes new duties and establishes new relationships with the citizenry. It is gratifying that the public is highly supportive of the system in the face of moderate levels of hostility. In rural India particularly, support and self-confidence levels, though apparently affected by personal hostility toward administrators, are rather high despite such hostile feelings. As the bureaucrats in the field assume less authoritarian postures and techniques, and convince the public of their service-functional and instrumental role in the system, our data suggest that hostility will decline and all but the most hard-core traditionalists will come to accept the new bureaucracy, support it, and participate cooperatively with it.

The administrator:
Social background,
personal orientation,
training experience,
and job perspectives

chapter 5

Our study of citizen attitudes toward administrators would not be complete without analysis of the administrator himself. The preceding chapters have explored a variety of factors which help explain differential patterns of public perceptions. But the bureaucratic subsystem consists essentially of citizen and administrator interacting with each other, and reacting to each other. Theoretically, the administrator is acting upon his images of his role, his career, his public. And it is this set of administrator perspectives, and consequent behavior, individually and collectively, to which the public is responding. It is necessary, therefore, to describe the bureaucratic context or contexts within which the citizen is located, and, if possible, to link that context to citizen response.

In designing this portion of our study we selected agencies relevant to the geographical areas in which our public sample was located, representing local, state, and national levels of authority, and representing both the historic, standard administrative system and the newer Community Development bureaucracy. We decided to interview officials in the police, postal, and health agencies in both urban and rural Delhi, to interview Community Development officials in rural Delhi, and officials in the Delhi Transport Undertaking in urban Delhi. Further, we desired, insofar as possible, to interview officials at two hierarchical levels — at the level of officials directly in contact with the public (police constables, bus inspectors, village level workers, etc.), and if possible at the level immediately above (police superintendents, doctors in charge of health clinics, Community Development officers, etc.). We were not able to completely fulfill this latter objective for the DTU and the urban postal service. Finally, we selected these officials by a procedure which emphasized the identification of officials with the eight villages and twenty-five urban mohallas in which our public lived. This would permit as tight a fit as possible between the officials in our study and the public in our study.[1]

Another important factor was our particular interest in developing a theory which focused on the conditions and criteria most useful for determining the extent to which Indian administrators are democratic and welfare-state oriented in their understanding of their roles and responsibilities. The components of democratic orientations to which we paid particular attention included: acceptance of the democratic system and a willingness to perform within it; a responsible awareness of the needs and demands of the public; sensitivity to the public in the sense of being service oriented and clientele conscious, rather than being exclusively preoccupied with private organizational goals and tasks; adaptability and accountability, defined as a willingness to be reasonable in implementing rules, and a recognition of the need to explain and justify administrative actions and decisions; and, finally, humility with dignity, by which is meant the ability to respect the citizen while also respecting one's own professional status. The absence of these component orientations would, indeed, be suggestive of a paternalistic, if not authoritarian, set of role perceptions, smacking of pre-Independence India, and certainly not conducive to the achievement of administrative goals in a system strongly reliant on citizen cooperation.

---

[1] In certain of our administrative subcategories we interviewed not a sample but every available person of a particular category. Thus we interviewed all block development officers in our areas, all extension officers, all Panchayat secretaries, all village level workers, all medical officers in charge, all postmasters, all police station house officers, all assistant subinspectors. Further, for a second category of officials we interviewed a sample of 50% or more: compounders, midwives, lady health visitors (9 of 10), head constables. Finally, for one category — police constables — we interviewed approximately a 10% sample, randomly selected. These interviews provided us with both a rich diversity of administrative types as well as sufficient geographical concentration, thus permitting analysis of hierarchical differences, agency differences, and patterns of congruence between administrators and the public in the total Delhi area as well as in particular geographical sectors.

Closely tied to this conceptualization of the democratic administrator was the concept of the welfare-state administrator. Two basic components were uppermost in our minds. One concerns the distributive orientation — does he feel that he as administrator has the positive responsibility of improving human welfare, solving social problems, and allocating economic justice? The second component concerns his egalitarian orientation — does he believe that administration must be conducted in such a way as to treat all citizens equally and fairly, in a nondiscriminatory style, with particular awareness of the validity of the needs and rights of the have-not sectors of Indian society? By operationalizing these concepts and testing their incidence in our study it was our hope to collect valuable evidence and to work toward a meaningful and realistic theory of democratic administration in a developing society.

The personal backgrounds of administrators

Description of the personal backgrounds of adminstrators is useful in at least two ways. It tells us what social sectors of the population these officials come from, and whether agencies differ in social origins. It also can indicate whether within agencies there are social gaps between the higher and lower echelons of officials.

Our data (Table 5.1) reveal, first, that the lower social strata of Indian society are poorly represented in these agencies. The lower castes have less than 10% of these positions, those with a primary school education or less are found generally only among the police constables (26%), and those with low family incomes are found in sizeable numbers only among constables (67%) and postal officials (31%). There is a considerable spread among age groups, with a surprising number found in the age category of "30 and under." Hindus dominate all agencies, as might be expected in the Delhi area. The Community Development administrators differ from the others in two important respects: they tend to be younger, especially the supervisory officials, and they have a larger percentage of non-Hindus among the line officials.

A second type of finding concerns the hierarchical differences within agencies.[2] There is high congruence in these agencies between staff and line on the social characteristics of caste status and religion. This may be very significant, suggesting a recruitment process which is both nondiscriminatory and hierarchically balanced. The colonization of particular agencies by certain castes does

---

[2]Note that we could not differentiate hierarchically from our data for the postal and DTU agencies.

5.1 Social characteristics of Indian administrators

Variable	POLICE		HEALTH		COMMUNITY DEVELOPMENT		POSTAL	DTU
	Staff	Constables	Staff	Compounders	Staff	Line		
1. AGE								
30 and under	14%	39%	27%	32%	48%	35%	23%	0%
31 to 40	49	58	27	27	52	43	37	24
older	37	3	46	41	0	22	40	76
2. RELIGION								
Hindu	91	91	86	91	87	61	91	88
Other	9	9	14	9	13	39	9	12
3. EDUCATION								
Illiterate or primary	0	26	0	0	0	4	9	0
Secondary	66	71	0	95	68	87	77	100
Higher	34	3	100	5	32	9	14	0
4. CASTE								
Brahmin and upper	21	24	43	53	38	24	56	44
Middle caste	76	70	57	42	52	70	35	44
Lower caste	3	6	0	5	10	6	9	13
5. FAMILY INCOME (monthly)								
Under 150 rupees	11	67	3	5	9	13	31	0
151 to 250 rupees	26	24	0	77	26	35	26	53
Over 250 rupees	63	9	97	18	65	52	43	47
Number of cases	35	33	29	22	23	23	35	17

not appear in our data but rather, a social mixture of caste groups. Thus 14% of the police staff are Brahmins while 21% of the constables are Brahmins; 7% and 10%, respectively, come from other upper caste groups; 70% to 76% are middle caste.

There are, however, other social status differences between staff and line in these agencies—in educational and income status. The latter is most striking in the police and health agencies. The greater majority of the staff are *relatively* well off (from 63% to 97%), but only a small minority of the constables and compounders make over 250 rupees a month. Among Community Development officials one does not find these social status differentiations—both staff and line are relatively well off.[3]

These administrative cadres, then, while under-representing lower status groups, do comprehend and reflect considerable social diversity. Hierarchical differences in educational and financial status are great, except in the Community Development cadre. These differences may be related to agency communication patterns, morale, role perspectives, and public response. Tensions may be modified or accentuated within these agencies by the balanced representation of caste groups.

Job tenure, mobility, and satisfaction

The administrators in our study have held their positions for varying tenures. From 25% to 40% of those in staff positions are fairly recent appointees, while line incumbents tend to have much longer tenures. The turnover of postmen is much greater than constables and bus inspectors, however. The line personnel in Community Development have a relatively balanced set of tenures, 50% having held their positions for over five years, and about 25% being recent appointees. If one combines this with the data on total job mobility while in governmental service (Table 5.2), the significance is clear. The staff personnel, as might be expected, have been highly mobile, with 33% or more having come rather recently to their positions at the time we interviewed them. The line personnel, however, show very limited mobility and are individuals who tend to have held their present positions for a relatively long time. As a matter of fact, we found the following percentages of line personnel in these agencies to have spent over 10 years in governmental service with no advancement:

---

[3] A detailed analysis by the three Community Development blocks in our study reveals different patterns, but high congruence. For example, in only one block was there significant representation of lower caste groups, but these were found at *both* the staff level (23%) and the line level (17%).

Police constables 61%
Medical compounders 50%
Community Development 32%

This leads to the query: Are the line personnel satisfied with their positions, or is there a morale problem in certain agencies due to the lack of upward mobility? A further question is: How difficult is it for staff personnel to motivate and commit line personnel, who have been on the job for a long period of time and non-mobile, to new perspectives in developmental administration? The important finding in these data is that many of these officials most closely in touch with the public have held their jobs for some time, suggesting an accumulation of experience, standardizing patterns of dealing with the public, and perhaps frustration. Has it been difficult, therefore, for such officials at the cutting edge of administration to adapt to new administrative norms in working with the public?

The majority of officials told us they found their jobs interesting (Table 5.3). Job satisfaction appeared to be particularly high in the health and Community Development agencies, where we found from 70% to 100% asserting that they "liked their work," although smaller proportions claimed their jobs were "interesting." The field personnel in Community Development seemed particularly satisfied. Combining their responses to these questions concerning job satisfaction with job tenure, we found a strong relationship between length of time in governmental service without career mo-

5.2   Tenure and mobility of officials by agency

	POLICE		HEALTH		COMMUNITY DEVELOPMENT		POSTAL	DTU
	Staff	Line	Staff	Line	Staff	Line		
TENURE IN PRESENT POSITION								
Less than one year	29%	3%	24%	5%	22%	13%	26%	0%
1 to 3 years	9	6	17	14	9	13	17	6
3 to 5 years	17	12	28	23	48	22	29	29
Longer	45	79	31	58	22	52	29	65
JOB MOBILITY								
No mobility	3	97	46	82	35	81	29	6
Upward mobility	97	3	54	18	65	19	68	94

5·3   Job interest and satisfaction for officials in various agencies

	POLICE		HEALTH		COMMUNITY DEVELOPMENT		POSTAL	DTU
	Staff	Line	Staff	Line	Staff	Line		
Is your job interesting?								
Yes	65%	67%	62%	64%	87%	74%	46%	59%
Somewhat-has reservations	30	21	38	32	13	26	37	41
No	5	12	0	4	0	0	17	0
How do you feel about your work?								
Likes his work	74	58	97	73	78	100	71	71
Has reservations	26	42	3	27	22	0	29	29

bility *and* job dissatisfaction. Thus 59% of the non-mobile police constables with long tenure had mild or strong reservations about their jobs; and 62% of health compounders with similar career patterns seemed somewhat frustrated. Community Development field personnel had shorter tenures and greater job satisfaction — only 34% of the non-mobile officials in the agency three years or more indicated any dissatisfaction with their positions.

There is potential for disaffection, then, in the agencies we studied. Large proportions of line personnel have not been able to advance. Their jobs are not interesting or satisfying to possibly one third of these officials. In the Community Development program the probabilities of tension and disaffection seem lower, despite long tenure without career advancement. Officials in Community Development work seem to be highly committed to their tasks and roles.

Emphases in training

A central question for a modernizing society like India is whether the administrative system has incorporated and is transmitting democratic and welfare-state norms to its personnel. Examination of the training function is relevant in this context. To what extent are training programs directed to the developmental requisite of an administrative cadre conscious of public needs, aware of the goal and value of public involvement, and committed to "good public relations"? The emphases in training perceived by the officials in these agencies whom we interviewed will indicate whether Indian bureaucracy is moving towards such developmental objectives.

Different proportions of the urban and rural officials in our study indicated that they had gone through extensive training programs. About 33% of the urban and 10% of the rural officials said they had not been exposed to any training programs for government work. Others had gone through brief training. But slightly over 40% of the urban officials and approximately 70% of the rural officials appear to have had considerable training for their present jobs. Most of these officials felt the training had been worth while.

But training varied greatly by agency. For the line personnel the following proportions in each agency said they had had *no* training or *very brief* training sessions:

	No training	Brief training
Police constables	3%	12%
Health compounders	41	23
Community Development	9	9
Postmen	59	18
DTU	82	12

The police and Community Development programs apparently subject their personnel to the most intensive training. This is true also for the police staff officers, only 3% of whom were never exposed to a training program. The Community Development staff personnel, however, appear less trained — 22% reported that they were not trained for the particular positions they now hold. This compares favorably, however, with the medical officer corps in our study, 54% of whom said they had not undergone training for their positions.

Obviously, the postmen and bus inspectors are left to learn on the job. In the other agencies only small minorities are not subjected to some type of training. The issue is, what is the content of this training? Particularly, does it communicate public relations aspects of the work, with what degree of emphasis, and in what substantive directions? We used a series of open-ended questions to get the respondents to tell us about the content of training programs and the nature of instructions given to them. The results of three of these are given in Table 5.4.

The agency with least emphasis on public relations is the postal service. As noted previously, less than 50% undergo a training program. Of those personnel who have had such a program, over

5.4 Emphasis on public relations in administrative training

	POLICE		HEALTH		COMMUNITY DEVELOPMENT		POSTAL	DTU
	Staff	Constables	Staff	Line	Staff	Line		
Training emphasis:								
Public relations emphasized	71%	73%	18%	45%	70%	74%	16%	18%
Public relations *not* emphasized	26	24	28	14	8	17	25	0
No training	3	3	55	41	22	9	59	82
Content of instructions in dealing with public:								
Democratic content	63	85	17	50	65	87	26	24
Bureaucratic content	9	0	0	5	0	0	0	0
Both contents	9	6	3	0	4	0	0	0
Not ascertained, don't know, and inapplicable	19	9	80	45	31	13	74	76
What does your superior emphasize?								
Public relations mentioned	79	85	37	55	70	61	49	88
Public relations *not* mentioned	18	12	48	45	30	39	40	12
Never see him	3	3	15	0	0	0	11	0

50% do not refer to public relations as a primary emphasis in that program. Again, about 50% of the immediate supervisors of post-men seem to emphasize public relations; the remainder are never seen or emphasize other aspects of the job. The supervisors of transport inspectors apparently are much more conscious of public relations (88% emphasize it); this may compensate for the lack of a training program.

The police and Community Development officials seem to be the most aware of the problem of maintaining good relationships with the public. Seventy per cent or more indicate that public relations is emphasized in formal training. What is equally interesting is the finding that supervisors of our respondents in police and CD communicated an awareness of public relations. Thus 80% of our police superintendents and station house officers report that they see *their* superiors *and* that these superiors emphasize the public relations aspects of the job of police superintendent. In turn, 85% of the police constables report that *their* superiors communicate the same emphasis.

The image of a police hierarchy transmitting down the line a concern for dealing with the public clearly emerges from these data. The same basic image emerges from our interviews with CD personnel. Thus, 70% of our "second echelon" respondents (block development officers, Panchayat secretaries, extension officers, etc.) report that they see *their* superiors and that public relations are emphasized. In turn, 61% of our CD line personnel report the same hierarchical transmission of concern for the public. There is, however, a sizeable minority of Community Development personnel who are either not trained or unaware of an emphasis on public relations in their training or in their relations with their superiors. These represent 33%, approximately, of CD personnel. They are a genuine problem for the system, as are the health personnel (no more than 50% of whom seem particularly aware of the public relations aspects of their job). Generally, however, the police and CD agencies seem self-consciously aware of public relations responsibilities, as a result of formal training and intra-agency communication processes.

The job orientations of administrators

We have examined the social background from which the administrator comes, his career status, and some of the organizational conditions to which he is exposed. These contextual influences obviously vary for particular agencies and within agencies. We come now to the critical question of the administrator's own perspectives toward his role, particularly his image of himself as an actor interacting with the public. Do the attitudes of administrators toward their public responsibilities and relationships also vary? It is one thing to find public-relations training programs, lower social class origins, and job satisfaction; or, conversely, no training programs, upper middle class origins, or job dissatisfaction. It is another to find democratic or undemocratic role perspectives correlated with such contextual influences. For a developing democracy such as India the incidence of democratic administrative orientations is a crucial test for the probable success of the system. The bureaucratic structure, which is above all a structure of the job and role perceptions of administrators, can provide us with significant clues about the movement of the system toward developmental and democratic goals.

A variety of questions were put to the officials, mostly open-ended, the responses to which we hoped would permit us to determine their orientations toward their jobs, particularly their orientations as officials interacting with the public. Aside from standard questions asking them to describe "the nature of your job," and "which duties take most of your time," we probed for specific orientations with the following types of questions: Do you find it at times necessary in your position to relax the procedures to do a more effective job? Do you find it possible to relax procedures? Do you think the public makes extra demands on you over and above what you do for them in the ordinary course of your job? (If *yes*) can you tell me something about the nature of these demands? Do you think it is necessary for you to explain to citizens the reasons for your decisions? How important do you think it is for your particular agency to get cooperation from the public? Why (or why not)? What kinds of cooperation from the public do you think you should get? And then this key question: Some people say that serving the public is most important; others say that following the orders of your superiors is most important. How do you feel about this? (Probe: If says both are, ask which of the two is more important.) These questions were useful in determining democratic role orientations by agency and by level within the hierarchy.

It is quite obvious from our data that the emphasis on public relations in the Indian government and society has impressed upon the large majority of officials the importance of getting public cooperation. An overwhelming number of them (88%) said that public cooperation was very important to their agencies; the remainder said it was somewhat important (with the largest concentration of these among urban health officials, 33% of whom gave this response). None said it was unimportant. Further, in certain agencies large proportions of officials sense the pressure of public demands for administrative service. This is indicated in the responses to our questions as to whether the public makes extra demands. Police constables and bus inspectors responded negatively to this question (only 12% indicating they were aware of such demands). The remainder seem particularly cognizant of public pressure: 67% of the CD officials, staff and line, and approximately 70% of the police staff personnel and postal officials. Although police constables and bus inspectors report little pressure for extra service, they are overwhelmingly aware of the need for public cooperation in their work—over 85% of the inspectors and over 95% of the constables said it was very important.

Despite an awareness that they are functioning in an administrative system and in a society with high expectations of cooperative citizen-administrator relationships, the extent of the commitment of the officials in our study to democratic roles and behaviors varies considerably. When we asked these administrators whether they thought it was "your job to treat everybody fairly," we found very few (only 10%) taking a negative position. Further, when we asked whether the official felt a necessity to explain to the public the reasons for his decisions, a somewhat larger proportion took the bureaucratic viewpoint, but over 70% in all agencies at both hierarchical levels responded affirmatively (Table 5.5). There were no significant agency differences. The Community Development staff officials were slightly more bureaucratic than in other agencies, but the differences are not great enough to be serious.

Much more evidence of a bureaucratic orientation was found when we asked about the relaxation of administrative procedures. The findings here are interesting. First, staff officials are generally inclined to admit the necessity for relaxing procedures. Over 66% of staff personnel in all agencies except police take this position, and approximately 50% of police staff personnel also admit to the necessity for being adaptive. But the line personnel are much more bureaucratic in their responses in all agencies except Community Development and the postal service. Whereas over 50% of line personnel in other agencies deny the need to relax procedures, only 17% of postmen and 24% of Community Development officials in direct contact with the public take this position. Over 60% of police constables gave bureaucratic responses to this question. This suggests a more pragmatic-adaptive approach to the public for Community Development workers and postmen than for other officials.

Second, although large percentages of officials see the need for

5.5   Specific job orientations of administrators

	POLICE		HEALTH		COMMUNITY DEVELOPMENT		POSTAL	DTU
	Staff	Line	Staff	Line	Staff	Line		
1. *Necessary to explain reasons for decisions (to the public)?*								
Yes	79%	75%	89%	77%	73%	86%	79%	100%
No	18	13	7	18	27	14	18	0
Don't know	3	13	3	5	0	0	3	0
2. *Necessary to relax procedures?*								
Yes, and does	36	25	17	29	35	57	59	27
Yes, but does not	18	13	54	12	39	19	24	18
No	46	63	29	59	26	24	17	55

relaxing procedures, many officials in each agency say they cannot or do not in fact modify procedures. Just slightly over 50% of all the staff officials in our study who see this necessity are pragmatic in their administrative operations, while 66% of line officials are. Community Development line officials and postmen, again, are the most willing to be flexible in administrative actions.

In sum, the officials in our study seem to have been indoctrinated with the idea of administrative flexibility in dealing with the public — staff personnel more so than line personnel. But, except in the Community Development and postal structures, only 25% to 33% do actually reflect this democratic norm in their behavior.

This evidence of a basic bureaucratic orientation is corroborated when we asked officials which is more important — "serving the public" or "following the orders of your superior?" Large minorities insisted both were (Table 5.6). But significant proportions placed greater importance on following orders — ranging from 3% among the medical officers, to 40% of the police superintendents, and 39% of the Community Development staff. It is interesting that except for the health officials, line personnel were more service oriented than staff personnel. It is significant also that the Community Development line personnel—the village level workers and their associates—seem least committed to the bureaucratic tradition. Over 80% of Community Development line personnel place high emphasis on serving the public.

The evidence presented here on the public-service orientations of agencies is conflicting. There are apparently individuals with democratic and highly bureaucratic perspectives in all agencies. On balance, cumulative evidence suggests that the Community Development village workers and line personnel are the most inclined to be democratic in job perspectives. The training program emphasizes public relations, the concept of adapting to public needs and working to solicit public cooperation appears to be transmitted in the Community Development hierarchy, and the majority of the personnel in the field manifest this emphasis in the answers they gave us concerning their jobs. Postmen have almost as consistent a set of democratic orientations, although their training program is poor. In the other agencies the evidence is mixed. Policemen, for example, seem democratic on some dimensions, but bureaucratic on others. The same is true for health officials and bus inspectors.

The extent of consistency in job perspectives by agency can be demonstrated by examining the responses of individual administrators on three of the questions we used: how important did he feel public cooperation was for his agency, did he relax procedures, and was serving the public or following orders more important. The distributions for selected sets of officials were as shown in Table 5.7. If a rigorous test of consistency is used, less than 25% of these line personnel measure up to democratic requirements.

On the other hand, almost all of them do occasionally respond in democratic terms, attesting to the penetration of the norms of public service and responsibility into the lower reaches of the Indian bureaucracy. If we call those who are consistent on at least two of

5.6 Conflict in primary administrative orientations: "Serving the Public" vs. "Following Orders"

	POLICE		HEALTH		COMMUNITY DEVELOPMENT		POSTAL	DTU
Primary Orientation	Staff	Line	Staff	Line	Staff	Line		
Serving the public	48%	45%	49%	50%	39%	65%	40%	35%
Following orders	40	34	3	27	39	17	29	35
Both	12	21	48	23	22	17	29	30
Uncertain; don't know	0	0	0	0	0	0	3	0

5·7   Consistency in democratic job perspectives

	CD line	Constables	Postmen	Health line	Bus inspectors
Consistently democratic on all three dimensions	26%	18%	29%	18%	12%
Democratic on two of the three dimensions	70	52	53	45	47
Democratic on one dimension only	4	30	15	23	35
Democratic on none	0	0	3	14	6

these dimensions to be democratic, the Community Development officials can be contrasted to bus inspectors — 96% of the former and 59% of the latter qualifying as democratic administrators. Postmen are close to Community Development officials, followed by the constables, with health line personnel closer to the bus inspectors in democratic perspectives.

We developed an "Index of democratic job perspectives" for all our officials, since we felt that reliance on one or a few responses would not properly permit us to type officials. In the index we used the three responses referred to above, as well as three other types of information: their reactions to and characterization of their training, whether they felt it was necessary to explain their administrative decisions, and their description of the nature of their jobs. Weighting public-relations-oriented responses as more important than other responses for this purpose, we scored each individual on all six items. Maximum score possible by this index was 12. Actual scores for respondents ranged from 2 to 11. The pattern of scores by agency and echelon is found in Table 5.8.

When all the responses are cumulated into our index we see more clearly the variation in democratic role perspectives by agency, at two levels of the hierarchy. The police are particularly interesting, for their staff personnel demonstrate the greatest awareness of democratic norms, but the constables are least aware of all the line personnel. Therefore, there is the greatest gap in the police force between superintendent and constable, with the latter most bureaucratic in his perspectives. This raises serious questions about the adequacy and penetration of their training programs. In health the distribution is fairly even between staff and line. If one takes those with scores of seven or more, 45% of the medical officers as well as the compounders are democratic, with, however, many more compounders at the low, or bureaucratic, end of the scale. Community Development presents yet another situation. The line personnel are far and away the most democratic, with 75% scoring above six. But the staff by this index are much less democratic — only 43% are "democratic." This suggests, then, a hierarchical gap also, but the reverse of the one found in the police force and probably very functional to the achievement of public cooperation, support, and respect. The postmen (on this index in contrast to earlier data—primarily because of training inadequacies) and bus inspectors do not as frequently reveal a respect for democratic norms as do the CD village level workers and their associates.

In sum, the balance in most of these agencies seems to be slightly on the bureaucratic side, although usually only small percentages show no real evidence of democratic job perspectives. CD is an exception for line personnel. For all officials in our study, 13% score high on this index, 35% are moderately democratic, 33% are moderately bureaucratic, and 19% seem clearly bureaucratic.

Factors related to democratic job perspectives

What distinguishes administrators with democratic as contrasted to bureaucratic attitudes toward their work? Why should some emphasize public service, relaxation of rules, sensitivity to public demands, concern for public cooperation, while others emphasize following orders, strict enforcement of procedures, unawareness of public demands or their propriety, and unconcern about public cooperation? We have already seen that agencies differ in their incidence and pattern of democratic job perspectives. This suggests differences *between* agencies as well as hierarchical differences *within* agencies. Agency norms may differ, and yet there may not be the communication or transmission of these norms within an agency. This is the paradox of the police force and Community Development, but in quite separate ways. In the police force there

5•8 Index of democratic job perspectives

Scores	POLICE		HEALTH		COMMUNITY DEVELOPMENT		POSTAL	DTU
	Staff	Line	Staff	Line	Staff	Line		
High (9-11)	30%	18%	7%	18%	13%	39%	9%	12%
Moderate high (7-8)	32	24	38	27	30	35	38	47
Moderate low (5-6)	32	42	45	18	52	26	30	35
Low (below 5)	6	15	10	36	4	0	23	6

5•9 Caste and democratic job perspectives

Index of democratic job perspectives	High caste	Middle caste	Low caste
ALL PERSONNEL			
Democratic (highest scores)	18%	18%	0
Moderately democratic	33	33	42
Tends bureaucratic	38	36	25
Bureaucratic (lowest scores)	11	13	33
Number of cases	*73*	*114*	*12*
ALL LINE PERSONNEL			
Democratic	13	19	
Moderately democratic	39	33	
Tends bureaucratic	37	31	
Bureaucratic	11	17	
Number of cases	*46*	*63*	*

*Too few cases for analysis

is a low incidence of democratic norms at the constable level, despite democratic norms at the staff level and an apparently comprehensive training program. In CD the opposite is true — democratic norms at the base of the structure despite low incidence of democratic norms at the staff level, *and* a training program. Are, then, organizational conditions contributory, or are other factors more helpful in explaining democratic job perspectives?

One might well expect that in India the social background from which an administrator comes would be related to his job perspectives. Our analysis revealed little evidence to this effect. One factor which is particularly interesting in this respect is caste status. As was demonstrated earlier in this chapter there is a mixture of caste groups in each of these agencies, although low caste groups are only minimally represented. From 20% to over 50% of the personnel have high caste backgrounds; from 3% to 10%, roughly, come from low castes.[4] But caste status seems to be only partially related to democratic job perspectives (Table 5.9). The high caste personnel are no more bureaucratic in job perspectives than middle caste officials. Approximately 50% of both groups, irrespective of the agency, fall into the democratic category. The few lower caste personnel in our sample do appear to be somewhat more bureaucratic, but the percentage differences do not present a striking contrast. Over 40% of

[4]See Table 5.1.

our low caste officials have developed democratic attitudes toward their jobs. This pattern of findings may indeed be very significant. It indicates that the caste system, the traditional bastion of conservatism, is no necessary impediment to development. Or, rather, that despite the caste origin of administrators they can and do develop democratic orientations toward their administrative positions.

Length of tenure in governmental employment might also be associated with job perspectives. One might expect the newer recruits to government service to be more amenable to, and supportive of, the democratic norms of the post-Independence administration. Generally, however, no relationship was found which seemed significant (Table 5.10). Actually, personnel with shorter tenure in governmental service seemed least democratic, and those with a medium tenure most democratic in their job perspectives. But the differences are not large. The number of cases was small for particular tenure groups for specific agencies, so a reliable analysis could not be made. Among the Community Development staff personnel, for example, we found long tenure in governmental service seemingly associated with bureaucratic perspectives, while the reverse seemed true for the CD line personnel. Perhaps the most important conclusion is that Indian public servants in our study who had a long record of government service were as likely to be bureaucratic as democratic in their job perspectives. This suggests that other factors *are operating and have been operating* to produce public servants with new democratic job orientations under certain circumstances and conditions.

There is a basis for some optimism in these findings concerning caste and tenure in relationship to administrative perspectives. They suggest that despite social structural and traditional organizational affiliations and commitments which might lead him in bureaucratic directions, the Indian public servant can and does adapt to democratic norms. In addition, we were interested in investigating the psychological predispositions of these civil servants to see what their latent authoritarian-democratic orientations might be, and then to compare this latent predisposition with the respondent's perspective concerning his administrative role. In developing such an authoritarianism index we explored the utility of the following statements, asking the respondent to indicate agreement or disagreement with each. (The proportion indicating *agreement* with each is indicated in parentheses.)

1. "A few strong leaders could make this country better than all the laws and talk." (85%)

5·10 Job tenure and democratic job perspectives

Index of democratic job perspectives	Short tenure (Five years or less)	Medium tenure (Five to fifteen years)	Long tenure (Over fifteen years)
ALL PERSONNEL			
Democratic (highest scores)	16%	22%	16%
Moderately democratic	27	38	34
Tends bureaucratic	39	32	35
Bureaucratic	18	8	16
Number of cases	49	78	83
ALL LINE PERSONNEL			
Democratic (highest scores)	21	20	18
Moderately democratic	18	45	31
Tends bureaucratic	36	25	33
Bureaucratic	25	10	18
Number of cases	28	48	51

2. "People can be trusted." (63%)
3. "Obedience and respect for authority are the most important virtues children should learn." (99%)
4. "The world is too complicated to be understood by anyone but experts." (84%)
5. "People are getting soft and weak from so much babying and coddling." (78%)

If "toughness," "strong leaders," an overwhelming respect for "authority," and a need for the "expert" are clues to personal authoritarian predispositions, these leaders appear so disposed. Except for item 2, the authoritarian response was high; in the case of item 3, so high that as a discriminating measure it was of no utility. Although one may question the validity and applicability of these statements (used widely in American studies) to India, in the absence of more valid and reliable measures these do, indeed, indicate that the Indian civil servant is basically authoritarian in his *personal* predispositions and view of the political world. The distributions for all the administrators in our study (excluding item 3) reveal this:

	Proportion of All Administrators
Four democratic responses	2%
Three " "	5
Two " "	24
One " response	45
No " "	24
	100%

The incidence of personal authoritarianism by agency is interesting (Table 5.11). Community Development officials are least authoritarian, with over 40% of these administrators tending to give democratic responses to these items. This contrasts to 18% in the DTU and line officials in the health service. The police fall in between — the constables slightly more democratic than the police staff, and postal officials as democratic as the police. Thus, though a high level of authoritarian response is found in all agencies, recruitment into the CD program seems to yield a higher proportion of officials whose latent predispositions are democratic.

The basic and primary query for us, however, is whether these latent personal predispositions correlate with job perspectives. Do we find that the administrator who reveals, by his responses to our

5.11 Personal authoritarian and democratic predispositions of agency personnel

Authoritarian-democratic index	POLICE		HEALTH		COMMUNITY DEVELOPMENT		POSTAL	DTU
	Staff	Line	Staff	Line	Staff	Line		
Two to four demo-cratic responses	29%	36%	21%	18%	48%	43%	34%	18%
One democratic response	45	31	51	68	43	35	43	47
No democratic response	26	33	28	14	9	22	23	35

statements about the political world, a tendency to be authoritarian in his images also to be the administrator who looks on his job in bureaucratic terms, and has little feeling for the public service aspects of his job? This is a critical problem, and our findings, as well as their meaning for Indian administration today, must be assessed carefully (Table 5.12).

We find in fact a peculiar non-congruence between manifestations of democratic orientations in *personal* predispositions and in *job* perspectives. Administrators with democratic personal predispositions tend only slightly to be less bureaucratic than the others. Over 40% of the former tend to have a bureaucratic job perspective. On the other hand, 50% of our authoritarian administrators indicate that they are inclined to be basically non-bureaucratic in the way they view their jobs.

5.12 Relationships between authoritarian-democratic *personal* predispositions and bureaucratic-democratic *job* perspectives

Authoritarian-demo-cratic predisposi-tion index	Job Perspectives Index:				
	Democratic (Score 9+)	(Score 7–8)	(Score 5–6)	Bureaucratic (Score under 5)	N*
DEMOCRATIC					
(score: 2+)	21%	36%	33%	10%	67
(score:1)	15	33	36	15	99
AUTHORITARIAN					
(score: 0)	19	31	37	13	52

*N=number of cases.

This suggests four possible interpretations. One is that these indices are not valid or meaningful for the Indian context. Further studies will help determine whether this is so. It should be accepted, however, that the degree of authoritarianism we found in our study may be tenable, as well as the extent to which Indian administrators genuinely espouse democratic role perceptions. A second interpretation is that Indian administrators compartmentalize these two syndromes — they can in fact be both authoritarian and non-bureaucratic, for example. This possibility should certainly not be ignored. A third interpretation is that there is a close linkage between predispositions and role or job perspectives, and that one of these two syndromes predominates (psychological predispositions), and that, further, when Indian administrators talked to us about their jobs they used democratic jargon which they really did not accept. This would mean that despite indications to the contrary that Indian administrators in the development bureaucracy are accepting democratic norms of behavior, they are still overwhelmingly authoritarian. This is indeed a possibility, but the variety of responses we have on which we built our index of job perspectives, relying both on direct and indirect questions, leads us to question this interpretation.

This leaves us with a fourth interpretation, that under certain conditions, primarily organizational, administrators who are latently authoritarian can take on genuinely democratic perceptions concerning their jobs. And that these democratic perceptions, though conflicting with basic authoritarian predispositions, can predominate, reënforced as they are by organizational expectations, and be functionally related to a meaningful democratic performance. This is an optimistic view of the data, but one for which we find much supporting evidence.

Undoubtedly, administrative structures differ in expectations in this respect. We have found differences by type of agency both in the incidence of democratic job perspectives (Table 5.8), and in authoritarian-democratic predispositions (Table 5.11). A further test of the theory that organizational conditions are related to the development of democratic job perspectives is possible by analysis of the factor of training. The key question here is whether exposure to an in-service training program, and particularly a training program oriented toward the democratic and public service aspects of administration, seems conducive to the occurrence of democratic job perspectives in such agencies.

Our data suggest that the existence of some type of training program by itself may be a factor related to a democratic job perspective. Our three agencies whose officials reported to us with the greatest frequency that there was no training program—health, DTU, and postal—had the lowest scores on the democratic job perspectives index. The contrast between Community Development and the health line officials is perhaps the most striking. About 40% of CD officials compared to 7% of health officials were found in the highest score category on the democratic perspectives index. In the former there was an extensive training program, in the latter, virtually none, according to the reports of our respondents.

It is not, however, merely the existence of a training program which is relevant, but whether the training program was *understood and perceived as emphasizing "public relations."* The same training program in the same agency could be interpreted differently. As Table 5.13 indicates, there is a striking difference in job perspectives for those officials who perceived and did not perceive the training as emphasizing public relations. Over 70% of those who saw their training as emphasizing public relations had very democratic orientations. On the other hand, the existence of a training program not emphasizing public relations was no more efficacious in developing democratic perspectives than if there were no training program at all. Thus, a training program which does not get through to its personnel is of critical importance, and obviously many officials do not perceive training programs as oriented toward public relations.

5•13 The role of training in developing democratic job perspectives

Democratic job perspectives index	Training oriented to public relations	Training not oriented to public relations	No training program
High scores—democratic	72%	30%	34%
Medium to low scores	26	45	42
Very low scores	2	25	24
Number of cases	*103*	*44*	*62*

The importance of this factor of differential personal perceptions of training programs is seen by a careful inspection of the police and Community Development agencies. Both of these agencies reputedly had training programs which emphasized public relations. *But* not all police or Community Development personnel perceived the program as emphasizing public relations. About 25% of police officials and 15% of CD officials did not. These differential perceptions were related to differential job perspectives. These data can be summarized quickly, as follows:

Perception category	Percentage with high scores on democratic job-perspectives index	
	Police	CD
Perceived training as oriented toward public relations	63%	73%
Did not perceive training as oriented toward public relations	28	25

Note: Each per cent is the proportion of each perception category which had high scores on the democratic perspectives index.

Thus, within the same agency, despite the existence of a public relations training program, certain personnel for some reason are not aware of the program's emphasis. And this can produce significant consequences for their attitudes toward the public. It is these two interrelated findings which perhaps have the most significance for Indian administration today.

Admittedly, it might be argued that our reasoning here is circular: that obviously those officials who hold democratic jobs perspectives would be those who said their training emphasized public relations. For three reasons we do not believe this to be the case. First, we organized each variable differently, with different sets of questions, to minimize this overlap. Second, we asked the questions in a sequence which would separate the two variables in the minds of the respondent. And third, our data themselves show that this is not the case — not all officials who had democratic perspectives saw their training as emphasizing public relations, and vice versa. It is doubtful, therefore, that we are measuring the same phenomena with different sets of questions. Training perceptions may or may not lead to particular sets of perspectives; training programs which are public-service oriented may or may not be thus perceived; when they are seen as public-service oriented, they do indeed seem to have an impact on official role perspectives. Finally, despite a possible circularity, the finding that training perceptions and job perspectives are clearly linked in India is critical.

One final finding concerning the authoritarian predispostions of Indian administrators is interesting in connection with the above analysis. We find very little linkage between this latent predisposition and the administrator's perception of a training program as public-service oriented or not. For example, 68% of the CD officials who showed the highest scores on the authoritarian index perceived their training program as public-service oriented, compared to 76% with the lowest authoritarian scores—not a significant difference. (In the police agency the comparable percentages were 75% and 90%, respectively.) Further, if we look only at those officials who did see their program as public-service oriented, we see no linkage between authoritarian predispositions and job perspectives. Thus, among CD officials 70% of those with high authoritarian scores defined their jobs in democratic terms; and 75% of those with low authoritarian scores defined their jobs in democratic terms —again no significant difference. (Among police officials, the percentages were 62% and 64%, respectively.) This means that although relatively large percentages of Indian administrators indicate a latent personal authoritarianism, this does not interfere with their capacity to understand and see a training program as oriented toward public service; nor does it mean their total job perspective is warped by this latent predisposition.

Congruence and tension: A comparison of administrative and public attitudes

A critical problem in the analysis of any administrative or organizational subsystem is the measurement of the extent of congruence in perspectives between different levels of the system. In the study of administrative organizations we must be concerned with the different images of political reality held by the official cadres and their publics or clienteles. For India, it is particularly important to know whether administrators see the system as functioning in the same manner as the public sees it. If great disparities exist in the two images it may not only be difficult to mobilize support, but, more importantly, it may be difficult to change the system. Disparities would suggest perceptual isolation and unreality or indifference, or both. The ideal objective in the developing Indian system would be administrative cadres which could accurately predict and interpret public views and evaluations of the administrative system, whether or not there was congruence on personal preferences for policy goals. The greater the inability of administrators to predict and interpret, the greater the likelihood that misunderstanding, inappropriate expectations, and non-cooperation will develop.

In our study design we purposely asked both officials and citizens some of the same questions, in both urban and rural Delhi. A simple presentation of the distributions of their responses reveals the extent of congruence, or distance, in their perceptions.

5•14 Citizen-administrator perceptions of relations with each other

Relations are:	URBAN		RURAL	
	Official image of relations with public	Public image of relationship with officials	Official image	Public image
Poor	0%	18%	2%	15%
Fair	0	41	2	15
Good	86	24	96	55
Very good	12	3	3	3
Don't know	2	14	—	9

Obviously administrators have a much more sanguine view of their relations with the public than the citizens do. The estrangement is particularly noticeable in urban Delhi. Officials are very reluctant to say their relations with the public are poor or even fair, while 30% (rural) to 60% (urban) of the public perceive their official relations as unsatisfactory (Table 5.14). Insofar as these responses represent the true picture, the suggestion of a gap in mutual perceptions may be significant.

The same tendency—for officials to be optimistic and citizens to be cynical about their mutual relations is reflected in responses concerning the general role of the citizen in the Indian political system (Table 5.15). Over 50% of the administrators in our study feel that officials really care about citizen opinion, and approximately 50% of our administrators feel the citizen does have a say in what the government does. Public cynicism is more frequent, particularly in urban Delhi where 67% to 90% are not optimistic.

The difference between officials and the public is revealed in the patterns of responses to other questions. We asked both samples what the citizen should do if he had a problem with the government—should he go himself or should he get help from other (influential) persons or organizations? Over 50% of the officials felt that he could be successful by handling his problem personally —while only 25% of our public cross section were sanguine about the efficacy of personal effort unaided by assistance from others.

Further evidence of the low congruence in mutual perceptions emerges from our data on the extent of administrative corruption. We asked a series of questions of both officials and citizens related to this subject, including questions requiring them to estimate the extent of official corruption. The results reveal wide divergence in these estimates (see Table 5.16). Officials are inclined to minimize the extent of corruption, while a majority of the public is ready to charge officials with corruption. About 60% of our sample is convinced that half or more than half of the officials are corrupt; but only 20% to 30%, roughly, of the officials in our sample have the same pessimistic view. Although a very few of the officials claim that *all* officials are honest, they reject the idea that a majority is corrupt. If these findings are reliable reports of mutual perceptions, they suggest great differentials in the confidence which the public and administrators have in the integrity of the Indian administrative system.

We also asked officials to predict what percentage of the public would say that officials are corrupt. The discrepancies between these predictions and the *actual* public response were great (Table 5.17). From 33% to over 50% of the officials in our study seem to be poorly informed of the public's image of administrative corruption—they predicted that all citizens feel that administrators are honest. Or, to put it another way, less than 10% of our officials would admit that a majority of citizens would contend that officials

5·15 Comparative perceptions of the citizen's role by officials and the public

	OFFICIALS' PERCEPTIONS		PUBLIC PERCEPTIONS	
	Urban	Rural	Urban	Rural
Public officials really care quite a lot about what the ordinary citizen thinks.				
Agree	65%	56%	36%	53%
Disagree	28	39	51	39
Unsure	6	5	13	7
The average citizen does not have much say about what the government does.				
Agree	53	46	88	68
Disagree	41	50	4	26
Unsure	6	4	8	5

5•16 Estimates of administrative corruption by officials and the public

What per cent of public employees (officials) would you say is corrupt?

	URBAN		RURAL	
	Officials	Public	Officials	Public
None are corrupt	4%	7%	11%	12%
Some—but less than 50%	29	19	38	16
About 50%	9	17	8	9
Majority (or over 50%)	10	42	24	48
Don't know; refusal	48	15	19	16
Number of cases	*106*	*347*	*114*	*337*

are corrupt, whereas over 70% of the public say there is some corruption, and close to 60% of the public contend that at least one half of all officials are corrupt.

Obviously, officials were, first, reluctant to admit to official corruption, and, second, reluctant to admit that the public views administrators as corrupt. Despite disinclinations to frankness, however, these findings suggest, in conjunction with previous findings concerning the divergences in perceptions, that there is either considerable tension between officials and citizens, or unreality in mutual perceptions, or both.

Conclusions

In summary, then, our data suggest that despite caste backgrounds and different social status, and despite long tenures in the public service, democratic attitudes toward one's job can and have been developed in Indian administrators. Administrators who began their government service many years ago, presumably in the iron framework of the bureaucratic tradition, and who came from conservative, traditionalized milieus, can take on democratic perspectives. This despite a latent personal authoritarian predisposition for large numbers of administrators. The critical factor seems to be the agency they are part of, and the training program in this agency —whether they perceive this training program as emphasizing and demanding public service, sensitivity to public demands, and flexibility in working with the public. No doubt recruitment patterns differ also, with possibly more personnel predisposed to democratic norms and amenable to a public-service-oriented agency program recruited into Community Development work than into other agencies. But this by no means seems conclusive. Organizational conditions in an agency are basic. The pattern of supervisor-subordinate relationships and the communication of organizational expectations differs from one agency to the next. Where the relationships and communication system seriously demand administrative perspectives which are democratic, and where personal bureaucratic and authoritarian orientations are overcome, administrators will incorporate and exhibit consistently democratic attitudes. Apparently, this has been happening in India in certain agencies since Independence, despite caste, despite long tenure, despite the traditionalism in which most administrators have previously been reared.

It is difficult to identify any large numbers of the officials in our study as traditional, in contrast to modernizing. We did use two items in our questionnaire which might permit an exploration of this dimension. These two, on which we asked our officials to indicate agreement or disagreement, were:

5•17 Official predictions of public perceptions of the extent of official corruption

Predictions	Percentage of all officials predicting a given type of public response:		Actual perception of the public:	
	Urban officials	Rural officials	Urban public	Rural public
100% of the public would say there is *no* corruption	35%	56%	7%	12%
Less than 25% of the public feel officials are corrupt	19	28		
25% to 50% of the public say officials are corrupt	37	11	78	72
Over 50% of the public say officials are corrupt	9	5		
Don't know			15	16

1. "The way the government runs things today is better than the way things were run in the past."
2. "Rapid improvement in the economic and social welfare of the Indian people is not possible under the present democratic system of party government."

The distribution of responses to these two items for all administrators was as follows:

Consistently traditional on both	11%
Consistently modernizing on both	45
Not consistent	
Traditional on #1, Modern on #2	8
Modern on #1, Traditional on #2	35
Unsure on one or both	2

Various interpretations can be drawn from these data. From a pessimistic standpoint one can conclude that a minority have emerged completely from traditional orientations. On the other hand, only 10% of the administrative establishment seems still completely committed to traditional views, while almost 50% have adopted modernizing orientations. The remainder are in a state of transition. This is a more optimistic view and perhaps a more realistic statement of the condition of the Indian administrative service. What is particularly encouraging is that in the Community Development staff and line administration less than 5% of the officials are explicitly and consistently traditional in their responses (in contrast to 20% in the postal service, 20% among the health staff, and 15% among police staff personnel). There is considerable evidence, therefore, that Indian administrators are developing modernizing perspectives, especially in the developmental bureaucracy.

Finally, our analysis reveals a great distance between administrators and the public in their perceptions and evaluations of the system. The administrator feels the system functions relatively well, corruption is minimal, and that relations with citizens are good. Indian citizens in the Delhi area do not unanimously or consistently share these perceptions and evaluations insofar as our data reliably describe the state of mutual citizen-administrator attitudes. There is more tension and potential disharmony in the system at present than congruence and mutual understanding. As Indian administrators become more adaptive and democratic in their job orientations and public contacts, one can hope that these tensions will be reduced, reality perceptions will converge, and greater cooperative behavior will emerge.

Bureaucratic contact:
Its dimensions
and relevance
for public attitudes

chapter **6**

We come now to a central question and analytical problem in our investigation—what is the impact of administrative behavior on public attitudes and performance? This is a question which concerns us for pragmatic reasons, and also because of its significance theoretically for the development of the Indian society. In our introductory chapter we explained our larger theoretical concerns. Empirical examination of elite-citizen contacts and communication will hopefully lead us to an understanding of the Indian prospects for achieving political consensus and unity, for democratic involvement with new and transformed political institutions, and for public participation in social and economic developmental innovation. While looking explicitly at citizen-administrative contacts, and identifying the conditions and consequences of such interactions for specific types of behavior, we hope to uncover clues suggestive of the pattern of movement in India toward major societal goals.

In setting forth our data here we are concerned primarily with five specific theoretical propositions for the developing social and political system in India. These are:

1. If citizens are to be properly involved in the system and in the achievement of system goals, administrative contacts

with the public, if relevant, must be extensive, continuous, and *penetrate* to those sectors of the population most "traditional," most probably alienated, and most vital for the success of developmental goals.

2. If citizens are to be properly involved in the developing India of today, these administrative contacts, if relevant, should lead to greater *information* and knowledge, instrumental and substantive, about governmental programs, policies, plans, and goals.

3. If citizens are to be properly involved, these administrative contacts, if relevant, should result in greater citizen *belief* in, and support of, governmental actions and programs. One should not expect, however, that there will be unanimous agreement over goals or means, but rather a consensus by the large majority that programs exist which are worth while, and feasible.

4. If citizens are to be properly involved, these administrative contacts, if relevant, should inspire *confidence* on the part of the public in the integrity, efficiency, and bureaucratic style of officials, leading to a feeling that officials care about the citizenry, treat them fairly, and, thus, that the individual citizen counts in the system, and that his actions are considered meaningful for the system.

5. If citizens are to be properly involved, these administrative contacts, if relevant, should tap the realistic aspirations of the common man, appeal to these aspirations, whether strictly utilitarian or idealistic, and motivate the individual to *action* and achievement, which is significant for the citizen as well as for the system. (Discussed in Chapter 7.)

The goals then must be penetration, information, belief, confidence, and action. Our major query here is whether administrative contacts with the common man in India (Delhi State) in 1964 indicate that bureaucratic contacts are functional or dysfunctional in these respects.

The index of administrative contact

We asked our respondents a series of questions about their contacts with administrative officials which permitted us to develop an index of administrative contact for each person in the sample. We primarily focused on the following agencies in our study: Community Development (rural areas), Health, Delhi Transport Undertaking (urban), Police, and Postal. We asked about the frequency and/or nature of contact by each respondent with each of these sets of officials, with a maximum score possible of 14. Eleven per cent of our respondents had scores of nine or above, 5% had zero scores. Two other indices were also developed for the study, one based on general communication status (including newspaper readership, group or association memberships, and knowledge of leaders), and a second conceived as *political* leadership contact (including personal contact with village or local leaders and party leaders). The distributions in these two indices will be presented briefly, but are not employed analytically in this chapter. The individual items in the administrative contact index, such as frequency of contact with Community Development officials, as well as the index as a total score permitted us to classify our respondents in a variety of ways and to analyze the interrelations between type of contact and citizen action.

The basic distributions of our respondents by these three indices as well as their total communication score can be seen from Table 6.1. The urban population generally has higher scores than does the rural population. There is one notable and significant exception — that of personalized contact with political and governmental leaders. Almost 50% of the urban sample have no such contacts while less than 10% of the village population is out of personal touch with all political leaders and officials. This is a significant finding in its own right and relates to our penetration hypothesis referred to above. The average villager in Delhi State has less frequent occasion to see *administrative* officials. He may also be less involved with newspapers and group associations than is the urban resident, although his knowledge of local leaders may substitute for his lower level of newspaper readership and group memberships. But he is *personally* familiar with political and governmental leadership to a greater extent than is the urbanite. His overall communication status, therefore, compares very favorably with the urban resident. If we combine our last two categories we could say that in Delhi State less than 10% of the rural population seems isolated, while about 12% of urban residents may be isolated, in terms of their public communicative involvement patterns.

These indices are to some extent interrelated and cumulative, but by no means perfectly (see Table 6.2). The individual who has low exposure to mass media and social groups may also be isolated from administrative contacts. But he may also substitute other types of communicative relationships. In the rural area we find that 90% of the sample with low scores in general communication status are also limited in their administrative contacts, but the other 10% did have frequent contacts with administrators. On the other hand 60% of those with a high general communication status had infrequent administrative contacts. Alternative channels for communication and contact exist, therefore, for the ordinary citizen and these cannot be ignored in any development strategy.

The penetration problem

Seventeen years after Independence and after considerable training of the new administrative cadre, particularly in the field of community development, what was the extent to which the ordinary citizen was exposed to the new bureaucracy? Has the new administration established contact with the lower classes and with those living in apparently isolated and traditional villages, or is most of its contact with the upper and proximately urban strata of Indian society? Table 6.3 presents data relevant to these concerns. It reveals

6.1 The indices of communication status

Categories*	Administrative contact (maximum score = 14)	General communication (maximum score = 10)	Personalized contact with political and governmental leaders (maximum score = 12)	Total communication status score (maximum score = 36)
HIGHEST SCORES				
Rural	7%	3%	10%	7%
Urban	16	6	8	7
MEDIUM SCORES				
Rural	60	33	43	85
Urban	68	35	21	80
LOW SCORES				
Rural	25	54	38	7
Urban	14	30	22	12
ZERO SCORES				
Rural	8	10	9	2
Urban	2	29	49	1
	100	100	100	100

*The score categories varied, of course, for each index, but were applied consistently for urban and rural populations. The highest scores were as follows: for administrative contact (9 and above), in general communication status (7 and above), for personalized contact with leaders (8 and above), for total communication status score (20 and above).

6·2 Relation of general communication exposure to administrative contacts (rural only)

General communication status	Administrative contact rare or never (score 2 or less)	Administrative contact low (score 3–6)	Administrative contact medium-high (score 7–8)	Administrative contact high-very high (score 9+)	N*
LOW Score 2 or less	43%	47%	7%	4%	215
HIGH Score 5 or more	22	39	19	19	36

*N = number of cases.

first that the higher the social and economic status of the individual the more likely he is to have very frequent contact with administrative officials. Only 10% to 15% of the low castes, illiterates, and low income groups in both urban and rural areas report high frequency of contact, while upper income, educated and high caste groups are consistently higher. Second, the data show that urban subgroups are consistently higher in frequency of administrative contacts. For example, a comparison of the upper educational strata in urban and rural populations indicates a discrepancy of over 30 percentage points; upper income groups differ 20%, and upper caste groups differ 17%. Third, in actuality this results in much greater differentiations among strata, or more disparities in administrative contact, in the city than in the village. In the village the upper castes do not seem to be extremely privileged by having contacts with administrative officials to a greater extent than lower castes—a difference at the high end of the scale of about ten to eleven percentage points. But in urban Delhi there is much more distance between low and high caste groups—26 percentage points. For educational groups this distance seems to be extreme. Finally, it is clear that fully a third of the lower socioeconomic strata of the rural population in the area near the nation's capital rarely or never has contact with administrative officials. The record in the city is somewhat better. It is premature to be critical of this finding, pending further data. While on the one hand it is clear that the access of upper social and economic groups to the administrative cadre is much greater and more frequent than that of the low caste, illiterate, low income population, it also appears that administrative effort has reached downwards into the lower levels of the system to a considerable extent. The Harijans in the urban area, for example, report frequent contacts with administrators and few seem completely isolated. It is clear that considerable penetration has taken place, if one judges penetration by the single criterion of contact alone.

Our study design provided for the selection of eight villages which were classified by objective criteria as probably traditional, transitional, and urbanized-modernized. A complex variety of objective indicators was used, including occupational pattern, caste character (percentage from scheduled castes), degree of literacy, geographical location, communication facilities, educational institutions, transportation and roads availability, postal facilities, presence of governmental offices, and the like. If we look at the extent of administrative contacts by village type, we see that penetration has occurred where one would perhaps least expect it (Table 6.4). If one compares the three most traditional villages (A, B, and C) with

6.3 Administrative contact status for educational, income, and caste groups

| | ADMINISTRATIVE CONTACT SCORE: | | | |
| | Rural | | Urban | |
	Very high & high	Rarely & never	Very high & high	Rarely & never
EDUCATION				
Illiterate	12%	39% (207)*	14%	35% (84)*
Primary	35	26 (66)	23	24 (79)
Middle	40	24 (37)	48	7 (56)
High +	27	19 (26)	60	3 (125)
MONTHLY INCOME				
Under 50 rupees	15	34 (95)	23	23 (13)
51–100	18	48 (96)	22	27 (79)
102–200	22	16 (85)	41	14 (118)
201–300	29	38 (21)	50	7 (42)
Over 300	30	9 (23)	50	12 (82)
CASTE				
Low	14	34 (108)	16	20 (49)
Middle	21	34 (159)	–	– (9)
High	25	32 (63)	43	13 (206)
Brahmin			41	7 (46)
Harijan			26	26 (19)
Muslims			5	53 (19)

*( ) denotes number of cases.

6.4 Extent of administrative contact—traditional and modern villages

Administrative contact	Most traditional villages to most modern villages								Urban sample
	A	B	C	D	E	F	G	H	
Very high & high	21%	31%	32%	13%	32%	4%	8%	18%	38%
Medium	54	41	38	47	44	54	58	46	46
Rare or never	25	28	30	40	24	41	33	35	16
Never	0	6	6	7	5	13	13	7	10
Number of cases	*24*	*32*	*47*	*30*	*41*	*46*	*48*	*82*	

the three most modernized villages (F, G, H) one sees, in fact, greater exposure to the administrative cadre in the so-called traditional communities. From 25% to 30% in our samples from traditional villages rarely were exposed to administrators, but up to 40% were rarely exposed in the urbanized-modernized communities. Neither physical nor functional isolation, in a formal classificatory sense, nor traditionalism as determined by social or economic characteristics, therefore, seems associated with isolation from administrative penetration. Villages in the most isolated areas do see and interact with administrators.

The same finding emerges if we look exclusively at citizen contacts with Community Development officials alone. The *relative* extent of contact is high in the most traditional and isolated communities. In our entire rural sample 67% of the villagers were out of contact with CD officials. But in our most traditional village, 50% of our sample had some exposure to CD officials, compared to 42% for the most modernized-urbanized community. Similarly, all three of the most traditional villages reported a high frequency of contact equal to or surpassing the 26.5% figure for the total rural sample. Although one may feel that this degree of exposure to Community Development officials is too low for the rural sector—67% did not know CD officials or never saw them—one cannot say that the traditional or isolated communities are discriminated against by the development bureaucracy. Indeed, what evidence we have indicates that they are *relatively* well exposed among villages, although the exposure of the urban population is greater.

Knowledge of, belief in, and support for governmental action

Since public cooperation and involvement in development programs is so crucial in India, from the standpoint of governmental

6.5 Informational level by extent of administrative contact (rural sample)

Informational item	ADMINISTRATIVE CONTACT SCORE:					
	Very high	High	Average	Occasional	Rare	Never
1. No knowledge of Community Development program	29%	29%	48%	63%	67%	81%
2. No knowledge of ways government is trying to improve agricultural production	4	7	21	37	38	44
3. What does government want you to do in agricultural program? *Don't know	5	17	20	30	44	47
4. No knowledge of health services	9	5	10	23	22	48
5. Does not know where family planning center is	43	61	68	82	91	96
6. No opinion on what to do if one has a problem involving administrative agencies or officials	0	0	5	7	4	19
Proportion of Sample	7	12	19	29	25	8

*Farmers only

Note: Each percentage should be read as a proportion of those in each administrative contact category. For example, 29% of those with very high administrative contact had no knowledge of the CD program, etc.

objectives, the level of information of the public about such programs is a major focus of any inquiry. Roughly 16% of the urban
sample had no significant contacts with administrators, while 33%
of the rural sample had no such contacts. One query is whether
administrative contact was associated with greater knowledge about
such programs.

We used a variety of approaches to test the respondent's knowledge
of governmental activities, services, and goals; only a few are
presented here. In Table 6.5 the extent of ignorance about governmental programs and administrative services is illustrated for the
rural sample. It is obvious that administrative contact is related to
much greater knowledge about specific services and programs, and
is related to a better understanding of governmental expectations
concerning citizen action. Those with below average frequencies of
bureaucratic contact (over 60% of the rural sample) are extremely
and consistently ignorant about the Community Development
program (from 60% to 80% have no idea about its nature and aims).
On more specific questions concerning agriculture and the health
programs the ignorance is less apparent, generally, but still considerable. Of those with infrequent contact 20% to 50% have no specific
knowledge of the health services, for example.

The importance of general administrative contact, whether or not
there has been exposure to the Community Development bureaucracy, is demonstrated in Table 6.6. For those villagers who had
limited contact with administrative officials generally, exposure to

6·6 Relative impact on knowledge of governmental programs of general administrative contact and contact
with Community Development officials (rural)

Information item	Highest administrative contact scores		Medium administrative contact scores	
	High CD contact scores	Low CD contact scores	High CD contact scores	Low CD contact scores
1. No knowledge of CD program	33%	23%	35%	63%
2. No knowledge of ways government is trying to improve agricultural production	8	4	17	35
Number of cases	39	26	29	*131*

6.7 Level of information by frequency of administrative contact (urban)

	ADMINISTRATIVE CONTACT SCORE:				
	Very high	High	Average	Occasional	Rare or never
1. No knowledge of health services	47%	62%	63%	61%	88%
2. Does not know where Family Planning Center is	32	51	54	78	81
3. No opinion of what to do if R has a problem involving administrative agencies or officials	13	13	19	34	44
Number of cases	54	78	85	73	57
Proportion of sample	16	23	25	21	16

the CD bureaucracy significantly reduced ignorance about the aims and expectations of the CD program. But among those with a generally high level of administrative contact, the absence of contact with CD officials was not important.

In urban Delhi the extent of ignorance about governmental services is extremely high for those who have not had administrative contacts. The illustrative items in Table 6.7 suggest that in the vital area of health services over 60% of the isolated are completely ignorant. Even among those with a high administrative contact score, lack of knowledge of health services is widespread—from 30% to 50% have no specific knowledge. If one compares the rural and urban distributions, one notices differential patterns of ignorance. The rural population is very much better informed about specific health services—at least 33% of the rural population is more knowledgeable. (This is not true, however, so far as knowledge of the Family Planning Center is concerned.) The urban population, furthermore, knows much less about how to process problems with administrative officials. The citizen-official relationship in the village has apparently educated villagers on how to seek administrative action.

What is the impact of administrative contact for illiterates as compared to literates (a question of no little significance in a country with 75% illiteracy)? The evidence is mixed, but generally administrative contact seems to be a factor reducing ignorance of governmental services in urban Delhi, among both literates and illiterates. Thus, among illiterates not exposed to administrative services, 86% are ignorant of health services, while only 53% are ignorant if in frequent contact with administrators; the comparable figures for literates are 89% and 60%. It is a curious and significant finding that illiterates in all administrative contact categories are slightly better informed than literates on this particular item concerning the health services. On the other measures of knowledge, however, this is not so. Illiterates are extremely uninformed and uncertain about specific administrative services and about procedures for contacting administrative officials. On this latter point, those with an education who have also had frequent contact with officials are well informed on how to process grievances and problems through the administrative hierarchy. Getting an education in India does not, in short, seem to be very functional by itself to knowledge about governmental programs. Experience with the administrative apparatus seems more functional, for certain types of

6•8 The influence of literacy on level of information about governmental services (urban)

	ADMINISTRATIVE CONTACT SCORE:					
	Very high, high, and average		Occasional		Rare or never	
	Literates	Illiterates	Literates	Illiterates	Literates	Illiterates
1. No knowledge of health services	60%	53%	65%	54%	89%	86%
2. Does not know where Family Planning Center is	43	83	73	92	78	86
3. No opinion of what to do if R has a problem involving administrative agencies or officials	10	53	27	50	33	60
Number of cases	*179*	*30*	*48*	*24*	*27*	*29*

information, though among illiterates with such contacts considerable ignorance of administrative procedures and services persists.

Public support of governmental officials and programs

When one examines the degree of support for governmental officials
and programs in India (Delhi State), there are striking differences
for urban and rural populations, as well as for illiterates and the
well-educated. When asked what kind of job the central government is doing, less than 40% of the urban population said it is
doing a good or very good job, while about 55% of the rural population was supportive. The urban disapproval is widespread among
all educational classes; the rural disapproval is highest among
illiterates (only 47% approving). When asked to evaluate the job of a
specific set of officials, such as health officials, roughly the same
differences appear, although the support is from five to ten percentage points higher. The rural population and its educational
subgroups is consistently more supportive, but large segments of
the population, especially among the lower status groups, are very
critical of the central government and its programs.

The impact of administrative contact on these support levels can
be seen from Table 6.9. In rural areas those who are frequent inter-
actors with the bureaucracy have extremely favorable attitudes
toward governmental officials, local and central, as well as high
approval of the health and Community Development programs.
Those out of touch with the bureaucracy are much less supportive.
Less than 40% of those who are isolated say the central governmental officials are doing a good or very good job, under 60% feel the
Community Development program is worth while, and 50% or less
feel that CD officials are doing a good job. Health programs are
supported by overwhelming majorities in both urban and rural
areas. But urban residents are very critical of government officials,
local and central, and contact with these officials does not contribute
to a greater approval for the job they are performing. Administrative
contact, thus, seems much more functional to the development of
supportive attitudes in rural than in urban areas.

Public confidence in the bureaucracy

A general theoretical concern in any society is the nature and extent
of the public's belief that administrators are, as Morris Janowitz has
put it, "principle-minded," that is, guided by an interest in, as well
as observing rules providing for, impartiality and public service.[1]

---

[1] Janowitz, *op. cit.*

6.9 The role of administrative contact in developing belief in, and support for, governmental programs

	ADMINISTRATIVE CONTACT SCORE:					
	Very high	High	Average	Occasional	Rare	Never
RURAL Believe government officials are doing a good/very good job						
Village	88%	78%	75%	64%	58%	48%
Central government	89	51	67	47	54	39
Believe health services should be provided by the government	100	100	98	95	94	85
Believe Community Development program is worth while	100	98	66	63	60	52
Believe CD officials doing a good job	88	83	59	50	52	44
a bad job	3	5	22	27	19	11
no opinion	0	2	19	23	29	44
Rare, never						
URBAN Believe government officials are doing a good/very good job						
Municipal (Delhi)	17	35	22	30	23	
Central government	30	44	40	45	22	
Believe health services should be provided by government	98	90	96	89	81	

Can the citizen expect fair treatment from officials, or is political pull indispensable? In addition, does the citizen feel he can act alone in approaching administrators or does he need help? Finally, is there any effective redress if one feels that officials are not doing their jobs properly? Expectations of impartiality, realistic calculations as to how to approach administrators, and feelings of optimism concerning the efficacy of interactions with administrators — all are important components of the confidence perspectives in citizen-official relationships. Data on such components will tell us a great deal about the general problem of public citizen perceptions of authority as well as indicate for India what the potential is for citizen cooperation with development plans.

The general pattern of responses to questions we asked in the Delhi study in this substantive area revealed a pattern somewhat similar to those found in Detroit by Janowitz. For example, on the question of whether political pull is important in whether the government will help a private citizen, the distributions for Detroit in 1954 and Delhi in 1964 were as follows:

	Detroit	Delhi urban	Delhi rural
Yes, it plays an important part	41%	54%	70%
Yes, it plays some part	28	6	5
Depends	4	3	2
No	15	7	11

On the question: If you had a problem to take up with a government bureau, would you do it yourself or do you think you would be better off if you got the help of some person or organization? the following distributions were found:

	Detroit	Delhi urban	Delhi rural
Would do it himself	16%	25%	23%
Would get help	67	50	64

What we were particularly interested in, in the Indian study, was the extent to which administrative contact was related to these confidence perspectives. Table 6.10 presents the data.

The relatively high confidence in both administrative behavior and in the capacity of the citizen to act effectively in contacts with administrators is noticeable in the response patterns of the rural sample. But the peasant's perspectives appear to be somewhat inconsistent, if not naïve. For he feels that officials are impartial, but that political pull is also important, and despite this he is more

6·10 The relevance of administrative contact for citizen confidence in the political system

	ADMINISTRATIVE CONTACT SCORE:					
	Very high	High	Aver-age	Occa-sional	Rare	Never
RURAL						
Officials treat all citizens fairly	65%	59%	60%	58%	59%	48%
Citizens can act if officials are not doing their jobs properly	83	78	69	57	45	33
Would act by himself if has a problem with the government	42	24	30	19	19	19
Political pull is important in dealing with administrators	79	81	79	79	69	56
URBAN					Rare, never	
Officials treat all citizens fairly	44	36	36	42	33	
Citizens can act if officials are not doing their jobs properly	72	59	55	63	63	
Would act himself if has a problem with the government	30	32	21	26	16	
Political pull is important in dealing with administrators	65	68	71	44	47	

likely to attempt direct contact with administrators than is his much more cynical urban counterpart. The urban resident doubts the fair-mindedness of administrators and also has less self-confidence in dealing with them. These differentials are consistent for most of these administrative-contact-score categories.

Does increased contact with administrators seem related to greater confidence in the bureaucracy? Yes and no. Those with very high contact scores emphasize the role of political pull much more than the isolates—a 23 percentage point differential in the rural sector, and a 17 percentage point differential in the urban sector. But also an increased proportion feel optimistic about the success of citizen contacts with administrators, either in initiating actions or in reprisals. The data are not completely consistent on this matter for the urban sample but point in that direction. It seems then that although there may be some rural naïveté and considerable distrust of administrative impartiality and responsiveness to public demands (although probably no more so than in the United States), exposure to the bureaucracy in India brings with it a certain realism as to how administrative decisions are made.

In addition, those with high contact scores feel that the citizen *can* act. On the question: What would you do if you have a problem with the government? 44% of those with no contact with officials in urban Delhi had no opinion, while only 13% of those with high contact scores were at a loss as to how to approach such officials. In the rural sample there was more self-confidence, but whereas none of the respondents in the high contact categories had no opinion as to how to proceed, 20% of those isolated from the bureaucracy had no opinion on action alternatives. Administrative contact, then, may be functional to the achievement of greater realism about administrative behavior and greater self-confidence in dealings with administrators.

Patterns of citizen-administrator relationships in three blocks

Communities differ in their social and political characteristics; administrative systems vary by geographical area. Bearing these theoretical assumptions in mind, the critical question to explore in concluding our analysis is: Do differential patterns of administrative behavior appear to be related to differing levels of public support for the administrative system in India? In order to secure evidence on this matter we took the three developmental areas or blocks in which our rural survey was conducted—Alipur, Najafgarh, and Mehrauli—and examined the background and attitudes of all ad-

ministrative officials in our sample, on the one hand, and the attitudinal data for our public sample, on the other. By isolating these
data for these three basic geographical areas, we can demonstrate
different administrative system orientations and seek to link public
responses to these three administrative systems, hopefully arriving
at clues as to the relevance of administrative behavior for public
behavior.

Significant differences exist in public attitudes and relationships
in these three blocks. One of them in particular stands out as an
area with poor administrative-public relations. In Mehrauli, public
knowledge of the bureaucratic system, including instrumental
knowledge, is less than in the other two blocks.

More important is the much larger percentage of citizens who
see their relationships as unsatisfactory—57% in Mehrauli compared to 21% in Alipur. Further, our indices of administrative
support and political self-confidence, which summarize a great

6.11 Block differences in public attitudes toward adminis-trators

	Alipur	Najafgarh	Mehrauli
Perception of relations with officials:			
Poor	9%	9%	33%
Fair	12	13	24
Good	68	70	26
Very good	3	5	1
Don't know	8	3	16
Ignorance of administrative system (percentage of public in each block with no knowledge):			
Of village officials' performance	4	4	15
Of block officials' performance	11	8	19
Of central government performance	13	32	37
No knowledge of what to do "if you have a problem with a governmental official"	2	2	14
Number of cases	159	84	94

6.12 Variations in public support for administration and in political self-confidence—three blocks

	Alipur	Najafgarh	Mehrauli
Administrative support index:			
High support (7+)	21%	29%	9%
Moderate support (4–6)	67	57	46
Low support (1–3)	11	14	39
No support (0)	1	0	6
Political self-confidence index:			
High self-confidence (6+)	28	33	3
Moderate self-confidence (3–5)	57	51	59
Low self-confidence (1–2)	15	16	29
No self-confidence	0	0	10

variety of responses, indicate again that the Mehrauli population seems less supportive, more bewildered, or alienated, than in the other two blocks (Table 6.12). One finds very few people in Mehrauli who enthusiastically support administrators—9% compared to over 20% in the other blocks. Close to 50% of the Mehrauli public reveals low support for administrators, compared to 14% or less in the other blocks. Similarly, there are striking differences in the citizen's level of self-confidence in dealing with officials in Mehrauli and the other two blocks.

The intriguing question for us is whether the background, training, attitudes, and behavior patterns of the administrative officials functioning in these three blocks help to explain these differing patterns of public perceptions of, and support for, these officials. We tested many hypotheses and found that the personal characteristics and training of officials did not vary greatly in these blocks. We did find that there was some difference, though not striking, in the commitment of officials to democratic relationships. Thus, on our index of democratic job perspectives, the officials in the blocks were distributed as follows:

Official score	Alipur	Najafgarh	Mehrauli
High (most democratic)	56%	51%	44%
Moderate	31	30	44
Lowest	13	19	12

Similarly, on the question of whether serving the public or following the orders of the superior was most important, 40% of Mehrauli officials in our sample took the bureaucratic position, compared to 37% of Najafgarh administrators, and 34% of those in Alipur.

Much more suggestive is the finding that the extent of citizen contact with administrators was significantly different. The findings were:

Citizen contact scores	Alipur	Najafgarh	Mehrauli
High contact (9+)	12%	5%	1%
Moderately high (7–8)	9	25	5
Some contact (3–6)	44	44	57
Low contact (1–2)	28	21	24
No contact (0)	7	5	13

It is clear from this that citizens in Mehrauli block had more sporadic contacts with administrators—6% had high contact, compared to over 20% with frequent contact in the other two blocks. This may be due to several factors including public apathy, but it is probable that officials in Alipur and Najafgarh were more actively engaged in regular contacts with the public than was the case in Mehrauli.

Our data strongly indicate that the most critical difference between Mehrauli and other blocks is the extensive pattern of official contact with the public. Mehrauli officials do not differ significantly from other officials in background or training. They are inclined to be only slightly more bureaucratic in their orientations toward their work. But they seem to be much more out of touch with the public, with the result that a poor public image has developed of the Mehrauli bureaucracy. People see their relationships with Mehrauli administrators as poor or only fair probably because of their feeling that Mehrauli officials are out of touch. As a consequence, even those with rather frequent contact with Mehrauli officials are less supportive, as the following data reveals:

	Percentage of those in frequent contact with officials who score highest on our index of administrative support:
Mehrauli	0%
Najafgarh	16
Alipur	32

It appears that once an image of official bureaucracy develops it persists, despite the training, attitudes, or special contacts of certain citizens with officials.

Conclusions

In this very preliminary and exploratory effort we have sought to examine the extent to which the new bureaucracy in India has penetrated into those citizen sectors in India which are most critical for development, most probably passive, and most potentially alienated. Further, we have examined the relevance of administrative effort for increased knowledge about governmental programs, increased belief in and support for those programs, increased confidence in the citizen's capacity to cope with officials, and positive action to implement these programs. On balance the data suggest that administrative effort has paid off. Where citizens have been in contact with officials, particularly in rural areas, the experience seems to have been functional to citizen involvement in the system. This is not to say that the behavior of Community Development officials specifically, or the behavior of other administrative cadres, has been completely successful in India. As reported previously, many citizens are still completely isolated, and many citizens in contact with Indian officials have deep suspicions, basic dissatisfactions, and uncooperative attitudes. Nevertheless the bureaucracy is evidently having and can play an important role. These data are not significant only from the standpoint of achieving economic or social goals. They have important implications for the eventual development of integrative citizen perspectives, for identification of the citizen with the larger collectivity of the state, and for the involvement of the citizen in the modern bureaucratic apparatus of India which is so essential if national unity is to be achieved and, on the other hand, if bureaucrats are to act responsively.

Our study suggests that it is actual contact with the public in the field that counts—contact which is courteous and responsive, while efficient and fair. Our analysis strongly indicates that officials with democratic orientations who are actively involved with the citizens in the field, and not bureaucratically shut off from them, can and are having a tremendous impact on the attitudes and behavior of Indian citizens.

Public involvement with the Community Development and agricultural programs

chapter 7

India's Community Development program has been called a massive governmental extension service. Its aim has been to train and send out an army of competent officials to establish contact with rural citizens and help them improve their personal and village conditions of living, in health, education, transport and roads, communication, and agriculture. It is development and welfare oriented. In the last analysis its success depends on the commitment and support of the rural citizenry, both in attitude and behavior, toward the philosophy and goals of the program, as well as toward the personnel assigned to carry it out. While competent and dedicated extension officials are needed and adequate resources are essential, success is still contingent on the capacity of the system to motivate and activate the peasants and villagers.

We probed in great detail for information about the general levels of public knowledge, support, and cooperation with Community Development, and with the agricultural program in particular. Although we have alluded to some of these findings at other points in this report, we will here present a more complete analysis of our data. The key questions confronting us are, of course: Does the public know about the program and understand it; is the public positively supportive of it; and does the public's behavior indicate a maximal or minimal involvement, an involvement which is meaningfully related to the goals of the program? Above all, is the work of Community Development officials effective, as measured by the extent of the public's contacts with these officials and the relationship of this contact to citizen behavior?

General patterns of involvement

As already indicated (see Chapter 2), the rural public in our study revealed considerable general support for Community Development. Only 20% felt that Community Development was doing a "poor job," over 66% felt the program was worth while, and only a small proportion felt that there was great opposition to the program. On the other hand, only 5% had considerable knowledge of the goals of Community Development while over 50% were almost completely ignorant. Similarly, when asked to explain what the accomplishments of Community Development in their villages were, only 33% could mention any specific accomplishments, while 20% said nothing had been done, and over 40% said they didn't know what the accomplishments were. Improvements of roads and water facilities, and agricultural assistance were most frequently mentioned by those who were aware of accomplishments (Table 7.1).

7•1 Public recognition of the accomplishments of Community Development

What in your opinion are the most important accomplishments of Community Development here (rural sample)?

Nothing has been accomplished	22%	
Don't know about accomplishments	42	
Mentions specific accomplishments:	37	
Streets, roads mentioned		33%
Water and irrigation mentioned		22
Agricultural assistance mentioned		21
Schools mentioned		15
Health improvements mentioned		8

In terms of time perspectives, evaluations of the program also seemed mixed. We asked our respondents whether they thought Panchayati Raj had improved block administration in the past ten

7.2 Public evaluations of Panchayati Raj

In what ways has the formation of Panchayati Raj changed the block administration (rural sample)?

Changed for the better	20%
Changed for the worse	16
No change has occurred	25
Don't know or unsure	39

years. Only 20% saw a change for the better, 16% saw a change for the worse, while over 60% said no change had occurred, or they didn't know (see Table 7.2). Thus, although the rural public seems to approve and not oppose these governmental programs, they are not aware of, or extremely enthusiastic about the changes that have been made. The low level of public interest in Community Development, no doubt a major factor in this pattern of attitudes, is frankly admitted by villagers. Only 27% of our sample said they were very interested, while 32% said they had no interest (Table 7.3).

Support for the agricultural program

When we move beyond general evaluations to specifics, and ask particularly about the agricultural program, we see the relative impact of governmental programs on the attitudes and behavior of villagers and farmers in the Delhi area. The findings when viewed together reveal an interesting blend of perceptions concerning the relevance and irrelevance of governmental action. Farmers may not be self-consciously aware of what their specific responsibilities are, but for a sizeable proportion of the farm sample changes are taking place, *and* partially as a result of governmental encouragement.

7.3 Level of public interest in Community Development

Would you say that you are very interested in the Community Development program, somewhat interested, or not interested (rural sample)?

Very interested	27%
Somewhat interested	29
Not interested	32
Don't know, or no opinion	11

7.4 Social status differences related to knowledge of governmental agricultural planning

What are the ways in which the government has been trying to increase agricultural production?

	Mentions 3 or more ways	Mentions 1 or 2 ways	Mentions none or says "don't know"	N*
INCOME STATUS (monthly)				
Under 50 rupees	36%	28%	36%	50
51 – 100 rupees	37	30	33	87
101 – 200 rupees	55	22	23	87
201 – 300 rupees	76	5	19	21
over 300 rupees	70	4	26	23
EDUCATIONAL STATUS				
Illiterates	38	21	40	202
Primary schooling	55	32	13	62
Middle schooling	65	21	14	37
Higher education	76	20	4	25

*N = number of cases.

A first point to be noted is that when we asked the villagers to tell us what the government was specifically doing to increase agricultural production only 29% answered "nothing." However, when we asked them to tell us *"what does the government want you to do to increase agricultural production,"* only 15% could give a specific and relevant response. Most say they "don't know" or merely say they are to "work hard."

This tendency toward ambiguity is manifest in all social sectors (Table 7.4). True, the responses of the higher income and educational groups indicate that they have more awareness about governmental plans, and they are less likely to say they are completely uninformed. But specific knowledge of what the government wants farmers to do does not increase greatly or considerably by social status.

Despite such ambiguity as to their responsibilities, approximately 60% of the farmers claim that they have made changes in their farming methods or facilities in the past five years (Table 7.5). The number and types of changes reveal that the use of improved seeds, fertilizers, and insecticides are the most common changes which have been introduced (from 70% to 80% mentioning these three). But sizeable numbers of farmers are making more use of implements, subsidiary farm occupations (as vegetable or truck farming), different cropping patterns, etc.

In analyzing carefully the way farmers are working their farms, it is interesting to note the labor force utilization trends, as reported by our villager-farmers. We asked them whether they were relying more on their own labor today or whether they were using more hired labor, or if there was no change in the way they worked their farms. It is significant to note that of all farmers 39% are relying more on their own labor and only 6% are relying more on hired labor. To put it another way, of those farmers who have made changes in their methods of farming 70% are relying more on their own labor and only 11% are relying more on hired labor (see Table

7.5   Ways in which farmers have changed their farming methods in the past five years

GENERAL DISTRIBUTIONS	
Have not changed	40%
Have changed	60
TYPES OF CHANGES	
(Percentages based	
on the number	
of respondents who said	
they had made changes)	
Seeds	83%
Fertilizers	88
Insecticides	70
Implements	41
Subsidiary farming	40
More investment	33
Tractors	29
Cropping patterns	26
Water and irrigation	21
Marketing	12
Transportation	7
Storage	5
Tubewells	4
NUMBER OF CHANGES	
One	8%
Two	12
Three	14
Four to six	48
Over six	18

7.6 Changes in the utilization of farm labor

Are you relying more on your own labor today in the way you work your farm, or are you using more hired labor, or is there no change compared to five years ago?

Have made no changes at all	40%		
Have made changes	60		
But no changes in utilization of labor		10%	
Changes in utilization of labor		90	
Rely more on hired labor			6%
Rely more on own labor			84
SUMMARY			
(of those who have made			
some changes in farming)			
Rely more on own labor	71%		
Rely more on hired labor	11		
No changes in using labor	18		
SUMMARY			
(of all farmers in sample)			
Rely more on own labor	39%		
Rely more on hired labor	6		
No change in use of labor	55		

7.6). There are different possible interpretations of these data. But it appears plausible that much of the increase in agricultural production in the past five years or more may have occurred as the result of farmers working their own farms harder, without outside hired help. It may well be that hard work by the farmer and his family has been paying greater dividends in increasing production than the distribution of seeds, fertilizers, water facilities, or insecticides.

From our data, farmers want to make changes in farm methods in order to increase production. There is no great resistance attitudinally to such changes. At least 83% of our sample were interested in change, said that the majority wanted to make changes. Further, 60% revealed that they had made changes. When we probed we found that they felt that Community Development and governmental officials had encouraged them to make changes. When asked: "What prompted you to make these changes?" 66% credited the advice and prodding of CD and other governmental officials (Table 7.8). From 20% to 30% said their own initiative was at least partly

7.7 Public perceptions of how many people want to make changes in agricultural production

Does the majority of the people here want to make changes?

Yes	83%
No	14
Don't know	3

responsible. Thus although the great majority of villagers and farmers cannot clearly describe the goals of Community Development, or even specify clearly what the government wants them to do to increase agricultural production, over 50% are making specific changes, or have done so, and are working their farms harder by themselves. Although governmental prodding may be prompting such changes, it is the individual farmer's own hard work which is of tremendous importance in producing results. His own motivation plus governmental encouragement seem to have worked together to produce the increase in agricultural production.

The question arises — why have the 40% who have not made changes continued to operate today as in the past? We asked these farmers to explain their reasons in detail (Table 7.9). A great variety of explanations were given: "no need for a change," "the old way seems best," "don't know what to do," and "no interest." One segment of this group said frankly that changes would be too expensive or that they had very little land and thus could not make any changes. These two categories include at least 30% of those who had not made changes. Other responses may also have an undertone of financial inadequacy or economic futility. If we add these findings to the previous findings that many of the changes in agri-

7.8 Public perceptions of the role of Community Development in making changes in agriculture

What prompted you to make these changes in agriculture?
(Based on survey of 105 farmers who said they had made at least one change)

REASON	
Encouragement by CD officials or by government officials	66%
Own initiative solely	19
Village leaders, or friends-relatives encouraged	8
CD officials *and* own initiative	4
Village leaders or friends — relatives *and* own initiative	4

7.9   Reasons for not making changes in agricultural or farming methods

Based on those farmers who had not changed in the past five years

Too expensive	21%
Very little land	13
Don't know what to do	13
No interest	5
Old way seems best	12
No need, doing well	5
Other; no facilities	13
Don't know why	8
Not ascertained	12
Number of cases	*103*

cultural methods recommended by the government are not being undertaken by those farmers who are change oriented, the critical element of economic assistance can be seen if agriculture is to move ahead.

In order to secure some evidence that a change in governmental program might lead to even greater changes in agricultural production, we asked:

> If the government would promise the farmers that they would not lose money if they made these changes—by giving them credit and not insisting on repayment of their debts unless their crops improved with such changes in methods—do you think that the farmers would follow the advice of the government?

This question was patiently explained to the respondents by our interviewers and their reactions noted. We found that 85% said they

7.10   Potential for agricultural change: Credit incentives

Would you change if the government provided easier credit terms?

Yes, would change	86%
No, would not change	11
Don't know, depends	3
Number of cases	*205*

would make changes, and that the majority of farmers would make changes, if the government adopted this policy. Here then is evidence that the level of farmer effort to step up production might be jumped by 25% if such a new credit policy were adopted.

The willingness of farmers to make changes in their methods cannot be questioned. They see their standard of living as realistically related to such progress (Table 7.11), and they are interested in cooperating with governmental efforts. But more action by the government to relieve financial and economic impediments to such changes in agricultural production, and a much more serious effort in informing farmers about the goals and objectives of the program is necessary, if the government is to achieve its agricultural goals.

7.11 Perception of relationship between standard of living and increasing agricultural production

Do you think your standard of living would improve if you did improve your ways of farming and follow the advice of government for increasing farm production?

Yes, standard of living would increase	85%
No, standard of living would not increase	7
Depends; can't say; don't know	8
Number of cases	*206*

The importance of citizen contact with CD officials

Perhaps the most practical and relevant query in a study such as this is: Is there any evidence that the activities of Community Development officials produce results? Or, to put the question another way: Do citizens who have been in contact with CD officials have markedly different attitudes and behavior from those citizens who have not been in contact with these officials? It is one thing for rural respondents to tell us that the encouragement of CD officials was important to them. It is another matter to prove the interaction between peasant and official, and its relation to changed perspectives and behavior. The latter is not an easy consequence to document.

We asked our rural sample several questions to determine whether they had *official* dealings with CD officials, as well as *personal* acquaintanceship with them. Then we asked: How often in the past month have you seen these officials? Almost 66% of our sample never had any contact with these officials, while about 20% had frequent contact. The distributions were as follows:

	Total sample	Farmers only
Did not know officials —		
Never had contact	66%	59%
Knew officials —		
Saw them once or twice in the past month	6	8
Saw them rarely or on special occasions	1	—
Saw them three or four times in the past month	6	7
Saw them five or six times in the past month	2	3
Saw them more than six times in the past month	18	22
Don't know how often saw them in past month	2	1
Number of cases	*335*	*208*

The differences in contact by social status are significant (Table 7.12). Whereas over 70% of the illiterates and low-income members of our sample were out of touch with these officials, only 27% to 42% of the upper-income and well-educated groups had no such contact.

Though some social selectivity occurs in public contacts with CD officials,[1] a certain amount of penetration by the developmental

7.12 Frequency of contact with Community Development officials by social status

	No contact	Some contact	High contact (over six times)	N*
INCOME STATUS**				
Under 50 rupees	73%	7%	20%	51
51 – 110 rupees	78	11	11	92
101 – 200 rupees	60	20	20	85
201 – 300 rupees	55	20	25	20
Over 300 rupees	27	37	36	22
EDUCATION STATUS				
Illiterates	74	11	15	203
Primary	55	23	22	64
Middle	66	17	17	35
Intermediate and high	42	20	38	26

*N = number of cases.
**Based on monthly family income.

---

[1] In addition, there may well have been some purposeful selection in order to get things done.

7•13 The relationship of frequency of contact with Community Development officials to citizen evaluations of the program

	Community Development contact scores			
	Frequent	Some	Little	None
CD officials doing a good job				
Yes	84%	62%	63%	51%
No	11	35	26	20
No opinion	5	4	11	29
Accomplishments of CD?				
Nothing has been done	8	15	15	26
Don't know what has been done	21	38	30	47
Failures of CD?				
No failures	48	19	21	17
Don't know about failures	36	38	58	65
CD program worth while?				
Yes	90	81	80	60
No	0	15	5	10
Uncertain	10	4	15	29
Number of cases	61	26	20	228

bureaucracy is beginning to take place. One fourth of the poorest and most illiterate peasants do have some contact with these officials, and for 15% to 20% it is rather frequent. Further, despite lack of contact, Community Development aspirations and plans gradually percolate downward through the social status hierarchy. This speculation is not documented by our data, but it is suggested by the fact that 66% of our farmer respondents said that encouragement by CD officials was a factor in their changed farming methods, *although only 33% had personal or official contact with them.*

We can begin to see the possible consequence of contact with Community Development officials if we divide our respondents into those with frequent, some, or little contact and contrast their attitudes and behaviors with those who have had no contact whatsoever. It must be remembered that almost 66% of our respondents had no direct, personal contact whatsoever.

Evaluations of the job of CD officials and the accomplishments of the CD program vary by frequency of contact with these officials (Table 7.13). True, there is very high support for the program among those who have had no contact with the CD bureaucracy.

Thus, 50% say the officials are doing a good job, and 60% think the program is worth while, even though they are out of touch with the personnel involved with the program. But 84% and 90% of those in frequent contact evaluate the job and program favorably. And even a little contact with officials seems to increase the level of support. Those who have met CD officials are much less likely to point out failures in the program or to say it has accomplished nothing. The "don't knows" are still relatively numerous (21% of those in frequent contact say they do not know what the accomplishments are). But evidently information about Community Development is transmitted by these officials and produces much higher levels of support. It is interesting that those who have had contact with officials point to road improvements as the most outstanding ac- complishment (about 50% mentioning this), with improvements in irrigation, schools, and agricultural assistance mentioned next (by 25% to 33%).

The interest of people in the Community Development program is relatively high, even among those not exposed to the apparatus and personnel of the program (Table 7.14). One may discount these findings with the argument that people would be inclined to give affirmative, respectable responses. Yet there was considerable varia- tion among the contact groups. And even those in frequent contact were not inclined to say they were very interested. Contact seems related to interest. But the differences are not as great as one might expect. Above all, the potential for involvement seems high. Almost 50% of those not in contact with CD officials revealed some interest in the program.

Knowledge about the program is not restricted to those who have had contact with CD officials. Forty per cent of those respondents (farmers) out of touch with officials could mention three or more specific ways in which the government is trying to increase agri- cultural production. This compares to 64% of those in frequent

7.14 Interest in the CD program — by frequency of contact

	Community Development contact scores			
LEVEL OF INTEREST	Frequent	Some	Little	None
Very interested	42%	31%	26%	23%
Somewhat interested	40	35	21	26
Not interested	18	26	53	35
Don't know	0	8	0	16

7.15 The relationship of administrative contact to self-interest aspirations and positive actions in the agricultural spheres (rural sample — farmers only)

	General administrative contact score				
	Very high & high	Average	Occa-sional	Rare	Never
Feel standard of living would improve if followed the advice of the government in agricultural sphere	77%	65%	56%	71%	55%
Have changed ways of farming in past five years	70	56	34	39	25

	Contact with Community Development officials			
	Very high	Moderate	Low	None
Feel standard of living would improve if followed the advice of the government in agricultural sphere	76%	81%	56%	61%
Have changed ways of farming in past five years	83	67	33	32

contact and 58% who had some or a little contact. Thus, again, although the efforts of the officials may be paying off in more substantive and instrumental knowledge, there may be a general diffusion of knowledge through other bureaucratic or communication media, or a dissemination of knowledge through social groups or interpersonal association.

Action orientations relevant to Community Development

In our study we asked a long series of questions seeking to discover in detail how the farmer was working his farm, what changes he had introduced in recent years in the use of seeds, fertilizers, insecticides, in cropping patterns, marketing methods, and the like. In addition, we attempted to discover the nature of his financial and standard-of-living aspirations for himself and his family, and whether he felt he could or would participate in the government's program to increase agricultural production. This brings us to the heart of the question of the relevance of bureaucratic effort for economic and social change in India. In short, we were interested in discovering what role the Community Development bureaucracy played in moving farmers to cooperate with the Five Year Plan's objectives in the agricultural sector. We can present only a few of the relevant findings here, but they are highly suggestive (Table 7.15).

As already indicated, the farmers in our study were highly motivated to improve their economic status. The overwhelming majority of them had aspirations to improve their lot and were convinced that the proposals of the government would indeed assist them to improve their standard of living. As Table 7.15 reveals, the evidence does not suggest that contact with administrative officials, generally, or the CD bureaucracy, specifically, was instrumental to that end. True, 77% of those with high contact scores felt their standard of living would increase, but 71 % of those rarely in contact with officials had the same conviction. The same finding is true if one looks at exposure to the CD bureaucracy alone. But the striking finding is that *action*, as contrasted to aspirational *conviction*, differs markedly for those farmers exposed to administrative officials. Whereas 70% or more of those with high contact scores *did* change their methods of farming, only 25% to 33 % of those isolated from contact with administrators took action to improve their methods of farming. This is a significant difference and consistent as one moves from high to low contact with the CD bureaucracy. A much more detailed analysis is necessary to test the relevance of other variables. But these data strongly suggest that bureaucratic efforts were functional for translating aspiration, belief, or conviction into positive action.

When the farmers in our sample were asked to state specifically "what the government wants you to do," contact with officials seems relatively ineffective. Virtually identical proportions (15%) of those with frequent contact and no contact gave evidence of instrumental knowledge of governmental objectives. The paradox in these findings is that despite this inability to state the specific expectations of government for increasing agricultural production, those farmers in contact with CD officials did, indeed, reveal much greater evidence of changing their farming patterns. This is perhaps the most significant finding in this section of our study.

Conclusions

The Indian farmer and peasant is at the take-off period in development. He has in fact been altering his way of life and method of farming considerably. He believes in the Community Development program, is gradually getting more information about it, and is inclined to support it positively. Theoretically, the officials manning the Community Development bureaucracy can have a tremendous impact. Thus far this impact has been marginal and minimal. Even in the area surrounding Delhi less than a third of the farmers have been in contact with these officials. The level of knowledge about the program seems to be greater among the higher social and economic status groups. But penetration of the Community Development program's goals, spirit, and value is taking place, almost despite the inadequacy of bureaucratic efforts. Given continued governmental interest, perhaps policy changes providing greater incentives and assistance, and more direct contacts by these officials, our data suggest that much greater changes in farming behavior can take place. For India to move farther beyond the take-off stage, the Community Development effort must become more extensive, greatly intensified, and directly relevant to the economic needs and aspirations of the Indian farmer.

The bureaucracy and the developmental process in India: Trends and paradoxes

chapter **8**

Indians face many internal conflicts over the goals for their society and the implementation of these goals. These conflicts exist in the minds of the elite and the ordinary citizens. The Indian body politic is involved in a continuous debate, private and public, over the ideological direction of societal efforts and over the types of structures and tactics which should be utilized in the pursuit of these goals. Expert theories as to the direction, technology, and speed of development are legion in India. Often the common man, already in conflict between traditional and modernizing motivations, is further confused by incessant public controversy over the issues of development. Tarlok Singh, of the Planning Commission, in his evaluation of the third Five Year Plan, put the matter well in 1964:

> Unless the basic conflicts are resolved to the satisfaction, not merely of the elite and organized groups, but of the common man, who is bound to judge all policies and plans from the reality of his own living conditions and opportunities and the problems encountered from day to day, there can be no consistent and continuing pattern of development.[1]

[1]From a speech delivered by Tarlok Singh, Brij Narain Memorial Lectures, at Chandrigarh in the spring of 1964.

In a period of great transition, characterized by controversy and conflict, the Indian society has articulated new social aspirations to be communicated and implemented in part through new and old administrative cadres functioning through new or modified structures. Two fundamental questions confronting any analysis of modern India obviously are: What is the empirical evidence that the new and old administrative cadres are recruited and socialized so that they respond to these social aspirations and can mobilize public support for them? What is the empirical evidence that the Indian public is developing an awareness of the social goals of the new regime, is communicating with the development bureaucracy of the new regime, and consequently is responding positively to the developmental planning objectives of the new regime? These two key questions encompass much of the developmental crisis in India today. They are the central questions to which this empirical study is addressed.

The study of elite-citizen interactions may, indeed, represent only a partial window to the functioning of the Indian system. Nevertheless, it is critical not only for securing an image of governmental relationships, narrowly conceived, but also for developing a theory of the present patterns and probable prospects for welfare-state democracy in an India staggering with fantastic material and human needs.

Our study is admittedly only a beginning of knowledge and insight into these problems. It was based on interviews personally conducted with approximately 700 adults who represented a cross section of the male population of urban and rural Delhi, and 220 interviews with administrative leaders at the agency level of interaction with this public. In the brief survey of major findings presented here the reader is reminded again that these findings and generalizations are strictly relevant for the Delhi public and its administrative cadres.

One of the major observations emerging from our data concerns the unexpected patterns of public contacts with administrative officials. One can be both optimistic and alarmed at these findings. The opportunity for the citizen to be influenced by the regime through its administrative cadres (and for the regime to be influenced by citizens) is great, since 60% to 75% of the citizens in urban and rural areas have frequent contacts with these officials. Less than 10% seem to live in complete isolation from the bureaucracy. However, the new Community Development bureaucracy has yet to establish contact with a majority of residents in the villages. The image of the Community Development program as a vast network of officials covering the countryside and working with villagers daily on their problems is not borne out by the data. At least 60% of the villagers do not know the CD officials and/or never have had contact with them.

Bureaucratic penetration has occurred in the most traditional and isolated villages of Delhi State, among the low caste groups, the illiterates, and the very poor. This suggests that the citizen base of the political system is being expanded, that the regime is consciously attempting to contact remote sectors of the society, communicate with them, and involve them with the new system and its goals. Significantly, over 30% of our respondents in our most traditional and isolated villages had frequent contact with Community Development officials, whereas the rural norm was 26%.

Certain key differences in exposure of social groups to the bureaucracy, however, suggest critical restrictions on information flow in the Indian system. This seems to be less a caste-differential problem than one related to education and income status. In rural Delhi 73% of the well-to-do villagers have some contact with officials, compared with only 27% of those in the low-income group. Similarly, 60% of those with considerable education have some contact whereas only 26% of the illiterates do. Although penetration has been taking place, the Indian regime is out of direct administrative contact with the bulk of the lower social classes even in the area surrounding the capital city of India. The significance of this for involvement and political development need not be underlined. Without greater and more extensive governmental contacts, the common man must rest his image of the system on stereotypes laden with historical connotations, rumors and hearsay, indirect and informal secondary communication channels, or the local opinion and political leaders in the village with whom he has contact and whose information he cannot subject to reality testing. Whether this is dysfunctional depends on the local context, his potential role in the system, and the particular content of the information flow which he casually and informally absorbs and accepts.

The attitudes of Indian citizens towards their government, and its administrative officials particularly, is a complex and paradoxical mosaic of support and hostility, of consensus and critique. From 75% to 90% view governmental jobs as prestigious, 90% feel that health and Community Development programs are worth while, and less than 50% (20% rural) are critical of the job performance of central government officials. On the other hand, the majority feel that 50% or more of the officials are corrupt, large proportions (60% urban, 32% rural) say their dealings with officials are unsatisfactory, and the majority sense that their probabilities of gaining access to officials and being successful in processing their complaints with them are low. Over 50% feel officials in certain agencies are not fair, that the citizen can do little by himself, and from 60% to 75% feel that political pull is important in getting administrative action. Only a minority (22% urban, 37% rural) reveal no hostility attitudes toward bureaucrats. This is a peculiar blend of respect for authority and impatience with authorities, of desire for administrative progress and frustration at administrative tactics and style, of realism as to how things get done and bitterness that one cannot get things done, of confidence in the system and cynical appraisal of the system. On balance, Indian citizens tend to be supportive of the administration, though not consistently or enthusiastically so. Our composite index of support reveals that only 20% to 25% are clearly critical, apathetic, or rejective. In the villages, 80% are moderately or very supportive; in the city 66% are supportive. Similarly, our hostility index reveals no more than 20% to be consistently hostile, while 50% (urban) to 60% (rural) manifest virtually no hostility reactions. Indices, however, are summations of responses and hide nuances of sentiment and attitude. Even among those highly supportive of administration one finds an underlying hostility at the 20% level in rural areas and at the 40% level in urban Delhi. Thus, although the movement is toward consensus and support, conflict exists, and the consensus is tenuous or mixed with doubt. Perhaps the most significant finding is that one finds such basic support in cognitions of the bureaucracy, despite the existence of considerable latent hostility.

The image which persists in our data then is one of citizen acquiescence and support, as well as actual and potential disaffection. But the character of this public response varies for particular social sectors of the population. The upper status groups in urban Delhi are the most critical of administration, while at the same time being more informed. The educated and relatively wealthy criticize the job performance of officials, feel they are paying more taxes than they should, and are cynical or pessimistic about the efficacy of citizen action in relation to the bureaucracy. Urban low status groups are less critical, but also more pessimistic about the efficacy of citizen action, though less well informed about the administrative system. Rural citizens are least critical (particularly, those with low incomes), but also are very dubious about the efficacy of citizen action (particularly rural illiterates). It is somewhat disturbing to find that in the urban area, among upper caste members and the educated, one finds the greatest hostility to administrators, while among the rural illiterates one finds the least hostility. Illiterates seem most uninformed, but relatively highly supportive — no doubt a peculiarly saving element in the Indian system. Despite imperfect knowledge and ambiguous images, the lower classes are supportive. The suggestion is implicit that as educational level rises, as more information about the system is disseminated, and as certain types of contact with certain types of bureaucrats become more frequent, hostility and criticism also may increase. This is one of the important paradoxes of a developing society requiring solutions at the policy level, and also suggesting the need for new patterns and techniques of socialization. It also highlights the significant role of administrative behavior.

Much more optimistic are our findings concerning public responses to the administrative system in traditional as contrasted to the modernizing sectors of the society. We analyzed this relationship first, by comparing the attitudes of citizens in traditional-isolated villages and in more transitional-modernizing urban environments. We found the greatest support for the administration, and the greatest citizen self-confidence, in the small villages which could be classified as transitional-modernizing on the basis of our objective, aggregate criteria, and in larger villages where the modernization process is advanced. The greatest tension exists both in the most traditional small villages and in the larger villages in an incomplete stage of development. We found, further, in a second analysis based on an examination of respondents' attitudes, that the hard-core traditionalists who had a pre-development orientation to the system, are most hostile to the new administrative system — about 50% are very hostile — while those who have taken on more development-oriented and prospective, modern attitudes are much less so — under 20% are hostile.

The following theoretical interpretation of what is transpiring can be advanced. Our data indicate that the Indian administrative system is penetrating into the most traditional sectors and areas, with only very limited impact on those citizens whose thinking is retrospective and whose acceptance of the new order is slow. But citizens involved in the modernization process are responding more supportively and self-confidently if they see their demands and expectations in the process of realization and if they can tolerate the frustrations of the developmental pace. Where the transition process is beginning, slow paced, where demands are not being responded to and some are intolerably frustrated, then, despite government innovation and modernizing personal attitudes, citizens can be critical, cynical, and even hostile. This, too, is a basic paradox of the system. Hopefully, the paradox will eventually be resolved as bureaucratic efforts relate to and ameliorate citizen demands and expectations.

The relationships and interactions between Indian citizens and officials at the base of the administrative hierarchy are generally functional to the achievement of integrative and developmental purposes. There are exceptions to this, and there are certain conditions under which the public response, despite exposure to administrators, is negative. Our data suggest that hostility reactions can increase particularly in the urban area, as a result of bureaucratic contacts, and in rural areas as a result of contacts with particular types of officials. But, despite this possibility, the citizen who associates with these lower bureaucrats reveals attitudes and orientations which can be construed as salutary for political and social change.

If we utilize the criteria for an effective relationship between citizen and bureaucrat which were set forth in Chapter 1 and review the basic character and direction of our finding, we can see the evidence which supports this optimism. First, the involved citizen who is interacting with the administrative cadre is much better informed about the government's services and policies. His instrumental knowledge of the health services and Community Development activities, for example, is high compared to that of the non-involved, isolated citizen. A striking example is the contrast in knowledge about the Community Development program—only 29% of those with high contact scores were ignorant, while 81% of the isolated were ignorant. Second, the involved citizen is more likely to affirm that developmental programs are worth while, although these programs receive widespread support even among those not in contact with the bureaucracy. Third, in rural areas the involved citizen usually evaluates the job of governmental officials positively, a finding which, however, does not appear in the analysis of urban responses. Fourth, although the impact and relevance of contact with officials is minimal in this respect, citizens exposed to bureaucrats are generally more inclined to feel that these officials are democratically responsive and egalitarian than citizens with no such contact. Again, the difference is not significant in urban Delhi; but in the villages, for example, 65% of our respondents with considerable contact had affirmative evaluations, compared to 48% of those with no administrative contact. Fifth, as to the role of politics in getting things done and the efficacy of citizen action, generally we find that citizens who have been exposed to bureaucrats are both more realistic about the importance of political pull and more confident that the ordinary citizen can get action if officials are not performing their jobs properly. In rural Delhi the findings are striking in this regard — only 33% of the rural respondents who were isolated had optimistic views of the possibility of citizen action, contrasted to 83% of those citizens who were involved.

On these important criteria, then, the evidence points to the conclusion that citizen-administrative contacts are relevant and meaningful. As the polity is expanded and more citizens are involved with the regime their perspectives are more integrated than alienated. The net effect of bureaucratic effort is the mobilization of greater support for development. True, sizeable minorities of those in frequent contact with these officials are still ignorant of governmental programs (29% know virtually nothing about Community Development even though they rate high on exposure to CD officials). Also, 10% to 20% are pessimistic about citizen action possibilities even though they are frequently in touch with officials. And personal hostility to administrators can continue or increase despite bureaucratic contacts. But these are minorities. Their existence suggests the imperfections in administrative orientations and behavior or the presence of basic or transitional conditions which constitute a barrier to proper reciprocal relations between citizen and official in any society.

Perhaps our most impressive evidence is that the new Community Development hierarchy is getting through to the public, not merely in terms of physical contact in the field, but in functional terms. Those in the rural area in contact with CD officials see the program as worth while, generally approve of the job CD officials are doing, have a great interest in the program, and are becoming more knowledgeable about specific governmental expectations and plans. The most significant finding is that farmers exposed to CD officials are changing their ways of farming much more than the farmers isolated from bureaucratic influence. Only 32% of the farmers out of touch with the CD program are improving farming methods, compared to 83% of those frequently in contact with CD officials.

One may well argue that CD officials may be consciously selecting only those farmers who would be cooperative and, therefore, these data are not convincing. Although conscious selection may indeed be present, directly for strategic reasons, or indirectly, these findings cannot be explained away by this argument. First, the penetration of the bureaucracy into the least modernizing sectors of the society, into the most remote and traditional villages, and into social categories which are the least literate and leading the most marginal of existences, refutes the hypothesis that bureaucrats are working only with probably responsive villagers. Further, the response distributions for those who have had frequent contact, some contact, and no contact with the bureaucrats suggests that these officials miscalculated if they singled out only supportive farmers with which to work. That the total effort of CD officials is still only a fraction of what it might be cannot be denied, since 66% of our rural sample are still largely unexposed. But that this effort is both intensive and eclectic, motivated by the goal of *involving* citizens throughout the countryside, is obvious from our data. And this effort is beginning to produce a harvest of public response, even among the most illiterate and poverty-stricken elements of the population, which if multiplied tenfold will have a tremendous long-run impact on Indian society.

The administrator at the base of the hierarchy, at the cutting edge of governmental interaction with the citizen, is surely the vital cog in this system, up to the present and in the future. Can the official at this level, committed to innovation and democracy, facilitate the involvement of the citizen with these system aspirations? In studying five agencies (police, health, postal, Community Development, and municipal bus and transport) we found differing patterns of recruitment and job orientation. The officials in these agencies included few with low status backgrounds, except possibly in the CD hierarchy. The line personnel revealed very limited job mobility, considerable tenure and experience, and general satisfaction with their careers, particularly the field personnel in health and Community Development work. At most, 33% had reservations about their positions, but this percentage increased to over 50% for the non-mobile incumbents.

A major concern in our investigation was the character of the training program in each agency, its public relations emphasis, and how this program was perceived by officials. In health, postal, and the Delhi Transport Undertaking the training programs were limited. In police and Community Development the extensive training programs had heavy emphasis on public relations. Whether or not a serious training program existed, the great majority of these officials (over 80%) had clear understandings of the importance of good public relations. But this has not as yet freed many from their rigid bureaucratic commitments to strict rule enforcement and a skepticism concerning the need to explain decisions to the public. For 30% to 40% following orders is still a norm more important than serving the public.

Clearly, many of these officials are in conflict in the new administrative system, indoctrinated with the need for public relations but imprisoned by previous bureaucratic norms. Using an "Index of Democratic Job Perspectives" we found from 7% to 39% of our line personnel committed to democratic task perspectives, with the CD line personnel most oriented to public service. But not all of the remainder were rigid bureaucrats. The large majority seemed to be moving away from inflexible, arrogant, and impersonalized perspectives associated with traditional bureaucratic behavior. Our index suggests that far less than 25% of these officials had not begun to assimilate the new norms.

Considerable evidence suggests that despite their social backgrounds, long tenure, and limited training, the great majority of these officials are incorporating welfare-state and public service perceptions of their roles. Further, although a large proportion of these officials reveal latent authoritarian personal predispositions, no strong relationship exists between these tendencies and the assumption of democratic job perspectives. Perhaps the most important factor related to the existence of a democratic job perspective is the saliency and intensity of the training program emphasis on public service. Where officials did perceive the program as demanding actions and attitudes which were public relations oriented, there was a significant, indeed striking, increase in the proportions revealing democratic perspectives. The implications of this for governmental planning must be underscored. A subtle process of democratic socialization and communication is evident in these agencies. Sensitivity to public needs is high where the agency hierarchy communicates such an expectation and reinforces it with a training program whose accent is clear.

Finally, in an intensive analysis and comparison of citizen and official orientations and attitudes in three development blocks, the administrative subsystem was scrutinized closely. To explain why citizens in different, but adjoining, geographical areas can have divergent patterns of attitudes toward government and authority is not an easy task. In our exploratory analysis we found that although the characteristics of administrators were similar, the pattern of citizen-administrator contacts was not. Where the public was in contact with officials, citizens developed perceptions and evaluations of officials which were more supportive than in the areas where contacts were infrequent. Public images of government and its bureaucracy are elusive phenomena whose origins and maintenance are most baffling to determine or change. In a developing society like India the greater the distance between citizen and administrator, the greater the probability of apathy, frustration, and alienation. But where contact is high, and the linkage of citizen and administrator in a common cause is promoted, the greater the probability of support, self-confidence, and social change.

These, then, are the major findings and interpretations from one pilot study. They suggest many uniformities, they point to serious paradoxes and problems. India today faces a continued struggle of gigantic proportions to achieve a democratic and integrated society, to develop public confidence in and meaningful utilization of political institutions adapting to the needs of today, and to involve, motivate, and mobilize citizen support for programs of social and economic change. These three crises, elaborated at the outset of this report, must constitute the theoretical agenda for the scholar seeking answers to hypotheses, or for the politician seeking pragmatic answers to immediate problems. In the resolution of these crises the role of the bureaucracy in India is crucial. The expansion of opportunities for contact with, and influence upon, governmental leaders and decision making is not a luxury in a developing society like India. Nor is it merely relevant to democratic system goals, perceived by some as peripheral if not dysfunctional to developmental achievement. The expansion of the polity is a vital necessity for the success of large-scale innovative planning, predicated on public consent, support, and commitment. Unless the Indian public understands the meaning of the new society, fervently believes in it and in the citizen's participant role in the system, and manifests such belief with action, neither democracy nor development can be achieved. Although progress is slow, the interviews in this study reveal that a beginning has been made, that the Indian official at the cutting edge is having his impact on the development process. The public response to bureaucratic contact, as well as the public influence on bureaucratic behavior, is moving the Indian society—although very slowly—toward democratic relationships between the citizen and his leaders, as well as toward the realization of social and economic aspirations.

Appendix

a *The samples*

Delhi State had a population, according to the 1961 census, of 2,658,612. The overwhelming proportion, over 88%, is urban, residing in the capital city or its environs, separated by the census into three divisions—Delhi urban, New Delhi, and Delhi Cantonment. The state includes 573 square miles, with a population density of 4640. In the heart of the city, known as Zone II, the density in 1961 was 143,113, which was double the average for Calcutta districts, and six times that for Bombay. The population of the state has increased rapidly since the 1951 census, by almost one million, a 52% increase in ten years. The literacy rate for the state is relatively high and improving rapidly—52.7% in 1961 compared to 38.4% in 1951. At least 12% of the population belong to scheduled castes.

The rural area of Delhi territory, according to the census, had 276 villages, located in five Community Development blocks: Alipur, Najafgarh, Shahadara, Kaujawala, and Mehrauli. Actually, at the time of our study only 239 of these villages could be considered for our purposes, since the remainder had either been abandoned or incorporated by Delhi Municipal Corporation.

According to the census, the following was the distribution of villages by population size:

Population size	Number of villages	Percentage of male population
Under 200 inhabitants	25	1.0%
200 to 499 inhabitants	51	6.4
500 to 999 inhabitants	99	24.3
1000 to 1999 inhabitants	59	27.7
2000 to 5000 inhabitants	42	40.6

Our study selected two distinct and separate samples, one urban and one rural, each to consist of approximately 400 individuals. Our purpose was to look at urban and rural behavior separately. Although it would be possible to generalize about the total Delhi population, because of the different population sizes of rural and urban Delhi the two samples of 400 were not commingled in our analysis, nor should they be by the reader. We have in effect done two separate studies — one rural, one urban.

In selecting our rural sample the decision was made to select eight villages randomly from the total of 239, after classifying all villages on two criteria: population size and developmental status, objectively determined. A traditionalism-modernism objective score was arrived at for each of the 239 villages, by use of the following indicators:

1. Percentage of scheduled castes (zero to over 46%)
2. Literacy level (under 10% to over 38%)
3. Development block administrative status (headquarters, Panchayat center, etc.)
4. Distance from railway station, public road, or bus line
5. Governmental facilities in village: dispensary, primary health center, police station, post office
6. Type of schools, if any, in village
7. Community facilities — whether a market center, a community radio set
8. Assignment of a village level worker, midwife, to village
9. Percentage of population employed as cultivators, or in agriculture

The maximum score possible on this index was 42. The actual scores ranged from 3 to 40 for the 239 villages in this area. We classified all villages with a score below 9 as traditional, those from 9 to 13 as transitional, those with a score of 13 to 19 as modernizing, and those 19 and over as modern.

Combining the two criteria of population size and objective score on traditionalism-modernism, we developed the following strata or grid:

Proportion of total population (number of villages in parentheses)

	Traditional	Transitional	Modernizing	Modern
Population under 1000	3% (21)	13% (63)	13% (53)	— (3)
1000 to 1999	— (1)	10% (20)	15% (29)⎫	
2000 to 5000	—	8% (7)	14% (16)⎭	24%(26)

From each of the eight major strata thus identified we selected one village at random, and these eight constituted our primary sampling points.[1] These eight villages were located in three different community blocks. They ranged in population from 476 to 3929, and ranged in traditionalism-modernism score from 8 to 20. The number of interviews assigned to each village was proportional to the population size of each stratum from which the village was drawn. This procedure for drawing the rural sample assured us of villages in different population categories, and in different stages of development or modernization, as objectively defined. Though interviews were clustered in eight villages, it was a random probability sample, representative of the rural adult male population in Delhi territory.

Two other features of the rural sample should be noted. The decision was made to include males only in the basic sample because of the uncertainty that women would be available for interviewing. However, to test this technical assumption, and to compare male and female attitudes, a random sample of 50 women was selected in two villages. The interviews were conducted successfully (with a 96% completion rate) by the two women interviewers in our group. Finally, because the number of interviews assigned to one village was small (only 13) under our sample selection requirements, an additional sample of 17 was selected at random to permit (and to be used exclusively for) village-by-village comparisons.

In urban Delhi the basic geographical unit used as our primary sampling area was the "mohalla," the significant subdivision for political purposes and adaptable to administrative sampling objectives. There were 25 such mohallas or wards randomly included in our study out of approximately 80 such areas. The 400 interviews in urban Delhi were allocated almost equally to these mohallas because their population size variation was minimal. Three New Delhi Municipal Committee Areas were included in these mohallas.

The procedure for selecting respondents in villages and mohallas was random selection from the electoral lists. These lists, up-to-date for the previous local elections, were the best available. They were not completely accurate, as we subsequently discovered, but no feasible alternative was open to us without the expenditure of tremendous amounts of time and money.

---

[1]The four villages which fell outside these strata were combined with villages closest to them at the same population level. Thus each village had an equal chance of being selected.

Block listings and house listings, particularly in the high density sections of the city, would be misleading because large numbers have no house address. Our experience suggests that the electoral rolls are a fairly reliable list of adults. A more serious problem is the mobility and transiency of the population, both urban and rural, which makes the discovery of the whereabouts of respondents often impossible.

We used standard procedures in selecting our sample respondents from the list, employing a random starting point and a specified interval determined by the number of interviews we desired in a particular area, in relation to the total number of adults (males separately from females) on the given list. Because of the problem of transiency, we selected at random an alternate second sample in all urban mohallas to provide us with enough interviews if the original sample mortality was too high. No substitutes could be selected by our interviewers. They were given the names and addresses of specific individuals and required to interview only these individuals. As many as ten call-backs were made, as well as special trips to different villages or mohallas, to find individual respondents.

Despite our careful and determined work, the completion rate was not as high as we would have liked, particularly in urban Delhi. The rates were as follows:

Rural males   85%
Rural females   96%
Urban males   64%

The reasons for non-completion were varied:

Percentages of all interviews which were not completed

	Rural	Urban
Deceased; ill	9%	7%
Moved; not traceable	59	48
"Out of station" (working elsewhere, in army, etc.); not available	28	35
Refusals	4	10

Obviously, the major problems were residential mobility and the tendency to leave home for long periods in search of work or because of the requirements of work, or for other reasons leaving the family behind at the original residence. Refusals constituted no particular problem for us. In rural areas we spent time with the village leaders explaining the purposes of the study and becoming familiar with village conditions. When the interviewing began we usually found people cooperative. Interviewing often took place late at night or in the fields during harvest time. In certain villages some residents actually requested or demanded to be interviewed, particularly if they were leaders or factional representatives who had been left off our sample list. These non-sample interviews were taken and proved informative.

In selecting the administrators for our study our design required the following: (1) administrators who functioned in the geographical subdivisions (blocks, villages, mohallas) in which our public cross section lived so that our questions concerning contact and mutual perceptions would have the greatest relevance; (2) administrators in five agencies, three of which were identical for both urban and rural population (health, police, and postal), one which was exclusively rural (Community Development) and one exclusively urban (Delhi Transport Undertaking); (3) officials at two hierarchical levels in these agencies, at the level closest to the public, and at the level directly above these lower echelon officials. We decided to take all officials in certain categories, and a sample in others. Thus, since there were only three block development officers, we interviewed all three. But from the large number of police constables we selected a sample from only those blocks and mohallas where our public resided.

The following table indicates precisely who was interviewed in each of our administrative leadership categories, keeping the above purposes in mind:

| | SAMPLE TYPE | |
	Line officials (lower level)	Staff Officials (higher level)
Police	Constables (10%)	SHO, ASI, DSP (100%) Head constables (50%)
Postal	Subpostmaster, postman (100%)	--------
Health	Compounders (67%)	Medical officers, doctors (100%)
Delhi Transport	Inspectors (20%)	--------
Community Development	Village level workers (100%) Midwives, dais (50%) Lady health visitors (100%)	Block develop- ment officers, extension of- ficers, Panch- ayat secretar- ies, progress assistants (100%)

Thus, the 217 administrators in the study were representative of all officials in the respective categories in Delhi State. They either included *all* available officials in a particular category in our subdivisions, (which had been randomly selected), or they were a randomly selected sample. The cooperation of the agencies assisted considerably in this selection. For example, the total list of police constables was made available to the project, from which a sample could be selected. The officials themselves were very cooperative also. Time was willingly given for personal interviews, often of several hours' duration, and no more than two or three officials refused interviews. With such a wide variety of officials, geographically dispersed, this part of the study was the most difficult. The interest in the project, however, was considerable, and largely responsible for its successful completion.

In this first effort, although the sample selection process was complicated and completion rates at the urban public level not optimal, we feel highly satisfied with our results. Adaptation of accepted procedures in other societies to the Indian society was possible. Scientific requirements were not compromised. Many lessons were learned for future work. But the sample selection process was essentially sound and rigorous, as were the other field procedures in the project. We are confident, therefore, that our data are highly reliable and permit the detailed and precise analysis presented in this report.

Appendix

b *The questionnaires*

Governmental official interview schedule

1. Let's start with some questions about your job. I want to be sure I understand your position. Can you tell me about the nature of your job? (Probe for job description as respondent sees it).

   a. Are there any other duties that you have?

   b. Which of these duties seem to take most of your time?

   c. What is your rank or designation?

   d. How long have you worked in this position?

   e. How long have you been a governmental employee?

   f. What positions did you have before this one? (Career details in chronological order)

   g. Do you find your job very interesting, somewhat interesting, or not interesting?

h. Do you think this job is in keeping with your qualifications and abilities?

i. Do you feel that you have enough authority to decide the things you should decide, or not enough authority?

j. Do you find it at times necessary in your position to relax the procedures to do a more effective job?

k. Do you find it possible to relax procedures?

l. Some people like their work; others think of their work as only a means of livelihood. How do you feel about your work?

m. Could you tell me a little about your training for this position: What training program did you go through?

(If *yes*) What sorts of things were emphasized in this program of training?

n. Was your relationship to the citizen or the public discussed during this training?

(If *yes*) What were you told about the way to deal with the public?

o. Do you think this training has been valuable to you in your job?

p. In what respects? Can you give me any examples of how it has helped you?

2. Now, I would like to have you tell me a little about the people you work with. Who is the immediate superior to whom you report? (Name and designation)

a. About how often do you see him?

b. How well do you know him? Aside from your official relationship, do you know him personally?

c. How well does he know your job?

d. What sorts of things does your immediate superior emphasize when he talks to you about your job? (Probe: What sorts of things seem to be most important to him in the way you perform your job?)

e. Has he ever discussed with you the problem of your relationship to citizens — the public — and the way you should deal with them?

f. What sorts of things does he emphasize in discussing your relationship to the public?

g. Have you ever had any difference of opinion with him about the way you should handle the public?

h. Have you ever been warned about your work?

(If *yes*) What was that?

i. Is there an official policy on public relations—dealing with the public—for your agency? Or are there *any* written rules and regulations in your department regarding dealings with the public?

(If *yes*) What are the main things it emphasizes?

j. About how often in the past six months would you say you have been issued directions or memoranda from your supervisors about the way in which you should deal with the public?

k. Who is the person at the top of your agency? (Name and designation)

l. Have you met him?

m. Do you think he is aware of the type of work you do?

n. Has he ever talked to the employees like yourself about the way in which you should do your job?

(If *yes*) What sorts of things does he talk about?

o. Does he discuss your relationship to the public at all, that is, how you should treat the public?

3. Do you think the public makes extra demands on you over and above what you do for them in the ordinary course of your job?

(If *yes*) Can you tell me something about the nature of these demands?

a. Do you think it is necessary for you to explain to citizens the reasons for your decisions?

b. Some people say that serving the public is most important; others say that following the orders of your superiors is most important. How do you feel about this? (Probe: If says both are, ask which of the two is more important.)

c. Have you ever happened to hear criticisms about the performance of your duties from members of the public?

(If *yes*) What sorts of things do they criticize you about? Do you think this criticism is fair or unfair?

d. How important do you think it is for your particular agency to get cooperation from the public?

e. To what extent does your agency get such public cooperation, in your opinion?

Why or why not? (Ask for both cases)

f. What kinds of cooperation from the public do you think you should get?

g. What per cent of the public do you think would say that people in your type of position are efficient?

h. And what per cent of the public do you think would say officials like you are courteous in their dealings with the public?

i. And what per cent do you think would say that officials in your position are corrupt?

j. In general, what do you think of your relations with the public — are they good, bad, or indifferent?

4. What are your plans for staying on in your present position? Do you expect to stay for a long time, do you expect to move to a higher position, or would you like to leave as soon as possible?

a. (If *leave* or *move up*) What type of position would you like to move to?

b. (If *leave*) What are your hopes for securing another job?

c. If you had an opportunity to take a position in private business, do you think you would take it?

Why or why not?

d. Some people say that a large number of people working for the government are corrupt. Do you think this is so?

e. Generally, what per cent of public employees would you say is corrupt?

f. What per cent of employees in your own agency would you say is corrupt?

g. (Ask health and Community Development respondents.) Do you approve of the government spending money for the type of activity your agency is performing, or do you think the government should not be engaged in this type of activity?

h. Do you feel that all citizens are treated fairly and equally by the people who work in your agency, or are some types of people treated favorably and others less favorably?

i. (If discrimination is indicated) What types of people are not treated fairly?

j. Do you think it is your job to treat everybody fairly, or do you think you have to give some people special treatment?

k. (If have to discriminate) Which groups do you have to favor?

l. Are there any difficulties or problems in your agency in serving the public?

(If *yes*) What are they?

(If *yes*) What improvements do you suggest?

5. The Congress party, which is in power, has been talking for some time about governmental programs designed to achieve "the socialist pattern of society." What do you think that means?

a. Do you think the government is achieving that goal, or not?

b. Do you think the government should try to achieve that goal, or not?

c. For your own type of work and your agency, what do you think is necessary for the government to achieve, or what can the government do through your agency to achieve that goal?

d. Do officials like you ever discuss such matters as governmental policy, programs, and goals among yourselves?

e. How often would you say that you do discuss such matters with fellow workers—very often, often, occasionally, rarely, never?

6. We are very much interested in your viewpoint on current issues in India.

a. First, how do you feel about this statement: "To improve the welfare of our people, the government should nationalize more private
businesses, industries, and banks"? Do you agree or disagree,
or don't you have an opinion on this?

(If has opinion)   On this question of nationalization, is the government going too far, doing less than it should, or what?

b. How do you feel about this statement: "Government should control
the prices of food"? Do you agree or disagree, or don't you have an
opinion?

c. And this statement: "The government should control house rents."
(Agree, disagree, no opinion)

d. And on this question of house rents: "Do you think that the government is going too far, doing less than it should, or what?"

e. Which party comes closest to your opinions on these matters?

7. We know that there are many reasons why people don't vote in elections. Could you tell me whether you voted in the last election in 1962
for the Lok Sabha?

(If not)   Why was it you did not vote?

a. Generally speaking, what political party do you support?

b. (If can't say or independent)   Well, what party would you say you
are closest to?

c. All in all, does it make much difference to you personally which
party, whether Congress or some other party, is in control of the
government?

d. Did any of the parties contact you during the last election campaign
in 1962 for your vote?

e. Do you know any political party leaders in this area personally?

(If yes)   What are their positions and parties?

f. Some people think that political pull — knowing the right person —
plays an important part in whether the government will help a private citizen with some problem he has; other people don't think so.
In your opinion, does political pull play an important part or not?

g. Do you feel that you have to provide more service to certain party leaders and their friends than to others?

h. In general, if you were to advise a citizen who had a problem and needed governmental help, would you advise him to go personally to the department concerned, or to get the assistance of a person who was on friendly terms with the governmental official or agency concerned?

i. (If mentions direct approach) If a citizen needs a special service or wants to get things done very quickly, would you still advise him to go personally to the department or to get help from someone who is known to the department?

j. Have you ever had any experiences yourself which indicated that political pull helps one get service from the government?

(If *yes*) Would you explain that to me, please?

8. Now I'd like to read some of the kinds of things people tell me when I interview them and ask you whether you agree or disagree with them, or whether you aren't sure.

a. The average citizen doesn't have much say about what the government does.

b. Public officials really care quite a lot about what the ordinary citizen thinks.

c. The way the government runs things today is better than the way things were run in the past.

d. Rapid improvement in the economic and social welfare of the Indian people is not possible under the present democratic system of party government.

e. Human nature being what it is, there will always be war and conflict.

f. A few strong leaders could make this country better than all the laws and talk.

g. Most people who don't get ahead just don't have enough will power.

h. People can be trusted.

i. Obedience and respect for authority are the most important virtues children should learn.

    j. The world is too complicated to be understood by anyone but experts.

    k. People are getting soft and weak from so much babying and coddling.

9. What daily newspapers do you normally read?

    a. Do you think the following ways of getting news about the government are important?

        Newspaper
        Radio
        Publicity literature
        Government officials
        Discussions with friends
        Others

    b. Which one of them, or any other, do you think is the most important?

10. Here is a list of the types of groups in this area to which people belong. Would you look at it and tell me to which of these organizations you belong?

    a. (For each group) Would you say that you attend most of the meetings of this group, about half, just a few, or none?

    b. (For each group) Are you on a committee or do you hold any office in this organization?

    TYPES OF GROUPS

Labor unions	Professional groups
Religious groups	Political groups
Business civic groups	Resident associations
Neighborhood clubs, centers	Women's clubs
Language or regional groups	Charitable groups
Sports teams or clubs	Other groups (specify)

Special questions for particular officials

Community Development

1. Are there any leaders in this area (village, community) whom you know and see a great deal of?

2. What leaders are they? (Probe: a faction leader, caste leader, etc.)

3. What do you see them about? What are they leaders of?

4. Are the leaders in this area willing to cooperate with you and your program?

5. What types of leaders are least cooperative?

6. Do you think that the amount of money the government is putting into your agency—that is, your budget— is too large, just about right, or too little?

7. Do you think that for the money spent on your agency, the taxpayer is getting back his money's worth in service?

8. Do you feel that people participate enough in your program?

9. What per cent of the people in this area would you say are not interested in cooperating with your program?

10. What types of people are least cooperative and what are their characteristics?

11. What can be done to get the cooperation of these people?

Police officials

1. Do people ever give wrong information to the police deliberately?

   (If *yes*)   Can you give me an example of that?

2. Are there any particular groups in this area which have stronger feelings against the police than others?

   (If *yes*)   In what respects and what groups?

3. Do you think the public generally fear the police, respect them but do not fear them, or neither?

Postal officials

1. When people come to the post office, do you think they are patient and considerate enough of postal officials?

   (If not)   In what ways are they not considerate?

2. When a person who comes to the post office has not prepared his letters or packages properly for mailing, do you ever have any problem in explaining this to him?

   (If *yes*)   What do you think is the basic difficulty in such situations?

Delhi Transport Undertaking

1. Do people usually wait for their turn in boarding the bus, or do they break the queue?

   Why is that?

2. Do you think people generally treat officials like yourself with respect, or not?

   Why is that?

Health officials

1. Do people come to you for advice on health problems when it is almost too late for treatment, or do they usually come well in time for treatment?

2. Have they seen anyone else for treatment before they come to you?

   (If *yes*)   Who do they see before coming to you — other doctors, untrained personnel, or others?

3. Do you think the members of the public have confidence in health officials like you generally, or not?

   Why is that?

4. Is the ordinary citizen with whom you deal grateful, critical, or indifferent to you for your help?

   Why is that, in your opinion?

5. Do you think people usually follow the advice which you give them in connection with their own health problems?

6. Do you think people are interested in ways of preventing the development of health problems (such as vaccinations and sanitary practices) or are they more interested in curing diseases after they have developed?

Why do you think that is so?

7. What would you say is the major problem you have in dealing with the public in the area of public health?

Background data

Well, that completes the regular part of the interview. As I was telling you, we don't take the names of the people on our surveys, but we do need a few facts about them, such as age, marital status, and so forth. Would you help me with these specific items of information?

1. Age

2. Sex (by observation)

3. What is (or was) your father's occupation?

4. Marital status: single, married, widowed, separated, divorced

   Number of children

5. Religion: Hindu, Muslim, Christian, Buddhist, Sikh, other

   Do you regularly engage in any religious worship?

6. Education: illiterate, primary, middle, high, intermediate, degree, M.A. and above

7. How long have you lived in your present residence?

   Where did you live before you came here?

8. Where is your permanent residence?

9. Place of birth

10. Do you own your own home, are you buying, or do you rent?

11. Mother tongue

12. Caste

13. What is your monthly family income?

    How much of this is the income of the head of the family?

Citizen cross section interview schedule[1]

1. What do you think of the officials in Delhi Corporation? Do you think they are doing a poor, fair, good, or very good job?

2. Now, how about the Delhi State Administration? Do you think the officials are doing a poor, fair, good, or very good job? How do you mean that?

3. And how about the central government—do you think those officials are doing a poor, fair, good, or very good job? How do you mean that?

4. Now I would like to ask you about some particular government services. How do you feel about the postal service here? What kind of job are the postal employees doing?

   a. Do the postal employees serve the public to the best of their ability in delivering letters, handling the savings accounts, and taking care of parcels?

   b. How often in the last month have you gone to the post office?

   c. Can you remember any experiences with postal employees which were unsatisfactory?

   (If *yes*) What were they?

5. Now I would like to ask you about the health services and facilities. Do you think the officials in charge of the nearest dispensary or hospital are doing a poor, fair, good, or very good job?

   a. Have you or anyone in your family ever gone to the dispensary or hospital?

   b. (If *yes*) Which of the following do you go to—corporation dispensaries, C.H.S. dispensaries, hospital?

   (If more than one mentioned, ask which most often.)

   c. How often in the past year would you say that you or members of your family have gone to the dispensary or hospital?

   d. Are the health officials courteous or discourteous to you?

   e. (If *no* to 5a.) How is it that you or your family members have not been to the dispensary or hospital?

---

[1]Questions 1 and 6 were asked in urban Delhi only.

f. Do you think it is necessary for the government to provide these health services?

g. What are your reasons for your opinion?

h. Do you think that all people are treated fairly by the health officials, or isn't the treatment equal and fair?

i. (If favored) What kinds of people are favored, in your opinion? (Probe for status where only names are indicated.)

j. Suppose you found out that a health official was not performing his job properly. Could you do anything about it?

   (If *yes*) What could you do?

   (If *no*) Why not?

k. Do you know whether you have to pay for any of these health services?

l. Do you know how to keep from getting smallpox?

   When was the last time you were vaccinated for smallpox?

   Have any other members of your family been vaccinated for smallpox?

   (If *yes*) Which ones?

   (If *no*) Why have you not been vaccinated?

   Where do you go to get vaccinated?

m. Do you know where the Family Planning Center is in this area?

   (If *yes*) Have you gone to it in the past year?

   What kind of job do you think the Family Planning Center is doing?

6. Let's talk about another important agency. Some people think that the Delhi bus service (DTU) is doing a good job, but others are critical of that service. How do you feel?

   a. Would you approve of turning the bus system over to the private companies?

(If *yes*)   Why is that?

(If *no*)   Why not?

b. How often do you or any members of your family use the bus — daily, several times a week, or occasionally?

c. If you have a complaint against the bus service, is there anything you can do?

(If *yes*)   What is that?

d. Have you ever used the complaint book on the buses?

e. Do you think the bus fare is high, reasonable, or low, in terms of the service you get?

7. What kind of job do you think the police are doing here — poor, fair, good, or very good?

a. Why do you think that?

b. Have you ever had any personal experience with the local police?

(If *yes*)   What was that?

c. In your opinion, what is the most important job that the police do here?

d. On what kind of problem would you go to the police for help?

e. Do you think they would be helpful to you?

f. Do you think the police are courteous or discourteous to citizens?

g. Do you know any policemen here personally?

h. In general, do you think there is corruption in the police department?

(If *yes*)   Would you kindly explain what you mean?

i. Do the police do a good job in preventing crime?

j. Do you think it is your responsibility to cooperate with the police in preventing crime?

k. If somebody got involved in some trouble with the police, do you think the police would mistreat or beat him up?

General questions

8. In general, if you had a problem to take up with a governmental department or municipal office, would you do it yourself, or do you think you would be better off if you got the help of some person or organization? (Do it myself, would get help from other person, would get help from some organization, would get help from both, no opinion, other)

9. In general, would you say that your dealings with public employees were poor, fair, good or very good?

10. Some people think that political pull — knowing the right person — plays an important part in whether the government will help a private person with some problem he has; other people don't think so. What is your opinion about it? (Yes, pull is important; pull is sometimes important; no, pull hardly matters; depends; no opinion)

   a. Could you tell me how you mean that?

   b. Have you or anybody known to you had any experience which indicated that political pull helps a citizen?

   (If *yes*) Would you explain to me what happened in that case?

11. In general, would you say that you discuss the working of the governmental departments and officials with your friends very often, often, sometimes, or never?

12. We'd like to know what people think of government jobs and government work. If these jobs were about the same in kind of work, pay, and so forth, which has the most prestige — that is, which do you think the most of?

	Government	Private
Clerk		
Night watchman		
Doctor		

Note to interviewer: Read the above question as follows: "Which job do you think the most of — clerk in a government office or clerk in a private firm?" Do the same for all three and record the answers above.

13. If the pay were the same, would you prefer to work for the government or for a private firm?

   a. Why?

   b. In general, would you say that you get more courteous service and attention in dealing with governmental employees or in dealing with the employees of private companies?

    c. Why do you think that is so?

14. How many of the government officials would you say are probably corrupt — more than half, about half, just a few, none, don't know, can't say?

    a. Do you think there is corruption in the assessment or collection of levies?

    b. Do you think there is corruption in connection with the services in dispensaries or hospitals?

    (If *yes*) Do you think this is because governmental employees are not paid enough?

15. In terms of what the government gives the public in help and services, do you think that the government gets back from the public more, less, or about the same?

16. Some people feel that they pay more taxes than they should, considering what they get from the government. How do you feel about this?

17. What are the main sources of income for the government?

18. Do you happen to know how much money a person had to make last year before he had to pay an income tax?

19. Now I'd like to read some of the things people tell me when I interview them and ask you whether you agree or disagree with them, or whether you aren't sure.

    a. People like me don't have any say about what the government does.

    b. Public officials really care quite a lot about what people like me think.

    c. Sometimes politics and government seem so complicated that a person like me can't really understand what's going on.

    d. If something grows up over a long time, there is bound to be much wisdom in it.

    e. The way the government runs things today is better than the way things were run in the past.

f. Human nature being what it is, there will always be war and conflict.

g. A few strong leaders would make this country better than all the laws and talk.

h. Obedience and respect for authority are the most important virtues children should be taught.

i. People can be trusted.

20. What daily newspapers do you normally read?

Name of the paper ⎯⎯⎯⎯⎯   Language ⎯⎯⎯⎯⎯

a. Do you think the following ways of getting news about the government are important?

Newspaper	Discussions with friends
Radio	Local party workers or leaders
Publicity literature	Other
Government officials	

b. Which one of them, or any other, do you think is the most important? Which is least important?

21. Could you tell me whether you voted in the last election in 1962 for the Lok Sabha?

a. And how about the last election for the Panchayat? Did you vote in that election?

(If *no*) I notice that you did not vote. Why was that?

b. Generally speaking, what political party do you support at election time?

(If can't say or independent) Well, what party would you say you are closest to?

c. Have you ever helped campaign for a party or a candidate during an election campaign, for example, by putting in time or contributing money?

(If *yes*) Which party was that and when?

d. Almost all of the parties organized public meetings in the last campaign. Did you attend any of these meetings?

e. All in all, does it make much difference to you which party is in control of Delhi Corporation or central government?

f. Did any of the parties contact you during the last election campaign?

(If *yes*) How was that? Which parties and in what way?

g. Do you think it would be helpful for you to go to a party leader if you needed assistance on a domestic or personal problem, or had a problem in connection with service from a government department?

h. Have you ever gone to a party leader for such a purpose?

i. Do you know any party leaders in this area personally?

(If *yes*) What is their position in the party, and which party is that?

22. We are also interested in your opinions on the political issues and problems of India today. Would you agree or disagree with these statements?

a. The government should control the prices of food.

b. The government should not control house rents.

c. The government should not increase the taxes on the rich.

d. To improve the welfare of our people, the government should nationalize more private businesses, industries, and banks.

23. Who would you say are the three most important leaders in your mohalla?

a. Why would you say that they are influential?

b. Do you know any of these leaders personally?

24. One of the ways in which people spend their time is in clubs and organizations. Here is a list of such groups in the Delhi area. (Hand over list.) Would you look at it and tell me to which of these types of organizations you belong?

a. (For each group) Would you say that you attend most of the meetings of this group, about half, just a few, or none?

b. (For each group) Are you on a committee or do you hold any office in this organization?

TYPES OF GROUPS

Labor unions	Professional groups
Religious groups	Political groups
Business civic groups	Resident associations
Neighborhood clubs, centers	Charitable groups
Language or regional groups	Other groups (specify)
Sports teams or clubs	

25. How would you describe the social class to which you belong — upper class, middle class, working class, lower class?

26. Has your own and your family's standard of living improved, remained the same, or gone down in the past five years?

    a. In what way?

    b. When you think about what really matters to your family, what are your wishes and hopes for the future? (Probe: What kinds of things would you like to have?)

    c. What do you think you can do to achieve these wishes and hopes?

    d. What would you like to have the government do in order to make these wishes and hopes possible for you?

    e. How many rupees per month do you think it would take to provide your family with the standard of living you would like to have?

Special questions for rural citizens

1. We would like to get some of your ideas about what sort of job the government is doing. First, what do you think of the government officials in this village? Are they doing a poor, fair, good, or very good job?

    a. And what about the block officials? Are they doing a poor, fair, good, or very good job?

    b. How has Panchayati Raj changed block administration?

2. The Community Development program here is also an important part of the activity of the government. Some people say that CD officials are doing a good job; other people are critical of it. How do you feel?

a. What would you say are the most important purposes of the Community Development program here? (Probe: Are there other purposes, or goals, or activities that you can think of?)

b. Who are the officials in the CD program in this area?

(If knows)   How often in the past month have you seen any of these officials?

c. What in your opinion are the most important accomplishments of Community Development here?

(If mentions any)   Why have these accomplishments been possible?

d. And what are the important failures, if any?

(If mentions any) What are the reasons for this (these) failure(s)?

Why is that?

e. Do you ever discuss the CD program with your friends or associates or neighbors?

f. Who are the people here who are opposed to CD?

And who are the people who are in favor of it?

g. Would you say that you are very interested in the CD program, somewhat interested, or not interested?

3. As you know, the government has been trying to increase agricultural production. Can you tell me if you have heard of any ways in which the government has been trying to increase agricultural production? (Probe: Do you know of any particular programs the government has started to increase productivity?)

a. What do you think the government wants you to do to increase production?

b. Have you changed your ways of farming in the past five years? (Probe, using the check list below.)

Check list of changes in farming techniques:

1) seeds
2) fertilizers and manures
3) insecticides
4) implements

    5) subsidiary occupations—poultry, fish, dairying, vegetable farming

    6) more investment

    7) use of tractors

    8) cropping pattern

    9) water and irrigation

    10) marketing methods

    11) transportation methods

    12) storage methods

    13) using tube wells

c. Is there any change today in the way you work your farm?

    (If *yes*) Are you relying more on your own labor, or on hired labor, or what?

d. (If changes made) What prompted you to make these changes?

e. (If no changes) Why is it that you have not made any changes?

f. What do you feel is the major reason why some farmers do not want to make these changes?

g. Does the majority of people here want to make changes, or not?

h. If the government would promise the farmers that they would not lose any money if they made these changes — by giving them credit and not insisting on repayment of their debts unless their crops improved with such changes in methods — do you think that the farmers would follow the advice of the government?

i. Would you?

j. Do you think your standard of living would improve if you did improve your ways of farming and follow the advice of the government for increasing farm production?

4. What is a Taqavi Loan? Who can get it and on what conditions?

Background data

Well, that completes the regular part of the interview. As I was telling you, we don't take the names of the people on our surveys, but we do need a few facts about them, such as occupation, age, and so forth. Would you help me with these?

  1. Age

2. Sex (by observation)

3. Marital status: single, married, widowed, separated, divorced

   Number of children

4. What is your (or your husband's) occupation?

   a. (If retired or unemployed) What was your job; what work did you do?

   b. What is (or was) your father's occupation?

5. Religion: Hindu, Muslim, Christian, Buddhist, Sikh, other

   Do you regularly engage in any religious worship?

6. Education: illiterate, primary, middle, high, intermediate, degree, M.A. and above

7. How long have you lived in your present residence?

   Where did you live before you came here?

8. Place of birth

9. Do you own your own home, are you buying, or do you rent?

10. Do you plan to move from this neighborhood in the next year or so?

    (If *yes*)   Where do you plan to go?

11. Mother tongue

12. Caste

13. What is your monthly family income?

    How much of this is the income of the head of the family?

14. Would you say you are satisfied, or dissatisfied, with the mohalla you are living in now?

    Why do you feel that way?

befor V.W. Dealer turn Left and wes
12th Aven.

321 12th Av. Am. Legend.

best buddies

sisters of the heart

soul sister

friends forever

kindred spirits

sister-friends

SISTERCHICKS
Down Under!

girlfriends

pals for life

chum

confidante

gal pals

ally

true blue

"I read *Sisterchicks in Sombreros,* and I couldn't put it down. Every time I pick up one of Robin's books, the theme seems to speak to *exactly* what I am going through in my life at that exact moment!"—KELLI

"I just discovered the Sisterchick novels, and I love them! I identify in so many ways with Robin's characters. Her books have not only taught me about myself, but they've taught me so much about the personality of our wild and wonderful God."—ANDREA

"While I was reading *Sisterchicks on the Loose!* I realized I had shut God out of my life for far too long. I got my heart right with God, and a week later I met a new friend who has almost instantly become my Sisterchick! My life would be so empty right now if your book hadn't showed me what was missing. Thank you, Robin!"—DARLA

"I just finished *Sisterchicks do the Hula!* and had to tell you how wonderful it was! I really can't put into words how this book touched me, deep down in my soul. Like I was thirsty for something and your book was a cool drink of water. As I was reading the last page, I had tears in my eyes, not wanting the story to end and thankful that I could come along on the journey also. Thank you so much!"—LISA

"I just had to write and tell how much I love your Sisterchick books. My best friend and I love reading them together. Your books go into a place deep in my spirit and remind me that God IS a faithful and a loving Father. We both agree that you have a way of saying things that express exactly how we feel but didn't know how to say it!"—MELISSA

"I just finished *Sisterchicks do the Hula!* and I loved it! Actually, I found myself sneaking into the bathroom away from my loving husband and ever-present children to read more. You have written marvelous fiction that leaves me feeling closer to God."—MARY

"A coworker has me hooked on your books, and they are fabulous! A bunch of us at work decided that we're Sisterchicks, and we can't wait for the next adventure, because we're all going to read the book simultaneously and discuss it at lunch. Thanks for making work a fun place to be all of a sudden!" —LAUREN

"I am from the UK. Last weekend I bought *Sisterchicks on the Loose!* I can honestly say I never in my life read a book so fast! I laughed out loud, even cried in places, and struggled to put it down. It made me realise I, too, have a Sisterchick who should be treasured."—TRACEY

"A friend gave *Sisterchicks do the Hula!* to me for my birthday. I couldn't put it down. I'm thirty-five and feeling way too old for my age. Thank you for the breath of fresh air. I felt like God had you write it just for me!—KARA

"I just finished *Sisterchicks on the Loose!* and loved it. In fact, I devoured it. I hated to see it end. It had to be one of the best books on friendship that I have read. Love your sense of humor; I laughed out loud many times reading it. You have such a heart for Jesus and a wonderful spirit."—DEBBIE

"Thank you for the return trip to Oahu this morning! [*Sisterchicks do the Hula!*] It is snowing and sleeting outside, but I was enjoying the beautiful blues that only Hawai'i has. Thank you for giving me a 'garland of hosannas' and for reminding me to do the hula with God's rhythm of grace." —MARBARA

OTHER BOOKS BY ROBIN JONES GUNN

Gardenias for Breakfast

SISTERCHICK NOVELS
Sisterchicks on the Loose!
Sisterchicks Do the Hula!
Sisterchicks in Sombreros!

THE GLENBROOKE SERIES
Secrets
Whispers
Echoes
Sunsets
Clouds
Waterfalls
Woodlands
Wildflowers

GIFT BOOKS
Tea at Glenbrooke
Mothering by Heart
Gentle Passages

www.sisterchicks.com • www.robingunn.com

a sisterchick™ novel

SISTERCHICKS
Down Under!

ROBIN JONES GUNN

Multnomah® Publishers *Sisters, Oregon*

SISTERCHICKS DOWN UNDER!
published by Multnomah Publishers, Inc.

© 2005 by Robin's Ink, LLC
International Standard Book Number: 1-59052-411-X

Sisterchicks is a trademark of Multnomah Publishers, Inc.

Cover image of women by Bill Cannon Photography, Inc.
Painting referenced on p. 161 is entitled *The Sea Hath Its Pearls*
by William Henry Margetson

Scripture quotations are from:
The Message
© 1993, 1994, 1995, 1996, 2000, 2001, 2002
Used by permission of NavPress Publishing Group
The Holy Bible, New King James Version © 1984 by Thomas Nelson, Inc.
Holy Bible, New Living Translation © 1996
Used by permission of Tyndale House Publishers, Inc.
All rights reserved.
HOLY BIBLE: EASY-TO-READ VERSION
© 2001 by World Bible Translation Center, Inc. and used by permission.

Multnomah is a trademark of Multnomah Publishers, Inc.
and is registered in the U.S. Patent and Trademark Office.
The colophon is a trademark of Multnomah Publishers, Inc.

Printed in the United States of America

For information:
MULTNOMAH PUBLISHERS, INC. • P.O. BOX 1720 • SISTERS, OR 97759

ISBN 0-7394-5251-7

Acknowledgments

With a grateful g'day to the wonderful people who contributed to this story:

Ross, my one true love.

Bill, my visioneer.

Don, Doug, Brian, and Kevin, who sent me down under in search of a good story.

Bruce and Paul, who met me in Sydney and gave me a bag of Cheerios to feed the kangaroos.

Mike, Noel, and Ted, who showed me the best of their beloved New Zealand.

Susanne, you are a gifted hostess. Thank you for opening your heart and home to me. Loved your Pavlova!

Frances, thank you for taking me to corners of New Zealand that will never leave my heart.

Carol, Joanne, Penny, Robin, Tania, and Tracey, you amazing women proved my theory to be correct: Sisterchicks are everywhere!

Mostly what God does is love you.
Keep company with him and learn a life of love.
Observe how Christ loved us.
His love was not cautious but extravagant.
He didn't love in order to get something from us
but to give everything of himself to us.
Love like that.

EPHESIANS 5:2

Prologue

Age is just a number, right?

That's what I thought until three years ago when my younger brother opened his big mouth. He was on his way to Mexico to settle the legal details on some property his wife had inherited when he stopped by our home in southern California. His life seemed brimming with new adventures, while Tony and I were riding the overly-committed-to-the-schedule freight train we had been on since we got married.

Over dinner my brother joked about his receding hairline. "You know, Kathleen, you're halfway there yourself."

"No I'm not." I pulled at the strands of my straight brown hair to prove that my dependable mane wasn't falling out.

"I meant your age," he said. "You turned forty-five last month, right? You could be halfway done." He seemed to wait for me to do the math.

I always hated math.

I felt as if an equation had etched itself on the chalkboard of my mind: $45 + x = ?$

I didn't know the answer.

What had my forty-five years added up to so far? What was the value of x that would fill the remaining years? What would the sum of my life be? And what risks was I willing to take to solve the equation?

Apparently God can use all things—including math—to prepare a hurried heart to respond to Him when He's about to do a new thing. If I hadn't been pondering the "value of x" for so many weeks after my brother's visit, I don't think I would have been ready for what followed.

In the middle of the night, Tony's old boss, Mad Dog, called from Wellington, New Zealand, to offer Tony a three-month position film editing at Jackamond Studios. Ever since the success of *The Lord of the Rings*, Wellington had become *the* location for up-and-coming filmmakers. Tony saw the job as the big break he had been waiting for. I saw it as an opportunity to step off the edge of my well-padded nest and take a free fall into the unknown.

After all, our daughter was in college, and we were no longer financially responsible for my mother-in-law's convalescent care. Tony and I could do this. We could leave everything for three months and have the exotic travel experience we had only dreamed about during our college days.

I always do my best thinking while shaving my legs in a tubful of bubbles. The two weeks prior to our departure for Wellington, I had the smoothest legs and the most wrinkled fingers in all of Los Angeles.

I'd thought through every detail and confidently arrived at the airport with everything I needed. Everything, that is, except one item I hadn't tucked in my suitcases or sent ahead in the boxes. I didn't pack a single friend. After spending most of my life in the same city, same church, and same circles, I suddenly was minus my built-in community of friends.

Looking back, I now see how unnatural it was to change a well-established migratory route in the middle of life and expect my wings to start flapping in rhythm as soon as I took the free fall. It shouldn't have been such a surprise that I fell so hard. After all, everything in my world had flip-flopped.

I think it was necessary, though, for me to tumble as far down under as I did. Otherwise, I never would have stumbled into the Chocolate Fish on a fine fall Friday in February with feathers in my hair. And that's where I found Jill.

If Jill were the one telling this story, she would say that's where she found *me*. But I'm saying that's where I found her. It had become clear that to solve the math problem written over this season of my life, I needed one more whole number. That little number was one. One new best friend. Jill.

Jill likes math. She sees math in art and nature and isn't afraid of the unknown equations. Two years ago when she and I stood in front of a painting at an Australian art museum in Sydney, she opened my eyes to the beauty of balance and symmetry, and that's when I began to make peace with math.

But before I flutter through our story, I will add one more important point. I believe the reason I found Jill wasn't so much because I was looking for her, but because she was waiting for me, hanging by her painted toenails on the edge of her own empty nest.

One

During the two weeks before we left for New Zealand, every day felt like a storm at sea. My husband turned into a ruthless commander, as the intensity of it all swept us through our final days in California. When the storm subsided, I found myself washed up at an unfamiliar airport on the underside of the globe.

The only comforting sight was the grinning face of Tony's boss, Marcus, aka "Mad Dog," who met us at the baggage claim in Wellington. He punched Tony in the arm. "What did you think of that flight? Was I right about its being a marathon film fest? How many did you watch?"

"Five. No seven. No, I think it was five." Tony's adrenaline-induced gaze seemed frozen on his face.

Mad Dog adjusted his frayed corduroy cap. "Do you want to eat something first or go right to your new place?"

"Home," I said, as if it were a secret password that would lead me into this new world. All I needed was my new space around me so I could start fluffing up things the way I liked.

Then I would be ready to remind myself why this had been a good decision.

"Home it is. Hope you guys like this place. I told you how hard it is to find housing near the studio, didn't I?"

"You did," Tony said. "And we really appreciate all you did to find us a place. I'm going to owe you big time."

"You can pay me back with a few hours of overtime." Mad Dog loaded our luggage into the back of a van he had borrowed from Walter Jackamond Studios.

"How many hours are a 'few,' Marcus?" I asked.

He let out a single gut sound that resembled a cross between a cough and a guffaw. In the twelve years we had known him, I still hadn't gotten used to his laugh.

"You have to start calling me Mad Dog," he said. "No one here knows me as Marcus. And when I say a few hours, I mean…"

He didn't finish his sentence, but I realized I already knew the answer. For the next three months, Jackamond Studios would occupy my husband's every waking hour. Not only because they were behind schedule on the project for which they had hired Tony, but also because my husband never did anything halfway.

"Hey, it's Gollum!" Tony pointed to the roof of the terminal. An enormous model of the bald, grim-faced Middle-earth icon peered down on us, looking like a gigantic alien that had fallen to earth and gotten his foot stuck through the roof.

"I guess we're not in Kansas anymore, Toto," I said.

Tony gave me a gratuitous wink at my attempt to make a joke. I gripped the car door's handle. Not because of Tony's wink or Gollum's glare, but because Mad Dog was driving on the left side of the road.

Tony laughed. "This is wild!"

"You'll get used to it," Mad Dog said. "Only took me a week when I moved here. Maybe less."

I expected an oncoming car to ram into us any moment. Everyone was going the opposite from what my brain said was correct. Mad Dog drove past a row of low-rise buildings, and I tried to take it all in. Stop lights, a normal-looking city bus, lots of small cars, billboards—and all of a sudden an Esprit store. All the evidences of Western civilization were here; yet it felt so different.

"There's the Embassy," Mad Dog said with reverence. He pointed to a pale yellow vintage square building. Fixed on the roof was another creature born in Tolkien's imagination. This one looked like a swooping black dragon with a long neck.

"How strange that the U.S. Embassy would have a dragon movie prop on top of it," I said.

Mad Dog and Tony both looked at me as if I were an alien creature who had just stuck my foot through the roof and landed in the same car with them.

"What?"

"Kathleen," Tony said patiently, "that's not the U.S. Embassy. That's the Embassy Theatre. And on the roof that's a fell beast ridden by a Ringwraith."

I kept a fixed expression and didn't blink, waiting for Tony to give me a few more hints as to why that should ring any bells.

"Remember the photos we saw of the premier? Opening night?"

"They still had Gollum on the roof of the Embassy for the premier," Mad Dog said. "Maybe that's why you didn't recognize it."

"Oh, yeah. I'm sure that's the reason." I diverted my gaze out the window. I hoped I wouldn't be tested on any more *Lord of the Rings* trivia before we completed the last few miles of a very long journey to our new home.

We turned onto a narrow road and followed a pristine bay that skirted Wellington like a fancy azure petticoat. Thousands of houses dotted the low, rolling green hills that rose from the bay.

I noticed that some of the trees were beginning to drop their leaves. Autumn was coming to the globe's underside. At home I had left budding jacaranda trees. My going away party at work had been decorated with fresh tulips and spring daffodils. Here, the leaves were turning gold.

I was in a flip-flopped place, inside and out.

Mad Dog slowed the van as we entered a residential area. "See that house over there?" He pointed at a tidy bungalow that was about eight hundred square feet big.

"That place just sold for the equivalent of two hundred and fifty thousand dollars. U.S. dollars. Not New Zealand dollars. Like I said, it was amazing I found a place near the studio for the exact rent you said you wanted to pay. And it comes with a refrigerator."

I should have known when he listed the refrigerator as a plus that I should brace myself.

"If you don't take it, another guy at work wants it."

"I'm sure we'll want it," I said.

Tony voiced his agreement.

Mad Dog stopped the car. "This is it. What do you think?"

I peered out the car window at another bungalow-style house. The first thing I noticed was the grinning figurine standing his post in front of a narrow row of yellow and orange mums. I'd seen a number of lawn gnomes in my day and a pink flamingo or two, but this was the first ceramic hobbit I'd ever seen guarding a flower bed.

"Cute," I said with a smile. "But the hobbit definitely needs to go."

Mad Dog let out his guffaw laugh. "You'll have to clear that one with Mr. Barry, the landlord. What do you think of the garage?"

The tiny building that was separate from the main house had a window in front with curtains. It reminded me of the toolshed my father had built in our backyard when I was a girl. My two sisters and I wanted to turn the shed into a playhouse, but Dad never let us.

"The garage is cute, too." I turned my attention to the main house. The bungalow appeared to be freshly painted in a soft shade of celery green with white trim around the two front windows. It was much smaller than our home in Tustin, but I could make this cottage into "our" place for three months.

"You think this will work for you?" Mad Dog asked.

"Yes." I nodded and looked to see if Tony agreed. He did.

"You got a good woman, Tony." Mad Dog reached into the back of the van for our luggage. "Last week a guy who came down here from Canoga Park left after ten days on the job. His wife said she couldn't live in such primitive conditions. She said he had to decide between her or the job. He picked her."

"Good choice." I looped a shoulder bag over my arm and reached for another bag.

Mad Dog looked at me with his eyebrows raised. "If you say so."

I headed for the front door and was at the doorstep when

Mad Dog called, "Kathleen, over here." He was standing by the garage's side door.

I stumbled through the grass and past the lantern-holding, smirking hobbit and wondered if the house key was hidden in the garage. Or maybe Mad Dog wanted to give us the full tour before we went inside the house.

He opened the garage's side door. Tony stepped in first. I followed, and the lights turned on. Literally.

This was it. We were "home."

Barely breathing, I dropped both the shoulder bags and stood in the middle of our garage apartment. The single room came with a bed covered in an overly bright floral bedspread, a corner table, two metal patio chairs, a sink, an armchair, a hot plate, and the prized feature—a dorm-sized refrigerator.

"Bathroom is back there." Mad Dog pointed to a door that looked as if it should open to the backyard.

I looked at Tony. He wasn't moving. Or blinking.

With quiet steps, I wove my way through the furniture to the closed door and opened it. The newly built bathroom/laundry room/storage room/closet space was nearly half the size of the entire garage apartment. The room had been beautifully finished and was by far the nicest part of the apartment. The white curtains fluttered as a cool breeze came through the open window and coaxed me to breathe again.

I looked at the bathtub, my usual place of retreat and reflection in times of stress. The inner sanctum was defiled by a wooden drying rack propped up inside it. Over the rack was draped a pair of men's briefs. Not just any briefs, but giant-sized briefs.

The cry of distress that had been welling up inside me came out in two unexpected words. "Jumbo briefs!"

"What?" Tony came over to me.

I pointed and blinked so I wouldn't cry.

"Who would've left their underwear in here?" Tony asked.

"They look a little too large to belong to the garden hobbit," I said in a pathetically squeaky voice.

Mad Dog cracked up, his cough-laugh bouncing off the walls. "You keep that sense of humor going, Kathleen, and you'll be fine."

I pressed my lips together and felt my heart swell with empathy for the wife from Canoga Park. Perhaps she had been the tenant in this toolshed before us. Her departure might have been the reason Mad Dog was able to find a place for us. Perhaps the jumbo briefs were her husband's and had been left in their hasty departure.

"You paid the first month's rent already, right?" Tony asked.

Mad Dog nodded. "I had to grab the place as soon as it opened up, since nothing else is for rent in this neighborhood. You'd have more options if you decided to buy a car."

Tony glanced my way. Our discussions about simplifying life during these three months had sounded so noble and appealing when we were in California working out a plan. We agreed that we needed to do this without the expense of a car. Obviously both of us thought the amount we had set aside for rent would have resulted in a lot more living space than it had.

"What can I do to help you guys settle in?" Mad Dog asked. I recognized in his voice a commendable effort to put a positive spin on the situation.

"We can take it from here." Tony stepped into the other room and checked out the premium unused space under the bed.

"You'll need some groceries." Mad Dog apparently wasn't

willing to leave so quickly. "I can drive you to the store, unless you want to walk down to the dairy. That's what they call the corner market around here. Or, hey, I know a great place for fish and chips. You have to eat fish and chips your first day here. We could all drive there now."

Tony looked at me, and I returned his numb gaze. I wasn't ready to sit with another seat belt around me for any reason. Even if food was waiting at the end of the journey.

"Do you want to stay here, Kath? I'll take a run with Mad Dog to get some food." Tony opened the refrigerator, as if sizing up how much space he had to fill. His mind was always editing, arranging, and adjusting to fit the parameters of a given situation.

Once Mad Dog left, I would let Tony know that too much information had been edited from our housing arrangements. This place was not going to be okay. Not for ninety days and ninety nights. Not when Tony was the one who would be going to work every day, and I would be the one sitting here with nothing to do.

We don't have to stay here. We can find another place. This is just for a night or two. We won't even need to unpack. This is very temporary.

"Anything you want me to bring back for you, Kathleen?"

I mouthed the word *chocolate.*

My knowing husband nodded. "Anything else?"

"After the chocolate it doesn't matter."

Tony and Mad Dog opened the door to leave, and there stood our landlord with his large fist raised, as if he were about to knock. He was huge. Gigantic enough to fit into the briefs occupying the hallowed bathtub space.

In a deep voice with a New Zealand accent, Mr. Barry

boomed out his greeting. Then he ducked the way I remembered Gandalf ducking to enter Bilbo Baggins's house in the Shire. Mr. Barry seemed to fill the room. Suddenly the joke seemed to be on me. I was the hobbit!

I tried to keep my jet-lagged self from bursting into laughter. Not a friendly chuckle sort of laugh. Welling up inside me was the sort of unladylike, explosive laugh that accompanies any truly successful preteen girls' sleepover.

I couldn't hold it in. The laughter spilled out. I couldn't help it. I'd never before met a giant's underwear before I met him.

"Jet lag," Tony said graciously.

I composed myself, and Mr. Barry told us all the important specifics of the apartment, including trash pickup and making the next rent payment. I only half listened, confident we wouldn't be here by the time the trash was ready for pickup.

As soon as all the guys left, I flopped onto the surprisingly comfortable bed. My head was pounding.

How many days do we have before Tony starts work? Three? No, wait. What day is this?

We flew out of LAX on Tuesday night. We lost a day when we crossed the international date line, so that made today Thursday. At least I thought it was Thursday.

I am so lost. What are we doing here?

I promised myself that regardless of what day it was, before Monday arrived, Tony and I would be settled in a real nest. All I had to do right now was float a little longer.

Tony and Mad Dog returned with a bundle of newspapers that Tony placed on our tiny table. He pulled back the pages. In the center were half a dozen large pieces of breaded, deep-fried fish and a mound of French fries. The excess oil from the fish and chips had soaked through the thin paper on which the fish were separated from the layers of daily news. I found the odor of the oil on the dried newspaper ink inviting.

"Here's the malt vinegar." Mad Dog pulled several small plastic packets from his back pocket. "You have to try it with the vinegar."

I sat in the armchair and enjoyed the fish and chips while Tony unpacked the groceries.

"I'm not sure where we're going to put all this food," he said.

"I told your man he was buying too much," Mad Dog said.

"Tony, all we needed was some snacks, milk, and Cheerios to get us through breakfast tomorrow."

"Did you say *Cheerios*?" Tony held up a package of what looked like little red-skinned sausages. "This is what they call *cheerios* around here."

"No cereal Cheerios?"

Tony shook his head.

"Oh."

Three months without my favorite breakfast food felt almost as shocking as the first sight of this garage apartment. It was all I could do to keep from crying. Over cereal. Or maybe it really was the jet lag. My throat hurt, and one of my ears hadn't popped yet. I just wanted to go home.

Mad Dog left after the fish and chips were devoured. Tony leaned against the closed door and looked around. "Well, what do you think?"

I told Tony every single thought down to my opinion of the obnoxiously bright floral bedspread that dominated the room.

Tony selected that problem as the first he would attempt to solve. "You think it's too bright? Really?"

I was fired up and let my words fly. "It's so blazingly bright that I feel like we could gather around and roast hot dogs in the visual heat it gives off."

"Or roast cheerios." Tony grinned.

"That's not funny." I clenched my jaw.

"Kathleen, relax! It's just the name of a breakfast cereal."

"Apparently it's not! Not in this country, at least!"

Tony laughed at my fury, and that was his mistake.

Two

To retell all the things that were said and done during our first two weeks in that toolshed apartment would have no redeeming value. I will simply confess that the worst in me met the worst in Tony, and I don't ever want to go through an experience like that again.

The conclusion was that we weren't able to find alternate housing. We didn't buy a car. Tony "stopped by" the studio within five hours of our arrival in Wellington, and I became a studio widow much sooner than I'd expected.

My survival therapy included many long, hot baths; every variety of Cadbury chocolate available at the corner dairy; a stack of magazines; and a lot of sleep in our comfortable bed with the bedspread turned to the plain side. I refused to eat any cheerio sausages, and I cried every day.

At the end of the second week of my extravagant self-pity, Tony came home on a bicycle. My project-energized husband had stayed his course during that horrible first two weeks with a fresh sense of definition and fortitude. I had been legitimately ill with a terrible head cold the first four or five days after our arrival and slept as much as I could. After I was better, I still wasn't "better."

"I got a bike." Tony wheeled it into the only open space by the sink and refrigerator.

"So I see."

"One of the guys gave it to me, because he bought a new one over the weekend. I thought you and I could buy another one and go for rides together."

I had no words to express to Tony what a bad idea that was. A bicycle wouldn't "fix" what I had. I hadn't ridden a bike since I was a kid. Why would I want to start again now?

"Did you go out this morning?" He motioned toward the stack of magazines beside me. I was still in my pj's, nestled under the covers, but Tony knew the only way I could get more magazines was by walking to the dairy.

"No, I already had these," I said defensively.

He came closer, scrutinizing the headlines and pictures on the covers. "What possible value do you gain from reading this sort of stuff?"

What Tony didn't realize was that he was talking disrespectfully of my friends. And in front of them, no less. The people in these magazines had been my only companions since we had arrived.

"Hey, do I start criticizing the way you spend your day the minute you walk in here?"

Tony raised his eyebrows but quickly edited his usual comeback. We'd already had this argument. A couple of times. He spent his days profitably, immersed in his dream job. Me? I had no reason to get up in the morning. In seventy-four days we would leave here, and I'd get back my life. But for now, the only option I could see was hibernation.

Tony positioned himself rigidly against the counter and lowered his voice. "Kathleen, listen."

I steadied myself for the worst. Whenever he edited his thoughts to a two-word sentence, and my full name was one of the two words, I knew it wouldn't be good.

"What do you need?" he asked.

"Not a bike."

"What then?"

"I don't know."

He seemed to be working very hard to get the next sentence to come out of his mouth. When it did, I knew he meant it.

"Do you want us to go back home?"

My first thought was, *Yes!* Then some long-buried competitive seed inside me sprouted, and I thought of how I'd barely lasted longer than the woman from Canoga Park. I could do better than that. Much better.

I stared at Tony but didn't give him any feedback with my words or my expression. This man, who was looking at me with sincere tenderness, had sold his father's rare coin collection to buy my engagement ring. He had been there for me every moment during our two miscarriages. In our wedding vows, I had drawn from the book of Ruth and promised, "Where you go, I will go; where you live, I will live. Your people will be my people, your God will be my God."

And now he was willing to give up his dream job to restore my sanity.

I hated what I had become. Instead of an adventurous

mama bird on a three-month sabbatical from work and routine who soared through new experiences, I'd tucked my head under my wing and folded up inside myself.

Blinking away a tear, I looked down at the magazine beside me. Details of a celebrity's messy divorce were splashed across the front.

"No." I shook my head and met Tony's gaze. "I don't want to leave. We need to stay here."

"Are you sure?"

I nodded, and with a firm voice I said, "Yes, I'm sure."

Tony looked as if he were trying to mask his relief and select his next words carefully. "Okay. Then if we're going to stay, and we both agree about that, what do you need to make this time in New Zealand work for you? You have to tell me what you need."

I paused. Not a single thought came to mind. Whenever my friend Patsy went on autopilot like this at work, she would say, "This is why they put the word *pause* in *menopause*." Were more changes happening inside me than I realized?

"I honestly don't know," I said at last. My voice was more tender than it had been in two weeks. "I don't know what I need."

"What about doing some travel while we're here? Mad Dog went to Christchurch a few months ago. It's on the South Island. He said it reminded him of Oxford, in England. You always wanted to go to England. You could go with a tour group or something. There's a lot more to New Zealand than Wellywood."

"Than what?"

"Wellywood. That's what employees at the studio call Wellington because it's a little Hollywood."

I realized Tony was even picking up lingo from the locals. The only local I'd talked to besides Mr. Barry was Mrs. Patel at the corner dairy, and she was from India.

"Look, Kath, this is how I see it." Tony reached for my hand. "It doesn't matter to me if you go on a tour. My point is that, for as long as I can remember, you've poured out yourself and your time for everyone else. I've felt bad that you've had to work for us to get by financially. You know that."

"I wanted to work. Besides, we live in an expensive part of the country."

"I know, but I thought that coming here would be a good thing for you, too. It wasn't supposed to just be for me. I never thought this experience would empty you. It was meant to fill you."

All the anger in my heart dissolved. I told Tony I wanted to be there for him the way he had always been there for me. He told me our marriage was more important than any job in any corner of this green earth. I knew he meant it. I also knew I could do a whole lot better at adjusting than I had. I hadn't even tried.

The next morning, with the warmth of my best kiss on his lips, Tony boarded his shiny new bike and took off for work, whistling like the happiest man in the world.

I took a shower, dressed, made the bed, opened the windows, and thoroughly cleaned our neglected living space. Then I took on the challenge of washing our garments from the previously untouched mound of dirty clothes. The garage laundry room didn't come with a dryer; so I filled a basket with the wet items and headed for the backyard.

It was nearly noon and a beautiful, sunny day with a softness in the air. I made my way to the umbrella clothesline in

29

the unfenced yard and pinned up our clean clothes. The saying, "airing your laundry," took on new meaning as I realized that, when you hang your clothes out to dry, you really do have fewer secrets from your neighbors.

"Wondered when we'd be seeing you." Mr. Barry's deep voice startled me.

I spun around. "Hello, Mr. Barry. How are you?"

"No complaints."

"Is it okay with you if I use the clothesline today?"

"I don't mind, if you don't mind."

"I was wondering, Mr. Barry. Is there a place nearby where I can get a coffee?"

I hadn't had what I considered a decent cup of coffee since we'd arrived. I didn't want to sound like a whiny American who was going through separation anxiety from her favorite barista, even if that was the truth.

"The Chocolate Fish is down the road by the sandy cove." He pointed me in the right direction. "Go right and follow the street around the curve for about a kilometer. You can't miss it."

"Thanks." I gave a friendly wave and went back inside for my wallet. If I was making a fresh start of it, nothing would help more than a grande mocha latte and a walk on the beach.

I was about a block away from the apartment when I heard a bird singing an unfamiliar twitter in the tree across the road. I was used to the doves' low cooing in two orange trees that separated our ranch-style home in Tustin from our neighbors'. The fragrance of the spring orange blossoms was just beginning to lace the air when I left home. I didn't recognize the scent in the Wellington air. The breeze had an Indian summer calm and warmth to it, but the scent in the air was sweet. Jasmine maybe? Honeysuckle?

Trotting past more cottage-sized houses, I rounded a bend and noted that larger, more elaborate homes were built on an imposing hill on the left side of the road.

Two more feathered friends overhead twittered the birdsong I didn't recognize. I stopped under the tree, peering up through the stained glass–looking leaves, trying to see what kind of bird was making that sound. A flurry of leaf rustling produced no birds, but a few leaves and feathers came raining down on me. I closed my eyes and waited for a leaf to touch my face. In southern California the seasonal changes were subtle. I was trying my best to enter into the New Zealand autumn.

Continuing on, I came upon the cove Mr. Barry had mentioned. Large granite formations jutted out of the water, providing solitary islands for the seagulls. Far across the blue-green water rose the neighboring hills of this irregular-shaped inlet. I stopped to look over the small, sandy beach. No one was in view.

Slipping off my shoes, I wedged my bare feet into the cold sand and quietly made my peace with God. I knew He never wasted any life experience. He had dreams for me even here in New Zealand. I believed that. But since we arrived, I hadn't asked Him what His dreams were for me. I'd only asked over and over what I was doing here. The answer to what I was "doing" in New Zealand so far had been obvious—nothing. But that was about to change. My heart was tender now. I was ready.

Across the narrow road from the turnout where I'd taken the steps down to the beach, I noticed a funky, elongated green building. The small sign in front told me this was the café Mr. Barry had mentioned.

Eager to sit on the covered front patio and sip a mocha latte, I dusted off my sandy feet and headed across the street. I entered the café and immediately was taken in with the charm and simplicity of the eclectic atmosphere. All the tables along the front windows were occupied except one. I went to that table and pulled out a brightly painted chair that bore the words: "Caution. Seagulls." The chair across the table bore a single red stripe and the neatly printed word: "Wellington."

Trying not to be obvious, I glanced at the woman sitting at the table across from me. She had beautiful, sun-kissed, tawny hair that fell smoothly to her shoulders. Her face was turned toward the window where her gaze stayed fixed on the endless sea. Translucent tears rolled down her cheeks while she did nothing to stop them, blot them, or in any other way acknowledge them. The tears seemed somehow fitting, as if this was her place to be right now, and the reason she was here was to shed tears.

All around us hummed the sounds of clattering plates, water running in a sink, and the buzz of half a dozen conversations spiked with a few dots of laughter. She didn't seem to notice any of it.

I spotted a message on the chalkboard that invited me to place my order at the counter. Beside the counter was a glass pastry case filled with sweets and rolls. Taking my place in line, I waited for the woman in front of me who had a toddler balanced on her hip. His New Zealand accent sounded adorable as he asked his "mummy" if he could have a "fluffy."

"Yes, Jordan. I ordered a fluffy for you and Logan. Now here's a chocolate fish for each of you."

"Yummy!" He took two candies from the woman at the register. The long, fish-shaped treats were covered with chocolate, and the first one immediately went into his mouth.

I smiled at the cute tyke and stepped forward to order. "I'd like one of those candies and a mocha latte."

"And just what have you done today?" the young woman asked in a friendly yet clipped manner. She seemed to be staring at the top of my head.

"Excuse me?"

"For the chocolate fish. What have you done to warrant a sweetie?"

I lowered my voice and tried to subdue my American accent, as I explained that I didn't understand what she was asking.

"Have you never heard that saying? You do something well, and someone says, 'Well done. Here's your chocolate fish.'"

"No, I guess that's one of many new expressions for me."

She tilted her head, and I thought she was trying to decide if she believed me or if I was making fun of what was apparently a well-known New Zealand saying. It turned out to be neither when she asked again, "So, what was your great accomplishment today?"

I felt heat race up my neck as my embarrassment rose. It was either that, or I was having my first hot flash.

This young woman had no idea what an accomplishment it had been for me to get out of bed and get myself here. But I knew. With my chin raised I declared, "I got up this morning."

She seemed to think I was making a clever joke. "Good for you. Have a chocolate fish. We'll bring your mocha to the table."

She handed me the soft, chewy treat. It was about four inches long and about as thick as a fluffy flapjack. The center was pink. It tasted like I was eating a chocolate-covered marshmallow. The burst of sweetness made me smile.

The woman with the beautiful, honey golden hair looked up at me as I slipped past her table. Our eyes met, and she offered me a half smile. A few tears still glistened on her fair skin. She, too, looked up at the top of my head.

Popping the last bit of the chocolate fish into my mouth, I cautiously moved my hand to the back of my head to see if my hair was sticking up. I discovered two white-tipped feathers caught in my hair. Then I remembered the trees I'd passed under and how I'd stopped to close my eyes and listen to the chittering birds.

"A little souvenir," I said with a shrug and a nervous laugh. "From my walk over here."

I tucked the feathers into the pocket of my jeans and headed for my waiting chair, but she stopped me.

"You're an American!" the woman said, her Yankee accent echoing mine.

"Yes." I swallowed the last of my fish and checked my lips for any stray bits of chocolate.

"Have you lived here long?"

"Just two weeks. My husband is working on a project at Jackamond Studios."

"Really?" She looked as if that bit of information struck a chord.

"What about you? Do you live here?"

"Yes." She paused before adding, "We moved here six years ago. Just like you, we came because my husband was offered a job at Jackamond."

"Really! I'm Kathleen, by the way. Kathleen Salerno."

"Jill Radovich." She motioned to the vacant chair across from her. "Would you like to join me? Or are you waiting for someone?"

"No, I'm all alone." Even though I'd been telling myself the same thing for a week, suddenly the hopelessness I'd attached to that phrase was gone. Being alone also meant being open and available for whatever possibilities might come my way.

"Did you by any chance come from California?" Jill asked.

"Yes, southern California."

"What part?"

"Orange County."

She leaned forward, and I noticed all her tears were gone. "What part of Orange County?"

"Tustin."

"What street?" Her smile told me she had heard of Tustin.

"Schilling. It's off of Seventeenth and..."

Jill nodded, her expression brightening. "I know exactly where Schilling is. My maiden name is Schilling. Your street is named after my grandfather. He owned all the Schilling Orange Groves."

"You're kidding!"

"No. I grew up in Tustin. Do you know where the two-story Victorian house is with the wraparound front porch? It was turned into a restaurant."

"Yes, the Fontaine Restaurant."

"My grandfather built that house. We lived there until I graduated from Foothill High School."

"You went to Foothill? So did I!"

We compared the years we were at Foothill and found that Jill had graduated four years ahead of me.

"We were almost there at the same time!" Jill said.

"This is unbelievable! My husband, Tony, and I have a house less than three blocks from the Fontaine Restaurant. As a matter of fact, we have two huge orange trees in our side yard.

They were there when we moved in. I'm sure they were planted by your grandfather."

Jill pressed her lips together, and for a moment neither of us spoke.

She drew in a steady breath. "I remember the day the bulldozers started uprooting the trees to clear the grove."

"That must have been awful for your family, seeing all those trees go."

She nodded. "Some of the trees were diseased and needed to be taken out. Actually, a lot of them were in distress. But not all of them."

"The reason we have the two trees is because I guess some hippy guy hung a hammock between them in an effort to save them."

"A hippy guy?" Jill's gray eyes widened.

"That's the way we heard the story. When we moved in, we were told that this wild hippy guy camped out between the trees and stopped the bulldozer from knocking them down. The builders worked around him, and the trees are still there."

Jill looked as if that was the best news she had heard all day. "I can't believe this. Those two trees are in your yard?"

"Yes. They're nice and healthy, huge and full of oranges every year. I'm so glad that loony guy put up his hammock." I leaned back, trying to read Jill's expression. "I'm sure you must have heard that story before."

"As a matter of fact I have," Jill said. "That loony guy, by the way, was my husband."

Three

Both my hands flew to cover my face, as the waitress brought my mocha latte and placed it on the table in front of me. Without looking at Jill between my closed fingers, I said, "I am so sorry! I can't believe I said that."

Jill laughed and reached over to pull away my fingers. "It's okay. Ray *was* a hippy in those days. And he's been called worse than loony, so don't worry about that either."

"Well, then I'll say this with all sincerity." I put my hands in my lap and leaned forward. "Because of your husband, I have eagerly opened my windows every spring for the past twenty years, and our whole house has filled with the fragrance of orange blossoms. He did a wonderful thing saving those trees. I'm the one who has enjoyed the reward of his zeal."

"The reward of his zeal," Jill repeated. She teared up, and I felt bad for making her cry again. Swallowing hard, she paused before saying, "Thank you for telling me that today. It means a lot."

Feeling hesitant to say anything else, I sipped my mocha and glanced at Jill's tears as they wandered over her lower lids and silently rolled down to her chin.

"Ray and I met in high school." She looked out the window. "Ray was really something back in the seventies. Every mother's nightmare of the kind of guy she didn't want her daughter to bring home. Long hair, leather sandals. He was ready to protest injustice anytime and anywhere."

Jill's moist cheeks lifted as she smiled and turned back to face me. "I was a goody-goody and a cheerleader, which was a combination that Ray found irresistible, or so he always said. He was determined to win me over, and once Ray Radovich put his mind to something, well...you might as well give up opposing him."

I nodded my understanding. "My husband, Tony, is the same way. He and I met in the parking lot at a concert. We started talking as we were walking in, and then we sat next to each other. That was it. We were pretty much together after that."

"What concert?"

I hesitated slightly before answering. I didn't know if telling Jill that Tony and I had met at a Christian concert would polarize us. I'd experienced that sort of distancing from women at work who were friendly and open toward me until they found out I was a Christian and very involved at church. Their assumptions about me took over at that point, and they pulled away, as if I were on a campaign to convert them instead of to become their friend. I didn't want that to happen with Jill.

Nevertheless, I was a Christian and not ashamed to say so. That's who I was, and I couldn't pretend otherwise.

"Tony and I met at a Christian concert. A church in Costa

Mesa used to have free concerts every Saturday night and—"

"Yes! In a circus tent, right? It was out in a bean field or strawberry field. Not far from South Coast Plaza. You went there, too? Ray and I went every week after we became Christians our senior year of high school."

My mouth dropped open, and I shook my head in amazement. I was thrilled to hear Jill say she was also a Christian. "That means we could have been at the same concerts, because Tony and I used to go all the time, too! Can you imagine?"

"We might have even sat next to each other but never met."

Jill and I ran through a list of the most memorable music groups and came to the conclusion that we definitely were at least in the same place on the same nights.

"You have no idea what this means to me right now," Jill said. "Meeting you, finding out you're a believer, talking about home and Ray and high school days…" She choked up and reached for my hand to give it a squeeze. "This is the best thing that could have happened to me today."

"Me, too," I echoed, giving her hand a squeeze back. I wished I could express to her how sincerely I meant it.

"I only live a few blocks away. I knew I had to get out of the house today. It took me all morning to pull myself together because…" She reached for a napkin to dab her tears and didn't finish her thought.

She didn't need to. I understood more than she could imagine. "I know what you're feeling, Jill. It's okay. You're going to be okay."

It struck me that I didn't know exactly what she was feeling. I only knew what I was feeling. The reassurance was more for me than it was for Jill. We were both going to be okay. I just knew it.

She looked out the window and then back at me with a soft expression. "I didn't know what I needed today. All I knew was that I had to get out of the house. Now I know why."

Again I nodded my understanding.

"There's something Ray used to say about answered prayer: 'If you feel a deep hunger but don't know what you want, just ask God to order for you. That way you'll always get whatever is the best on the menu.'"

I started to leak my own sorry tears and chased them with a silent confession. I had spent the last week so lost in myself and unresponsive to God that I hadn't asked Him to order anything for me. Yet He still gave me exactly what I needed to fill the emptiness.

"God is so good to us," I said in a whisper.

Jill's nod was slow in coming, but when her head began to bob, a trickle of laughter followed. "I feel like we're in high school again. I can't control any of my emotions."

"I know." I fanned myself as I felt my temperature spiking. "And I think I'm starting to have hot flashes." Lowering my voice I leaned closer and asked, "Forty-five is pretty young for this, isn't it?"

"Not necessarily. Stress can really mess up your body's rhythm."

Our conversation turned to details about our bodies, and the pros and cons of hormone therapy. After that we slid into other girls-only topics. For the next hour, our heads were bent close as we did what clear-hearted women do so well. We opened the door, let each other come in, and warmed ourselves by the fire of our spirits.

That's when I realized that my new "home" in this place of upside-down living wasn't an ugly garage with a blazing bedspread and defiled bathtub. My home was my heart. And today, at last, my home was clean and ready for company.

As the afternoon light dimmed, Jill looked at her watch. "Do you need to get home soon?"

"No, not really. What about you?"

Jill shook her head and in a thin voice said, "No one is at my house waiting for me."

"I know what you mean. Tony hasn't yet come home early enough for us to eat dinner together." With a sigh I added, "I think I have a bad case of DENS."

"What's that?"

"Delayed Empty Nest Syndrome."

"I don't think I've ever heard of that," Jill said.

"Me neither. I just made it up!"

We laughed, and I told Jill how our home had been Grand Central for many years. We had only one daughter, but she had many friends, and our place seemed to be the designated hang-out.

"What about you? Do you and Ray have children?"

She held up three fingers. "All boys. Or I should say *men*. The two oldest are both married and settled in California. James, our youngest, is going to Victoria University here in Wellington, but he moved into student housing at the term change. It's been very quiet around my house since he left."

"I know what you mean. We had exchange students living with us the first two years Skyler was in high school, and her senior year my nephew moved in and stayed until this past Christmas. As soon as he moved out, we remodeled the kitchen, but that was barely done before we came here. I'm not used to being alone."

"It's not so great, is it?"

"The only advantage seems to be there's a lot less laundry." My quip reminded me of the clothes I'd left hanging on the line. I told Jill I'd better head back to take down the clothes before the sun set. I could imagine all of Tony's jeans turning stiff in the cooling air.

"Is there anything you need to help you get settled? Groceries? Anything for your house?"

"No, our apartment is too small to even hold the things we shipped over."

"Let me know if you think of anything. Anything at all." She wrote down her phone number, and we agreed to meet here again next Tuesday for coffee.

"Unless," Jill added, as we rose and were heading for the door, "you think of anything you want or need, and then we could squeeze in a shopping trip."

"I actually wouldn't mind a new bedspread."

"Then let's go find you a bedspread. What does tomorrow look like for you?"

Our plans were quickly formulated, and Jill asked if I wanted to look for anything besides a bedspread.

"I don't think so. To be honest, I shouldn't be making such a big deal about this bedspread. Tony thinks I should be able to endure this one for three months, but it's really obnoxious."

"Three months?" Jill stopped walking out of the café and looked at me. "Why do you only have to endure it for three months?"

"Tony's position at the studio is for three months."

"It is? Then what?"

"Then we go back to California."

Jill looked surprised.

"Didn't I say something earlier about this being a tempo-rary position?"

"If you did, I didn't catch it. And that is possible, with all the laughing and crying we were doing. But seriously, three months isn't long enough."

"Not long enough for what?" Ever since we arrived I'd been counting the days until we could leave, and now Jill was telling me our stay was going to be too short.

Before Jill could give me the answer that seemed to be for-mulating in her mind, we were interrupted by the sound of a long, flat car horn. We were standing outside the Chocolate Fish, and apparently we were blocking a prime parking spot. We hopped out of the way.

"Excuse us," I muttered with plenty of sarcasm.

"Don't worry." Jill waved at the driver. "It's Tracey. She's a permanent fixture here at the café."

A petite, energetic woman with very short, very red hair hopped out of a vehicle that made me stop and stare. The 1952 classic Chevy truck had a rounded hood and roof, and lots of shiny chrome on the front grille and bumper. The buffed-to-a-shine paint was sunshine yellow. Someone had taken good care of that little gem.

"Hallo!" The woman came toward us all smiles and gave Jill a hug.

"Tracey, this is Kathy Salerno. She just moved here. Her husband is at Jackamond. You won't believe this, but it's like we had parallel lives in high school, but we never met until today. We've spent the whole afternoon comparing our lives."

Tracey greeted me with an unexpected hug. "You both had to come all the way to Kiwi Land before you could meet each other inside my little café. Lovely! Welcome, Kathy!"

43

I wasn't used to being called Kathy. I'd always been Kathleen. The more lighthearted Kathy had never been activated, because I viewed that as a name reserved for the popular girls—the cheerleaders and homecoming queens.

With a lump in my throat, I realized that Jill had renamed me. In this new place of global turnabouts, I was being accepted as one of the popular girls by Jill, a former cheerleader, and Tracey, a rich girl with a cool car.

"Your truck is gorgeous." I felt a little nervous that I might say the wrong thing and be banished from the group. "My uncle used to refurbish old trucks. He would have loved this one."

"We call her Beatrice the Dazzling Bumblebee," Tracey said. "Bea for short."

"She's a honey, all right." I hadn't realized I'd made a bee-related pun, but Tracey laughed generously.

"Did your uncle let you drive his refurbished trucks?"

"No, never."

Tracey glanced at Jill and then back at me with a mischievous glimmer in her eyes. "Then you'll have to take Bea for a spin to make up for lost opportunities." She held the car keys out to me and gave them a jingle.

I looked at Jill. Her expression told me that not every visitor to the Chocolate Fish was extended such an offer. I felt as if this was part of my initiation to the cool girls' club.

"Are you sure?" I asked.

"Of course. Come on. It's a perfect evening for a drive."

I bravely headed for what my brain said was the driver's side. Tracey was right behind me, chuckling and saying, "Other side. You're the driver."

"Oh, of course!" I laughed nervously, my American ways showing through.

I peered into the cab and saw the steering wheel was huge, and as soon as I settled in behind it, I discovered it had a lot of "play."

I took my position with a thrill I don't think I'd ever felt, even when I was in high school. I had been a goody-goody like Jill. I played it safe, taking very few risks. Driving someone's "honey bee" down what felt was the wrong side of the road wasn't a huge risk as opposed to, say, bungee jumping. But for me, this was a nerve-wracking leap into thin air.

My heart was pounding as Tracey pointed out the gears on the steering column and reminded me to put in the clutch with my left foot before shifting. A pullout button on the front panel adjusted the throttle.

"And you say you never drove one of your uncle's vintage trucks? Not even when he wasn't looking?"

"No, this is all new to me."

"Well, Bob's your uncle," Tracey said.

"Actually, my uncle's name was Harry."

Tracey gave me a strange look, and then her face lit up and she laughed, as if I had just made another clever joke.

"No, Bob's your uncle," she repeated. "We say that here. *Bob's your uncle.* You don't say that?"

Jill leaned over with a dozen giggles sparkling in her eyes. "It took me a while to get used to that expression, too. It's like we would say, 'There you have it' or 'There you go.'"

"*Bob's your uncle?*" I repeated. "That makes no sense. Where in the world do you suppose that saying came from?"

Tracey flicked away a giggle-tear. "Guess we can't blame that one on the Americans. Go ahead and start up Bea. What's the saying where you come from? Surf City, here we come."

Jill applauded. "We will take credit for that saying, since we are a couple of California girls."

Tracey sang off tune, *"I wish they all could be California girls!"*

We laughed again, but as soon as the merriment dissolved, I felt the return of my nervousness about being behind the wheel of this imposing Queen Bee. With the mirrors adjusted and my feet in position, I turned the key, and the eager engine rumbled to life. My left hand was in place, ready to shift gears with a lever on our car that I would have used for the windshield wipers.

"Go for it, Kathy!" Jill cheered.

"Stay to the left," Tracey reminded me.

Easing off the clutch and giving Bea a thimbleful of nectar, I inched us away from the front of the café.

"Don't be afraid of her. Go ahead, drive like you mean it," Tracey said, as I picked up speed and headed for the right lane. "Stay left!"

"Oh, right"

"No, left," Tracey repeated.

"Right," I agreed. "Left."

"Just drive," Jill said with a giggle. "Keep the dividing line on your side of the car, and you'll be fine."

"Got it." I attempted a less-than-smooth shift into second gear and could almost feel the startled engine working with me to make the adjustments.

"She doesn't need much coaxing," Tracey said. "You're doing fine."

In an effort to stay in my lane, I overcompensated with the large steering wheel and promptly rolled up over the curb. A burst of nervous laughter spilled out, and I turned too far to the right before veering back to where I should be.

"You have the feel for her now," Tracey said. "Where to?"

"Why don't you drive back to your place, Kathy?" Jill suggested. "That way I'll know where to pick you up in the morning for our shopping trip."

"Shopping plans already, girls? Good for you."

"Do you want to come with us, Tracey?"

"Ask me another time. Tomorrow is a busy day at the café."

I kept my hands at ten and two o'clock on the leather-wrapped steering wheel and felt confident I could find our place, since I knew it was on the same road. All I had to do was keep this buggy pointed in the same direction for less than a kilometer, and we'd be there.

"Third." Tracey tapped my leg.

I knew she meant it was time to shift into third, and I did so with impressive smoothness.

"Well done!" Tracey praised.

I grinned. "Oh, yeah? Then where's my chocolate fish?"

Tracey laughed. "Very good! She catches on quickly, doesn't she?"

Jill laughed too, and somehow I knew I'd made it through this self-imposed initiation ceremony. I was cruising down the road like one of the cool girls now, head cheerleader, homecoming queen, brimming with glee and filled with pride.

And you know what they say pride comes before...

Exactly.

Four

As we motored down the road, I squinted to see out the window. In the glow of twilight, the houses I'd walked past earlier that afternoon now looked different. Just when I thought I recognized Mr. Barry's house ahead on the left, Tracey spouted, "Look out for the pizza delivery boy!"

I spotted a guy on the right, steering his bike with one hand and precariously balancing a pizza box in his other hand.

"Hey, that's—"

"Kathy, stay to the left!"

In an immediate response to Tracey's shouted warning, I cranked the steering wheel to the left, then back to the right, and then way too far to the left. This time my overcorrection popped us up over the curb, heading for a garden of mums. I slammed on the brakes, but it was too little, too late. All three of us winced and then shrieked as we heard and felt the deep thud of obvious impact with something in our path.

"What did we hit?" Jill was the first one out of the car. Tracey and I were right behind her.

In the steady beam of the headlights, the three of us peered at the victim, who lay flat on his back in the golden flowers. I drew in a horrified breath. His head was still attached. His small eyes and impish grin still seemed to be directed at me.

"The hobbit. I killed the hobbit!"

"Don't say that too loud," Tracey said. "It could be considered a national crime. Besides, I think he's okay. Help me get him back up."

"Kathleen?" Tony's voice coming toward us was accompanied by the faint scent of pepperoni.

Tracey whispered. "Did you order a pizza?"

"No, that's my husband."

Tracey and Jill snapped into formation beside me with their backs to the fallen hobbit.

"Hallo," Tracey said with calm cheerfulness.

"Good evening," Jill added, playing along with the innocent adolescent routine.

"Lovely evening, isn't it?" Tracey asked.

"Kathleen?" Tony looked at me, as if he still couldn't compute this extreme makeover from couch potato to highway hellion.

"Tony, these are my new friends, Jill and Tracey."

"Hi." He nodded and returned his incredulous stare to me. "Are you...are you okay?"

"Sure, I'm fine! We were just, you know, out driving around in Tracey's truck, and I parked kind of funny."

"You were driving?"

I nodded like a bobble-head doll riding down a bumpy road at fifty miles per hour.

Tony's expression was difficult to decipher. Was he still

stunned or was that boyish amusement on his face? "I, ah, I got a pizza for us," he said. "There's plenty. Tracey, Jill, if you want to come in and have some, you're welcome to join us."

"Thanks, but I have to get back to the café," Tracey said.

"I should be going as well," Jill said without moving.

"Okay. Well, nice meeting you both. Good night," Tony said.

"Good night," Jill said.

"Cheers!" Tracey peeped.

Despite our farewells, the three of us cruisin' chicks hadn't moved. I was hoping Tony would take the hint and go inside so we could get the hobbit back on his huge, hairy feet again. I was also hoping Mr. Barry wasn't home, or if he was, that he hadn't heard us or looked out to see what was going on.

"I guess I'll, ah…I'll take the pizza inside and see you in a few minutes, Kathleen."

"Okay."

"Well, good evening, ladies."

"Good evening," Jill and Tracey repeated in unison. The three of us inched our way to the right with synchronized steps. We had to keep our human shield at the proper angle so Tony wouldn't see the horizontal Frodo.

As soon as we heard the side door of the garage close, we turned and went to work putting everything back in order, trying hard not to let our giggles escalate to rowdy laughter.

"That was close," Tracey whispered.

Jill giggled. "I can't believe us! I haven't acted like that since…"

"Since far too long," Tracey concluded for her. "I'd almost forgotten what a great laugh you have, Jill. It's made my day seeing you like this. Kathy, you're the best!"

As Tracey was praising me, I was crouched down examining

the grille of her truck to see if I'd done any damage to her beautiful Beatrice. "You might be a little hasty with your kind words, Tracey. Look, I dented the grille."

She leaned close. "No, that was already there."

"Are you sure?"

"Of course I'm sure. You'd have to be a lot more aggressive than you were to damage this baby. Not that I'm inviting you to be more aggressive next time you take her for a spin."

"Don't worry. I don't think I'll be imposing myself on poor Bea anytime soon."

"And why not? Now that you've gotten used to her, she and I will let you drive her anytime you want."

"Tracey, you are so gracious."

"Aren't I, though?" The soft glow of the headlights brightened her whimsical expression as she gave me a hug. "Next time you come into the café, I'll have a chocolate fish waiting for you. You too, Jill. And don't stay away so long this time."

"I won't." Jill reached over to give my arm a squeeze before she climbed back in the car with Tracey. "See you tomorrow."

I nodded and waved. Tracey started up the engine. Bea seemed to slip into a contented buzz now that Tracey was behind the wheel.

Entering our apartment, I found Tony standing in the center of the room looking at me with his new, mysterious expression on his face.

"So that really was you outside."

"Yes, it really was me. The new, improved me."

"You know what I did?" Tony asked. "I actually walked in here and checked to see if you were in the bathtub."

"Why would I be in the bathtub?"

"Why would you be driving around town in a vintage

automobile with a couple of shrieking women and knocking down ornamental lawn fixtures?"

"Oh. You saw that?"

"I didn't actually see it, but I couldn't help but notice how the three of you were acting; so I added up two plus two."

Math. Math had never done anything good for me. Although, I have to admit that today, for the first time in a long time, I didn't feel as if my life was half over with only the boring part left. Today I felt as if the second half could hold more freedom to do the sorts of things I'd never had time for before. It was pretty fun not to feel responsible for everyone else in the family and to take a silly risk by getting behind the wheel of Beatrice.

"How bad is he?" Tony asked.

"Frodo? He's fine."

"The flowers?"

"Mum's the word!"

Tony stared at me without blinking.

I couldn't stop laughing. "Mum's the word," I repeated just in case Tony hadn't heard my joke the first time. He certainly wasn't as quick at picking up jokes as Tracey had been.

Tony gave me a long, sunken-eyebrow sort of examination. "Kathleen, are you taking some sort of medication that I don't know about?"

That deduction really cracked me up. "No! As a matter of fact, this is the first day since we've been here that I haven't taken a single pill. Not for a headache or a stomachache or sinus pressure. I'm finally all the way here, Tony. I know my body arrived on the plane two weeks ago, but the rest of me finally caught up."

At last my husband looked as if he was willing to accept

the new me. We sat down to eat the cooled pizza, and I gave him a thorough recounting of what had happened since he had left me earlier that day.

When I reached the end of my tale, I asked Tony what he thought of inviting Jill and her husband over sometime soon for dinner or at least coffee.

"Sure, it's a great idea. Did I tell you I cleared it with Mad Dog to take one of the vans tomorrow? I thought you and I could go do something."

"Tony, I told Jill I'd go shopping with her tomorrow. I'm going to look for a new bedspread."

"This one really bothers you, doesn't it?"

I glanced over at my vivid nemesis and was shocked when the first thought that came to mind was, *I guess it's not so bad.* Apparently everything around me was looking better now that I had my equilibrium back.

"Can you borrow the studio van a different day?" I asked.

"Sure. And if you're not going to be home tomorrow, I'll go in to work. I was trying to find ways to make you more comfortable here."

I thought Tony looked relieved that he didn't have two full-time jobs: one at the studio and the other at home trying to keep me from flipping out. I didn't know if I liked the idea of his agreeing to overtime and working on Saturdays, but I did like being his companion and counterpart again instead of his patient and sometimes opponent.

I fell asleep that night in my husband's arms, dreaming up plans for how Jill, Ray, Tony, and I could all fit in our apartment for a cozy dinner party. Or maybe with our limited space and furniture it would just be appetizers.

The next morning I was up before Tony, getting ready for

my shopping trip with Jill. I fumbled around looking for clean undies and realized I'd left the laundry on the line all night.

Dashing into the backyard in my pajamas, I was met by a steady morning drizzle. All our clothes were as wet as when I'd hung them out the day before. The drying rack in the bathtub became my only hope. The rack and the hair dryer. I stood shivering, my bare feet on the cold tile floor and my nose dripping while I shot hot air at my unmentionables.

Despite that setback, I was dressed and ready to go by ten o'clock. Although my elastic waistband was still a little damp. I missed my clothes dryer. I missed it even more than I missed my morning Cheerios, and I dearly missed Cheerios. A few days earlier Tony had brought home some Weet-Bix, a popular cereal, according to the guys at work. To me it tasted like Shredded Wheat without any sugar. My hunt was still on for a breakfast food that I would look forward to every morning.

Tony had a bowl of Weet-Bix and left on his bike before Jill arrived. I noticed that the sun had come out. The gentle world outside the door smelled fresh, new, and green. I could smell a dozen different foliage fragrances than the ones distinguishable in southern California. The warm, sweet, tropical scents mixed with the deep smells of an evergreen forest.

I ventured outside, wondering if I should take a chance and hang out the clothes again. I decided it was worth a try. As soon as I had all the damp clothes back on the line, I walked around to the front of the house and nonchalantly examined the mums. I was happy to see that the rainy night had worked wonders in covering the tire marks in the previously flattened grass. Only a few stems near the statue were snapped off. The hobbit looked no worse after his tumble.

I felt a soft poke from something in my jeans pocket.

Putting my hand in, I expected to find a pin of some sort but instead discovered the two white-tipped feathers I'd pulled from my hair yesterday when I had met Jill. With a smile, I returned to the apartment and tucked the feathers into a small plastic bag. My mind kicked into gear, and I mentally started to design a homemade card for Jill that featured two feathers on the front.

Grabbing a notepad, I jotted down possible lines for the inside.

Friends of a feather sip lattes together.

For my fine, feather friend. I appreciate you a latte.

So glad I fluttered your way. You made the day fly by.

With a silly streak rising I wrote,

When we're together, mum's the word.

The mum joke didn't sound as funny as it had last night, so I tried another route. But the sound of a car in the gravel driveway interrupted my creative writing spell. I quickly penned a final madcap line,

Spending time with you could become hobbit-forming.

Five

I see you decided to park in a more conventional spot than the one I chose last night." I greeted Jill with my hand up, shielding my eyes from the sun. It was strange watching Jill exit the "passenger's" side of her compact car.

"Good morning," she said in a tone that was much more subdued than I felt. I wanted to ask if she was okay, but she was the first to ask a question.

"Is Tony here?"

"No, he went to work."

"Would you mind if we went inside and talked before we go shopping?"

"No." I tried to stay lighthearted. "You can have a look at the bedspread and tell me if you think I'm loco for trying to replace it."

We went inside, and Jill diplomatically said, "I've seen worse." Looking around she added, "This is a nice apartment."

"It's tiny."

"But it's clean. Everything looks new. I'm sure you were told how difficult it is to find reasonable housing."

I nodded and led the way to the other room. She agreed that the bathtub was a bonus. Having Jill's positive input made me feel better about the apartment. It's amazing how a few sincere, affirming words from a woman you admire can change your opinion about something.

"Would you like a cup of tea?" I pulled out the box of tea bags from the packed kitchen cupboard.

"Sure. Thanks."

"It's not fancy tea."

"Gumboot is fine."

"Actually, the box says 'Bell Tea.' Is that okay?" I held it up so she could see the limitations of my hospitality and have a chance to decline the offer if she wanted.

"I'm sorry. I didn't mean to confuse you. Gumboot around here is what they call plain black tea. It's different than something like Earl Grey or green tea."

"So is Bell Tea a Gumboot tea?"

"Yes, and I would love a cup. Thanks, Kathy."

"Do you take cream or sugar?"

"A little of both would be nice."

"That's just the way I like my tea, too."

Yesterday Jill and I had slipped easily into the role of high school best friends. Today, in my ridiculously tiny, Susie Homemaker kitchen with my Easy-Bake Oven and box of Bell Tea, I felt as if we were playing little girls having a tea party. I almost wished I had decorated sugar cubes to offer instead of an unimaginative box of granulated white sugar.

"Mind if I use your bathroom?" Jill asked.

"Help yourself." With a tease I added, "Let me know if you have trouble finding it."

Jill wasn't laughing at any of my jokes. I decided to stop trying to be clever and to direct my efforts into putting together a nice tea party. To fancy up the sugar, I poured some into a freshly washed small bowl I'd found in the silverware drawer that I think was supposed to be for teriyaki sauce. Finding a fancy container for the milk was a bigger challenge. I decided the glass milk bottle would have to work. Tony had become enamored with the "old-fashioned" glass bottles as soon as he discovered them at the dairy, and we now had two.

I remembered the snapped-off mums I'd tossed in the trash bin the night before as we tidied up the scene of the crime. Rifling through the rubbish, I pulled them out and gave them a good rinse in the sink and a shake before transforming one of the empty milk bottles into a vase.

With my little tea party ready at the table, I poured the boiling water over the tea bags in our two yellow mugs.

"I have some cookies," I told Jill as she took her place at the table. "Unless you think it's too early for cookies."

"It's never too early for cookies. Especially Toffee Pops. Have you had these yet? They're one of my favorites."

I looked at the package in my hand. "I don't think I've tried these." I arranged several of the small, round, chocolate-covered cookies on a plate.

"This is wonderful," Jill said. "Nice touch with the flowers."

"Those are the ones from last night. Broken, thrown away, but look! I pulled them out, and they still have plenty of life and color in them."

Joining Jill, I placed the cookies on our table, and we had just enough room left for a folded napkin and a spoon.

"Well, this answers my question," I said, trying to rearrange the items in the limited space.

"What question is that?"

"Last night I told Tony we probably would have to settle for an appetizer party instead of a dinner party when we have you and Ray over. As you can see, we don't even have four chairs."

Jill's expression fell. She put down her cup of tea, and the stream of tears I'd seen on her face yesterday returned.

"Are you okay? Did I say something that upset you?"

"Kathy, I hardly know how to tell you this. I wish I'd said something yesterday."

"That's okay. You can tell me now."

"I need to apologize."

"Apologize for what?"

"When we met, I think I dropped into some sort of parallel reality. It felt so good that I stayed there a little too long."

"Yesterday was great fun," I agreed. "It was a little wacky once we got in Tracey's car, but there's nothing to apologize for."

"No, Kathy. Just listen, okay?"

I nodded and kept my mouth shut.

"It's about Ray. I would love for you to meet Ray. I would give anything if he and I could come join you and Tony for dinner sometime. But we won't be able to do that because, you see, my husband is gone."

"Oh, Jill!" I felt instant anger toward Ray. How could any man leave a woman as wonderful as Jill?

"It was two years ago yesterday, and that's why I went to

the Chocolate Fish. I needed to get out of the house." She let out a puff of breath and whispered, "Last year I spent the anniversary of his funeral at home alone, and I knew I didn't want to do that again."

I was so stunned I couldn't speak.

"I'm sorry, Kathy. I should have said something. It wasn't fair not to let you know. I meant to tell you. But then we started talking about Ray and high school, and in a strange way it seemed as if he wasn't really gone. And that was the nicest feeling I'd had in, well, two years."

"Oh, Jill."

A crooked smile kept her lips from trembling as she went on. "Being with you and thinking about Ray was such a sweet gift to me. You invited me to talk about Ray—to say his name without connecting it to his death. When you did that, something inside me started to heal. It was such a wonderful sensation to finally feel that healing. I couldn't bring myself to tell you the truth. So I let you believe what wasn't true. I am sorry, Kathy."

"Jill, it's okay. You don't have to apologize."

I went for a box of tissues and pulled my chair up next to hers. "I can't imagine what this has been like for you."

A few quiet moments passed before she said, "At first, I had a lot of support from people around me. They were there through the whole ordeal. So many people did so much to help me. But now they don't ask about Ray. Nobody talks about him. It's as if he vanished, and everyone has forgotten him. The worst part is that since Ray doesn't exist for some people anymore, that means I don't exist either. I've become the invisible widow of the great Ray Radovich. They don't see me."

I handed her another tissue.

"But you! Kathy, yesterday you saw me. You brought back my loony, youthful, hippy guy, and he was still alive to you. More than that, I was alive to you."

"Oh, Jill," I said with all the tenderness I felt in my heart. "You are alive. Very much alive. You're not invisible at all." After that, I didn't know what to say, so I put my arm around her shoulders, and together we swayed back and forth until all the tears were gone.

We didn't end up shopping that day. Instead, we talked for a long time over our tea and cookies and then drove to a lookout on Mount Victoria. Jill said I had given her a broader view of her life, and now she wanted to give me a broader view of the world I was living in. We parked in an open lot and climbed to a fortified lookout spot. Lush, green grass skirted the hilltop where several visitors had stretched out to take in the incredible view. Below us, on the many hills of Wellington, rose and fell thousands of rooftops like bits of red, brown, and gray tiles scattered across the green. Where the green ended, the soft blues began—either the blue of the ocean and the bay or the blue of the cloudless sky.

The wind began to push us around, taunting my ponytail, daring it to whip around and slap me across the mouth. Jill's golden locks were flipping out at ear level the way Marilyn Monroe's skirt flipped out in the photo of her standing over the air grate.

"What a view!" I called across to Jill.

She nodded and pointed out the airport, far below us. To our right was the bay, lined with tall buildings. In every direction we turned, we saw houses. Wellington was much larger and more spread out than I'd realized.

"Do you see the large ferry there in the harbor? That one goes to Picton on the South Island of New Zealand."

"How far away is the South Island?"

"The ferry takes about three hours to Picton. Maybe three and a half. If the weather is nice, it's a beautiful crossing."

"And how far away is Christchurch?"

"It's at least six or seven hours south of Picton. They have a train that goes from Picton to Christchurch. It's considered one of the most picturesque train rides in the world."

"Have you taken it?"

"No. We planned to once, when Ray's mom was visiting us. She didn't do well on the ferry crossing, though. The trip was stormy, and none of us felt like taking a long train ride after that. We spent the night in Picton and flew home the next morning."

"And you haven't been back to the South Island since then?"

"No. I'd like to go. Especially to Christchurch. Everyone says the town has a quaint, British feel."

"That's what Tony said. He suggested I take a tour there," I said.

"It's a nice time of year to go. Not too many tourists. It's the final outpost for all the major explorations to Antarctica. Did you know that?"

"No. How far south is it?"

"I don't know how far south it is, but think of it this way: Wellington is more or less in the middle of New Zealand. Auckland is at the top of the North Island and closer to the equator."

"Okay, I'm with you so far."

"And then Christchurch is at the other end of New Zealand on the South Island."

We started walking back to the car, both speculating on what the weather would be like now in Christchurch. Once inside, instead of starting the engine, Jill and I settled in and quietly looked out at the incredible bird's-eye view of the city. The wind raced through the lookout parking lot. All the world seemed to be spread out before us, colorfully painted with endless possibilities. It was a new world to me in many ways. One I was ready to embrace.

"You know," Jill said after our comfortable pause. "If you really want to go to Christchurch, let me know. I'd like to go sometime."

"With a tour group?"

"Not particularly."

"Me neither."

"Maybe we could go on a Sisterchicks adventure, just the two of us."

"A Sisterchicks adventure?" I repeated. "What's that?"

"That's what my daughter-in-law calls a weekend getaway. She and her best friend take one every year and call it their Sisterchicks adventure. I always thought it would be fun to do something like that. Ray and I used to travel together a lot, but I can't remember ever taking off with a girlfriend for a vacation."

"I've never gotten away like that, either," I said. "Tony told me I should do some exploring, but I didn't want to go by myself. It would be lots of fun to go with you."

"I think so, too. We can book our tickets on-line."

"Okay. Although I'll have to ask Tony to book mine at work because, as you may have noticed, I don't have a computer at home. Or a telephone. Or a television. But I have a refrigerator."

"And a bathtub," Jill reminded me.

"Yes, I have a nice bathtub. It's just that I haven't yet figured out how to get my bathtub or my refrigerator to connect to the Internet to book airline tickets."

Jill laughed. Like Tracey said the day before, Jill had a great laugh. Just getting close to her bubbly laugh made me want to join in.

"If you want, we can stop by my house after this and use my computer. But first we have one more place of interest to see." Jill started the engine.

"If it's the Embassy Theatre, I've already seen it," I said flatly.

"You know about the Embassy?"

"I didn't before Mad Dog drove us past on our way from the airport."

Jill stepped on the brakes and looked at me. "Mad Dog?"

"That's Tony's boss. Do you know him?"

She paused before saying, "Yes, I know Mad Dog."

Jill continued to back the car out of the parking lot. From her response to Mad Dog's name, I guessed Jill didn't have a good impression of him. Even though I knew he could have done plenty to earn his reputation with Jill, I felt the need to defend him—or at least to explain the nickname.

"Did you know that his real name is Marcus? My husband gave him the nickname at a studio party years ago. They did a commercial involving a high-strung poodle that kept chasing its tail instead of cooperating with the film crew. Tony took footage of the tail-chaser that they couldn't use, turned it into a clip, and set it up as a screen saver on Marcus's computer. After that Marcus got to be a little too good at imitating the poodle, especially as an icebreaker at parties."

"Oh," Jill said politely.

The topic of Mad Dog seemed to hang between us like an embarrassing pair of jumbo briefs on the invisible clothesline of our forming friendship. I decided not to bring up any more stories about Mad Dog.

Jill was the one who changed the subject. "Kathy, I want to thank you for something you said yesterday. It really helped me."

"What did I say?"

"When you were talking about Ray stringing the hammock between the orange trees, you said you had experienced the 'reward of his zeal.' I love that."

"It's true."

"I know." She glanced at me and then back at the road. "And you know what? I needed to hear that. Thank you."

"You're welcome."

We coasted a little farther down the road on the side of Mount Victoria, and Jill revealed she was taking me to see a famous movie spot.

"I should warn you that I'm not extremely reverent about *Lord of the Rings*. You saw what I did to the hobbit in the garden."

"You'll like this place," Jill assured me. "And even if you don't, please just pretend you're impressed because it's a special place for me. I was there the day they filmed, because Ray got special permission and...well, I'll just show you."

Jill pulled the car to the side of the road and turned off the engine. We got out and walked along what looked like a hiking trail that led into a densely wooded area. The dirt trail was covered with a carpet of dried, brown pine needles that cushioned our steps.

"This *is* beautiful," I said.

"I told you."

I stopped to touch the thick bark on one of the towering giants. "These trees are so old. They're ancient. Look at this trunk."

"I know." Jill nodded. "This is a wonderful place, isn't it?"

"It's amazing."

"Look how gnarled some of these trees are." She pointed to a particularly unusual tree. "You can almost see faces in the trunks. And look over there. The moss seems iridescent."

"Wow."

The farther we walked, the more enchanting the forest became. Sunlight slid through the high canopy of thick branches and seemed to ignite clumps of grass into vibrant green campfires, clustered in the open spaces. All across the forest floor, these emerald patches blazed with a natural glory that hinted at the hidden glimmers still tucked away in God's imagination.

"Right here." Jill stopped, and I tried to see what she was pointing at.

Six

Jill pointed to where the trail took a sudden dip. An outgrowth of lanky tree roots was exposed by erosion.

"Try to picture this spot with another tree they brought in and put right here. It was a tree they made in the props department. Any idea what scene they were filming?"

I sized up the setting.

"I'll give you a hint. It was when the hobbits left the Shire."

I looked around, and suddenly I could visualize it. "This is where Frodo and his pals hid, isn't it?"

"That's right." Jill moved to the trail's edge. "Right here."

"I remember that scene! The hobbits jumped off the road and hid under these massive roots. Right here! That's so cool!"

"You got it."

"And those dark horses came through here on the trail."

"The ring on the chain around Frodo's neck was calling out to the Ringwraiths."

"I can see it all. Wow! They didn't need to add many props, did they?"

"No." Jill was smiling. She seemed to be drinking in sweet memories of the place. No evil spirits on black horses were riding through her mind, as she gazed down the trail. "That was the first scene they filmed, and the rest of the project unfolded from that day."

We stood alone on the pine needle–padded trail, and I knew where I'd bring Tony the next time he borrowed the studio's van.

"Have I made a fan out of you yet?"

"Almost." I moved to the trail's edge, sizing up the hollowed-out spot.

"Kathy, what are you doing?"

"Come on, let's try it out. I'm not exactly hobbit-size, but I think we can fit."

Jill laughed. "You have to be kidding!"

"No, I'm serious. Come on!"

We were dressed in Saturday shopping clothes, but who cared? Edging over the side of the trail, we grabbed on to the extended tree roots and used them like a climber would use a rope.

"That looks roomy enough." I pointed to the largest hollowed-out area under the tree.

"This is the craziest thing I've done since..."

"Since you went driving with me yesterday? Come on, we can fit in there."

And indeed we did. We fit so well that the dampness from the rich, dark earth penetrated our clothes. I twitched at the thought of legions of creepy, crawly creatures jumping on me, as if I were their bus ride out of there.

"Listen," Jill said, holding her breath. We heard the steady pounding of feet coming our way.

"Joggers," Jill whispered.

"Should we jump out and scare them?" I whispered.

Jill covered her mouth so her giggles wouldn't escape. "I can't believe we're doing this."

"On the count of three," I whispered. "One, two, three!"

Instead of springing out of hiding like two slender, annoyingly perky cheerleaders, the width of our midlife frames wedged us together at the opening, and Jill's shirt caught on a protruding twig.

"Wait! I don't want to tear this shirt. Hang on." She tried to pull her right arm around to use both hands to release her shirt. In the flurry, my long hair caught on the buttons that ran up the sleeve of her cute shirt.

"Ow! Stop! Wait! Now I'm caught."

"Are you two okay?" One of the joggers stood looking down on us, his face expressing surprise. It just wasn't the same surprise effect we were trying for.

"We're fine," I said with my head tilted at an unnatural angle to the left. I groped to find the connecting button that was yanking the hair off my head. "Thanks anyway," I added cheerfully.

He didn't believe me. "Are you caught?"

"Yes!" Jill confessed the obvious. "Can you see from up there where my shirt is caught on the tree?"

He gingerly came toward us.

I didn't blame him for his caution. Why would two women be wedged under a tree root, appearing to be joined at the hip, with Jill's right arm suspended in midair and my oddly twisted head connected to her wrist? I'm sure we looked like freak show contestants who never made it to the big time and were forced to practice their talents for the unappreciative woodland creatures.

"I can see where it's caught," he said. "It's along the edge. If you can back up a few inches, it should come off on its own. In theory."

I could smell his sweat as he got closer, and for some reason the unpleasant odor was more of an irritant to me at the moment than our predicament.

"I think I can back up." Jill crouched and pulled her arm down. Consequently, my hair and twisted head went down with her.

"Ouch!"

"Sorry!"

"A little more to the left," the jogger said.

"Got it." Jill raised herself and moved forward untangled.

"Oww!"

"Kathy, I'm so sorry. Hold still. I can see where you're caught. There, got it."

Crawling all the way out of our hobbit hideout, we stood up straight and smoothed our hair and crumpled clothes. Then, as if we had practiced, we simultaneously brushed off our behinds with the same synchronized motions and turned to our jogger hero with what I'm sure must have looked like clown grins.

He sized up the situation. "All right then. Looks like you're clear. I'll be on my way. Cheers."

We stood in place, watching him jog on down the trail.

"I wonder which one of us he thinks is Lucy and which one is Ethel," Jill said.

I didn't catch on to her joke at first, but as soon as the *I Love Lucy* connection hit me, I snickered. "You can be Lucy."

"I think I was the Ethel in this caper because I let you talk me into crawling under that tree. You were the Lucy."

"I promise I'll never ask you to do that again."

"Yeah, right, Lucy. We'll see about that. You may not be able to talk me into crawling under tree roots again, but I have a feeling you'll come up with a few more stunts before this sitcom ends in three months."

"Three months?"

"When you go back to California."

The thought that popped into my mind was, *I don't want to leave.* I was astounded to realize I had experienced a mental turnaround from twenty-four hours ago, when I was making another big *X* on the calendar inside my checkbook register. That *X* represented the checking off of another day of exile in New Zealand. Today I wanted a big eraser so I could go back and capture every day of the two weeks I'd lost wallowing in self-pity. What a difference a day makes. What a difference a friend makes.

"How about some lunch?" Jill asked once we had shaken ourselves off and gotten back in the car.

We stopped at a deli and ordered turkey sandwiches to "take away" instead of "to go." The woman behind the register asked if we wanted a bag of *crisps* to go with our *sarnies.*

I turned to Jill for a translation. "Potato chips," she whispered. "To go with our sandwiches."

"Oh, no thanks."

I tried to pay, but Jill insisted I put my wallet back. "You can get the hokey pokey later."

"The hokey pokey? Does that involve putting my right foot in or my left foot out? Because I think we should coordinate our movements ahead of time, so we don't get stuck anywhere. I mean, not that something like that would ever happen to us."

The woman at the register was not amused, but Jill was.

"Hokey pokey is ice cream," Jill explained. "It's nice and creamy with bits of honey nougats in it."

"Ice cream? Why didn't you say so? In that case, I'll gladly buy."

We took our sandwiches to the car, and as we drove back to Jill's house to eat, I thought of how quickly I had come to feel the ebb and flow of friendship with Jill. In California I'd had the same friends for years. We formed a small circle and gathered regularly at church and school events. A few of us got together for lunch to celebrate our birthdays. We were close and comfortable and always there for each other.

With Jill I felt that same connectedness, even though we only had been doing life together for a few days. It felt luxurious to slip so quickly into the coziness of friendship.

Jill pulled up to a stop sign, and we waited for two older women to toddle across the street. They wore sensible shoes and matching hand-knit caps and scarves, and walked with their arms linked. The slow-moving women reached the other side of the street, where they turned together and waved at Jill and me with appreciative smiles. We waved back.

The world seemed to be full of friends.

No matter where a woman is, she can always find a pal.

Rolling through the intersection, we drove a few more blocks before turning up an inclined driveway. "Welcome to my humble abode," Jill said.

I expected a cottage-style home like Mr. Barry's, but Jill's house was closer to the water and looked like a beach house built in the sixties along the cliffs in Laguna. It had a raised front deck that was beautifully decorated with potted plants and sturdy metal lawn furniture. A canvas umbrella was opened over the glass-topped table, and sitting on the table, surrounding the umbrella's pole, was an elaborate metal candleholder with at least six loops. At the end of each loop was a votive candle in a glass holder. I could image how magical the candles must look when lit at night with the lights of the homes across the bay easily visible from the deck.

I noticed right away that all the flowers in Jill's planters were red, white, and blue with a few dashes of yellow added. At my home in Tustin, I used red, white, and blue flowers also.

We also had the same taste in furniture and decorations. Jill's home was done in neutrals. She had cream-colored walls, cocoa brown furniture, deep brown wooden table and chairs, and all her appliances were black. Majestic purple and shimmering, soft gold were the colors that accented her neutral foundation.

I never would have selected those two colors, but they were gorgeous. My accents were in blues and yellows. Somehow taking those shades several steps deeper to purple and gold made all the difference between zippy exuberance and quiet elegance.

"I love your house," I said, peering around the open living area and kitchen-dining area.

"Thank you. Ray insisted we buy it when we first got here. I thought we should rent and play it safe in case the job didn't work out for him, but he said the market value was going to skyrocket, and he was right. We bought this for a song, compared to California prices. The house was twenty-four years old when we bought it, so we had to make a lot of repairs. That turned out to be a bonus because it gave us a chance to change things to the way we liked them."

"You have a gorgeous home," I said. "So many beautiful paintings!"

"I taught an art appreciation class in California for nine years. When we moved here, I taught the same class at Victoria University for three years, but then they hired a full-time teacher."

"Did you paint any of these?"

"No, I only appreciate them. Would you like something to drink?"

"Sure. Whatever you have, I'll have the same."

"Is Fresh Up okay?"

"Sure. I've never had it before, but I'm willing to try it."

"It's juice. Nothing fancy. This one is apple-mango."

"Sounds good."

As I was following Jill into her kitchen, I stopped in front of a black-and-white photo hanging on the wall. I felt entranced by the beauty of the composition.

The picture was a close-up of an infant sleeping, balanced on the broad forearm of a tender father. The infant's head was cupped in the father's open hand, which was huge in comparison to the newborn yet so gently covering, protecting, blessing the tiny, naked miracle.

"This is amazing," I said in a low voice.

Jill joined me with two tall glasses of Fresh Up in her hands and looked lovingly at the picture. "That's my son. He's holding their firstborn. My first grandbaby. Lacey."

"She's beautiful! And this photo is so beautifully done. Who took the picture?"

"My son's mother-in-law. Our little Lacey-girl was only two days old."

I looked at the signature in the corner to see if I recognized the photographer's name. "Laurinda Sue?"

"Yes. She's amazing. Her work is really taking off. It's wonderful because her husband is a painter, and for years his work got all the attention. I guess the story goes that she was taking photographs for years but never showed them to anyone. I'm not sure what brought her work out of the drawer, but she's won a few awards, and one of her pieces is on display at a large hotel in Hawaii."

"Laurinda Sue," I repeated, certain I hadn't heard of her. "You said she's married to a painter?"

Jill hesitated, as if measuring if she could trust me with information that appeared to be a family secret. "She's married to Gabriel Giordani."

My mouth dropped open. "Your son married into the Giordani family?"

She nodded.

Gabriel Giordani's work was everywhere in the U.S. He was known as "The Painter of Hideaways" and had been popular for well over a decade. I owned a box of greeting cards with pictures of cottages he had painted. My mom had a print of one of his garden scenes over her fireplace.

"This is really extraordinary," I murmured, trying not to say anything ridiculous about the Giordani connection. Just in and of itself, the composition of the photograph was exceptional. It didn't need a Giordani endorsement.

"I love this picture," Jill said in a wistful voice. "Not just because it's of my son and my grandbaby, but whenever I look at it, I get a sense of comfort. I think it's because that's how I picture God holding me these past few years. I'm the fragile infant, and He's the strong, Almighty Protector who has held me in the palm of His hand."

Jill's words caused my throat to swell and my eyes to brim with tears. I had no response. I, too, was an infant, more aware than I'd ever been that God wasn't just looking down from His heavenly throne, the all-powerful judge evaluating all of my actions. He cared for me with such gentle mercy that He wouldn't allow me to fall out of my empty nest and tumble headlong into self-destruction. He caught me and held me securely in the palm of His hand.

Seven

Two days after Jill and I made our on-line travel plans for Christchurch, it rained buckets. For the first time since we had arrived in New Zealand, I reached for a small devotional book one of my friends had given me as a going-away gift. The reading for that day was from Ephesians 5.

One verse stood out to me, and I underlined it. "Mostly what God does is love you. Keep company with him and learn a life of love. Observe how Christ loved us. His love was not cautious but extravagant. He didn't love in order to get something from us but to give everything of himself to us. Love like that."

For a long time I sat listening to the rain hitting the garage's metal roof, sounding like rubber pellets. I didn't know if I had ever loved anyone extravagantly, the way God loved me. Finding Jill certainly had been an extravagant gift to me from God. I thought of all the people I had loved cautiously over the years. *What would my life look like if I started to love extravagantly?*

The next morning the sun was back, Tony was out the door early, and I was ready to trot down to the Chocolate Fish for a morning wake-up mocha.

I found Mr. Barry already out in his garden. He greeted me with a wave of his gloved hand from where he knelt beside the mums. He was trying to tie up the drooping stems. I waved back and thought how he seemed the sort of man who, by virtue of his build, was better suited for shouldering a plow and driving a team of oxen than bending low to fiddle with tying delicate knots in gardening twine.

"How are you this morning, Mr. Barry?"

"No complaints."

I noticed that Mr. Frodo was looking his cheerful self. I also noticed that the blooms on the mums had become so heavy in the rain that they bent in such a way that their golden faces appeared to kiss the earth.

Deciding that I better come clean as well, I bent my head and said, "Mr. Barry, I didn't tell you this yet, but a few days ago I was driving a truck, and I bumped into your lawn hobbit. He fell over, but we put him back up. I broke off a few flowers, but that was all. I don't think anything in your garden was hurt, but I thought I should tell you."

"I saw the whole thing," he said.

"You did?"

"The three of you were a box of budgies."

I wasn't sure what that meant, but I guessed it was something positive by the way he said it. "So you're not upset?"

"How could I be? Best entertainment I've had in a year."

Relieved and yet still feeling a bit penitent, I asked, "Do you need some help?"

He hesitated before nodding and moved back so I could get in there and bolster up the drooping blossoms.

"My wife planted these six years ago. Every year her chrysanthemums keep coming back."

I assumed Mr. Barry's wife had passed away. After going through all the emotions with Jill when she told me about Ray, I wasn't sure I wanted to open up any repressed feelings in this gentle giant. Instead, I nodded to the gunnysack marked Narcissus Bulbs. "Do you plan to put those in the garden today?"

"Thought I would. Might be nice to have some flowers here in October."

"I'd be glad to help, if you like." I knew my gesture wasn't exactly extravagant, but it was a first step toward loving someone without being cautious or thinking about what I could ask for in return.

"I don't mind if you don't mind," Mr. Barry said.

I picked up a trowel and asked where he wanted the first bulb to go. The rain during the past two days had made the earth nice and soft. Getting my hands into fresh, moist soil met some sort of basic need inside me. I felt happy the moment my fingers curled around the rich earth.

Mr. Barry asked if I wanted gloves, but I was enjoying the feel of the soil and told him I didn't have fancy fingernails that were in danger of breaking off.

"My wife used to paint her fingernails red. Bright red. She painted them every week. I liked her red fingernails. You could always see her hands moving about. Even from across the room."

"Did she paint her toenails, too?"

"No, she's always hated her feet. Hates her ears, too. Never wanted to wear her hair back like yours is now. Said she was afraid people would stare at her ears. Why are women like that? Dorothea has beautiful ears."

I noticed he was talking about his wife as if she were alive. I risked broaching a volatile topic and said, "I'd like to hear more about your wife."

"She doesn't say much, but she gets by."

I wasn't sure what that meant.

"She'd like to meet you."

"Okay. Would this morning be a good time?"

"Good as any."

Sliding the last few bulbs into the cool earth, I rose, dusted off my knees, and followed Mr. Barry into the celery-colored cottage to meet Dorothea. She was seated by the window in a wheelchair with a crooked expression on her face. When she saw me, her eyes brightened.

I went to her, slipped my hand in her quavering left hand, and introduced myself.

Dorothea made a soft sound in the back of her throat and kept looking at me. The fingers on her right hand were curled in, and her wrist was bent. I recognized all the symptoms. My grandfather had a stroke when I was young and lived with us a full ten years. The stroke incapacitated him on the right side and severely affected his speech, but his mind was all there. Was that the case with Dorothea?

I told her about my husband and what he did at Jackamond Studios. She took in every word, using her expressive eyes to respond.

Mr. Barry offered me a chair. I sat beside Dorothea, still holding her hand. Then I treated her to the delicacy my grandfather always wanted: I gave her news about what was going on in the outside.

First I told her about the bulbs we'd planted and how large the mums were growing. Then I told her about the views Jill and I enjoyed from the top of Mount Victoria. Dorothea's eyes didn't turn away from me even for a moment. She was a medium-framed woman with short white hair that poofed up on her head like a squiggly shower cap. I thought she had very dainty ears, but I didn't mention them. I didn't want her to think her hubby had been telling me secrets about her in the garden.

Clearly, Mr. Barry could help Dorothea in and out of her wheelchair and take care of all her basic needs. But no man can minister to a woman the way another woman can. I wondered if Dorothea had a regular stream of visitors. Even if she did, after spending an hour with her that morning, I decided that for the rest of our stay in Wellington, I'd be one of her regular visitors.

"I'm going to go," I said when her eyes began to droop. I guessed she probably napped a lot. "I don't want to wear out my welcome, but I'll come back and visit you in a few days. Okay?"

She made a gurgling sound in response.

"Good. I'll see you in a few days then."

Mr. Barry walked me out the front door. He cleared his throat awkwardly once we were where Dorothea couldn't hear us. "I'm in your debt," he said in a deep, yet faint voice.

"No, you're not. Tony and I are in your debt. As a matter of fact, Tony wanted me to be sure and pay our rent before next Tuesday. I'm going to be gone for a few days, and we didn't want to be late with the payment."

"All right." He raised his hand to wave as I took off down the street.

The sun was nearly halfway through its paces, but I was still a woman on a mission for a morning mocha. Some things, like a Chocolate Fish mocha latte, I didn't forget about regardless of how many pleasant interruptions blocked my way.

In the week that followed, Jill and I shopped for a new bedspread for me, comfortable travel shoes for her, and something extra special for Dorothea.

Jill came over the morning before we left for Christchurch and helped me give Dorothea my little going-away-for-a-few-days gift. I'd been over to the house to see her nearly every day. My topics of conversation had dwindled by the third visit, so I brought a novel with me the next time. She seemed to love being read to. Especially because the novel I was reading didn't seem the sort of book Mr. Barry might read to her.

When Jill and I entered, Dorothea was waiting for us. "Good morning!" I said. "I brought my friend Jill with me. Jill, this is Dorothea."

Their connection moment was tender but a little awkward. Jill didn't seem to quite know how or where to touch Dorothea. I'd seen visitors act that way with stroke victims before. My grandfather's friends would look at him as if part of him was broken, and they were afraid to touch any other part of him in case that area might break as well.

I slipped my hand in Dorothea's strong left hand and leaned close to press my cheek against hers. "Jill and I have a little surprise for you today."

Dorothea's eyebrows went up as I held out a small gift bag. I looked over my shoulder. Mr. Barry couldn't be seen, but I guessed he was in the kitchen, his usual place of retreat whenever I came to visit. He seemed to want to hear everything but not let me know he was interested in the novel or what I had to chat about.

"Are you ready for this?" I leaned closer and whispered, "Your husband let me know what color you liked. Or at least what color he liked on you."

I pulled a bottle of bright red nail polish from the bag along with a file, a top coat, and some cotton balls.

"What do you think, Dorothea? Would it be okay if Jill and I put a little color on your fingernails?"

The dear woman began to cry.

"Oops!" I said. "I forgot the tissues."

"I have some." Jill reached into her purse.

We pulled up chairs and positioned ourselves. Jill took Dorothea's flexible left hand. I knew how to handle the right one even though it was locked in a curled-up position.

"Let me know if this is uncomfortable in any way." I massaged the palm of her hand.

"Did Kathy tell you that she and I are leaving in the morning for Christchurch?" Jill asked, warming up to the situation once she started to file Dorothea's neglected thumbnail.

"Have you ever been to Christchurch?" I asked.

Dorothea made a response, but it was hard to tell if it was a yes or a no. I half expected Mr. Barry to answer for her from the kitchen, but when he didn't, Jill and I went on as if her contribution to the conversation had been clear.

"We're flying down and taking the train back," Jill said.

"And staying at a bed-and-breakfast. Jill found this place, and it sounds charming. Actually, all of Christchurch sounds lovely. We've heard that the leaves should be gorgeous."

Dorothea made a sound in her throat, and I said, "Do you want me to bring back some big autumn leaves?"

"Aaah."

I let her know I'd bring back a big bouquet of leaves and lots of stories from our trip.

Cheerfully working together, Jill and I lit up Dorothea's smooth fingernails. The red looked even brighter on her nails than it had in the bottle.

"Mr. Barry is going to love this," I whispered. "He'll notice these little holly berries from across the room and think it's already Christmas."

Dorothea's visceral laugh startled Jill, but I'd come to love it. It sounded like a thinner version of Mad Dog's guffaw. I enjoyed those rare puffs from her sunken chest as much as I enjoyed getting a little chocolate fish. It was like receiving a tiny reward for making Dorothea happy.

The manicure was a grand success. When Jill and I left, Dorothea couldn't stop waving at us with her left hand, as if she were the Queen Mum and we were her adoring subjects, which we definitely were.

"Poor Mr. Barry," I said with a giggle, as we crossed the yard back to the garage.

"Why do you say that?" Jill looked at me as if I were being mean.

"There'll be no living with the woman now that she has red nails! Did you see the way she was waving at us? That red-tipped hand will be ordering him all over the place. All she has to do is point, and the man will be powerless to deny her request. Yes, I'd say our work is done here for the day."

Jill smiled. "Wellington was running a little short on super-heroes before you arrived."

"The dynamic duo, that's us. And the dynamic duo has struck again! Armed with only a bottle of nail polish, Lucy and Ethel go where no man wants to go! With a few vibrant strokes we keep up the never-ending battle of finding ways to empower women everywhere!"

We enjoyed a good giggle in front of the hobbit. I thought the fellow should be happy. This was one of the few times the laughs weren't about him.

"What time should I be ready in the morning?" I asked, as Jill and I wound down and were about to go our separate ways to pack.

"Is seven okay? Our flight is at nine, but I like to be early."

"Me, too. And Tony wanted me to thank you again for letting him borrow your car while we're gone."

"No problem. Anytime. I'll see you in the morning." She gave me a hug. "You did a good thing today, Kathy. With Mrs. Barry. That was a good thing."

I basked in the glow of Jill's praise for a little while after she left. What Jill didn't know was that I hadn't really gone out of my way or done anything extraordinary with Mrs. Barry. I did what came naturally and comfortably to me, because I worked with elderly people every day. Jill never had asked about my job, and I hadn't told her. The topic had never come up.

I pulled out my suitcase from under the bed and wondered what conversational topics would come up on our trip to Christchurch. Jill hadn't told me exactly how Ray had passed away, and I didn't feel as if that story was one I wanted to ask for. If she wanted to give it to me one day, I would receive it, but I wouldn't ask.

When we were on the plane together the next morning, I thought Jill was about to give me the story of Ray's death. She mentioned that the studio had an office in Christchurch and how one of the other location managers had been on site in Christchurch the day of the accident.

But that was all she said. So Ray's death had been an accident. She seemed to be fighting against a wave of sadness after giving me that snippet of information, and I didn't want to start down a conversational trail that would set a somber tone for our getaway.

The Christchurch airport was a small building with a single conveyor belt for the luggage. It took us no time to retrieve our suitcases and head outside into the sunny day.

Climbing into the first cab that was waiting at the curb, Jill told the driver the name of our hotel. The cab appeared to be a family van that doubled as a cab. Delicate, white lace doilies covered the headrests.

"These are pretty," Jill said.

"Some of my wife's handiwork," said the driver.

He was a bald man dressed in a long-sleeved white shirt and a red and green plaid vest, and he welcomed us to his hometown by telling us a variety of details about the surrounding area. He had to be at least in his seventies. His grandfather, he said, had come from England and helped settle this province.

"You'll find my city to be the most English city outside of England. That's what I tell everyone who comes here. They all agree with me. You will, too."

"I'm sure we will," Jill said.

"What do you recommend we do while we're here?" I asked.

"It's a nice time of year to go punting. On the Avon. You can hire out a man, and he'll take you. Don't know that they'd let two young ladies such as yourselves hire out a skiff on your own."

His accent was tricky to understand, but I guessed he was talking about going on a boat on the Avon River so I said, "Sounds like fun."

The cab pulled up in front of our bed-and-breakfast, and Jill drew in an appreciative breath. "Look at this house!"

"It looks like the Fontaine Restaurant," I said. "Or I should say, it looks like the house your grandfather built."

"Did you see the front door?" Jill asked after we had paid our driver and started to pull our wheeled suitcases up the front walkway.

"I love the stained glass." I admired the attention to detail on this restored charmer. The walkway was lined with bright yellow marigolds and two large chrysanthemum plants at the bottom of the steps. The mums reminded me of Dorothea.

"Jill, let me get a quick picture of you at the bottom of the steps. I want to show Dorothea the mums."

We took turns posing by the flowers, on the steps, and at the front door next to the stained glass.

"How about one by the railing," I suggested.

"Oh, this porch brings back so many memories," Jill said. "I love this wicker furniture."

"Then let me get some shots of you in the wicker rocking chair."

She chuckled. "You're going to use up all your film in the first five minutes of our trip."

"Don't worry; it's digital," I said. "This is Tony's favorite of our three cameras. I think my limit on this one is five hundred shots, so keep on posing!"

Jill rested her hands on the back of one of the chairs and struck a chin-up, noble-woman-on-a-mild-afternoon pose with a closed-lip, contented expression.

"All you need is a parasol," I told her. "Or a tall glass of lemonade."

"How about this?" Jill reached for a china teacup and saucer resting on the side table. The cup was half full, as if someone had stepped away and might be returning for the final three sips.

"It's still warm!" She held the saucer in the palm of her hand and pretended to take a sip. "I feel like Goldilocks. You better take the picture quick before the three bears return."

The front door opened tentatively. Instead of a bear of any sort, a fair-haired woman in a billowy white blouse looked at us shyly. "Hallo?"

Jill was not the only Goldilocks in this fairy-tale setting.

"Hi." Jill laughed nervously and quickly returned the teacup to where she had found it. "We have reservations. The name is Radovich. We were just enjoying your beautiful porch."

"Thank you," our more relaxed hostess said. "Please come in."

We stepped onto polished dark wood floors and listened as she explained with a hint of a British accent where the *loo* was located down the hall.

"You are both invited to enjoy the front porch, of course, and feel free to make use of the front parlor and breakfast room anytime you wish."

We were shown to our room at the front of the house. The high ceiling was accented by a charming chandelier made from a lacy parasol hung so that the open part served as the shade.

"I love this light." Jill gazed up at the parasol. "I'd like to hang a parasol like this in my bedroom."

"I saw the idea in a magazine," our hostess said. "I still have the magazine. You're welcome to take it with you, if you like."

"Thank you. Yes, I'd love to see how to hang a light like this."

From the tall windows flowed sheer ivory curtains. The twin beds were separated by a gorgeous white table where an amber glass vase exploded with purple asters. On the dresser was an electric pot for heating water and an assortment of tea bags along with a china teapot and two matching china cups and saucers. Next to the teacups a plate of fancy chocolate truffles waited for us.

"This is charming," Jill said. "Everything about your home is beautiful."

"Thank you." Our hostess gave a humble bow, as she left us to settle in.

"Does it remind you a lot of the house you grew up in?" I tried out the bed closest to the window.

"Only from the outside. Everything inside is different—the floor plan, the ceilings, the staircase. But I love it, don't you?"

"I do. Especially our room. It feels as if we stepped into a party that's all set up and waiting for us."

"It does! So what are we waiting for? Let's start to party!" Jill lifted the plate of goodies and graciously offered me first choice of the chocolates.

If I hadn't already decided that I liked Jill as much as I did, that one gesture of offering me first choice of the chocolates would have cinched our friendship forever.

Eight

S o, what should we do first?" I was leisurely enjoying the last drop of tea from one of the china cups that had been waiting for Jill and me in our lovely B&B bedroom in Christchurch. The chocolate lifted our adventurous spirits, and we were ready to take on the town.

"We should find a map first," Jill suggested.

"I saw a rack of brochures in the front room when we came in. I'm sure a map would be there. I'll go see what they have."

"How about if I meet you in the front room in a minute? I'm going to change. It's a lot warmer here than I thought it would be."

I left Jill and browsed through the rack of travel brochures. The first brochure I pulled out gave information about one of the visitor centers that offered cultural presentations by the Maori.

On the back of the brochure the words, "*Ki mai koe ki a au, he aha te mea nui tenei ao,*" appeared over a photo of a Maori warrior complete with a tattooed face, frighteningly popped-out eyes, and an open mouth in a roaring expression.

Under that photo was a picture of a Maori man greeting another by coming nose to nose in a warm expression of friendship. The words under that photo were, "*He tangata, he tangata, he tangata.*"

"Are you thinking of going to Rotorua?" a voice behind me asked.

I jumped. I hadn't seen the man sitting in a side chair when I entered the front room. His dark, kinky hair looked how Mad Dog's might look, if he ever got it cut.

"I'm not sure. It looks fascinating."

"That's because we're a fascinating people." He grinned. Then he rose and came toward me with a book in his hand. "I'm Hika."

I introduced myself and explained that I was visiting.

"I live here." He grinned again, as if he knew a secret I wasn't in on.

I assumed he was renting a room. "It's a charming place, isn't it?"

Instead of agreeing with me, he thanked me for the compliment and said, "My wife and I bought this house five years ago. It was her dream to run an inn after I retired. Here's the picture of what it looked like when we started the project." He pointed to a framed picture on the wall.

"Wow! What a transformation."

"Thank you."

"That's a nice portrait." I pointed to a pencil sketch of an aging Maori man's profile. Over his shoulders he wore a cape of some sort.

"My grandfather," Hika said. "He was a Maori chief. I'm named after him."

"Really? My great-grandfather was a chief also. He was Navajo."

Hika's expression sobered. He tilted his head in reverent acknowledgment. It was as if he were honoring me as a descendant of a chief. I didn't quite know how to respond. That bit of lineage trivia had rarely prompted a response of respect in the past.

"And you?" I asked cautiously. I didn't want to say the wrong thing and have him stick out his tongue or pop out his eyes like the warrior on the back of the brochure, but I wanted to honor his heritage as well. "Have you always lived in this area?"

"No, I'm from the North Island. From Auckland." He said a few words that I couldn't understand, and I supposed them to be the name of his tribe. I didn't know how to ask further, because I didn't know if the Maoris were from tribes or clans or what.

"I know very little about Maoris," I admitted, holding up the brochure in my hand. "Maybe I should go to this cultural center."

"It's on the North Island. It will take you a day to get there." With a hint of mischief in his expression he added, "Since you are staying here for two nights, I don't think you should check out early to make the journey. We don't like it when our guests leave early."

"Don't worry; we're planning to stay both nights."

"Good. Now, if you want to know about Maori culture, I can tell you a few things. And what I don't know I can make up."

I smiled and lowered myself onto a chair in the parlor.

Hika took the chair across from me and told me how the Polynesian Maoris had paddled their way through the South Pacific in huge, elaborately decorated, dugout sailing canoes before settling in New Zealand at least a thousand years ago. Dutch sailors were the first Europeans to make contact with the Maori in the late 1600s. But four of the sailors were clubbed to death, and so the captain sailed on without exploring any more of New Zealand.

"A hundred years later Captain Cook and his crew showed up, and none of the sailors were killed this time. That was good for them, but it was not good for us, because the explorers left two things behind we did not need: guns and measles. More Europeans came bringing more civilization and more means of death. But then, I am telling you a story that is familiar to you."

"No. As I said, I don't know anything about the Maoris."

"I was referring to the story of the Native Americans."

I wasn't prepared to feel as sad as I did at the impact of his words. "Western civilization hasn't been good for indigenous people during the past three hundred years, has it?"

Hika pointed to the italicized words on the back of the brochure I was holding and repeated them in a deep voice. "*Ki mai koe ki a au, he aha te mea nui tenei ao.*"

"What does that mean?"

"It is the first part of the proverb. A question. 'If you should ask me what is the most important thing in the world, the answer would be…?'"

He waited a moment for me to respond. If I were in the middle of a Bible study group or a circle of friends from my church, I would know the expected answer. Jesus had made it clear that the greatest commandment was to love the Lord your

God with all your heart, soul, strength, and mind. I didn't know what answer Hika would expect here in this place of upside down. My guess was something like land or tribal rights, or freedom.

When I didn't jump in with a response, Hika said, "The answer is, *'He tangata, he tangata, he tangata.'*"

"And what does that mean?"

"'It's the people, it's the people, it's the people.'"

Hika sat back, waiting for the proverb to sink in. It struck me that this was the second part of the great commandment Jesus gave to His disciples: love your neighbor as yourself.

That's it. Love God and love people. Not one or the other. It's both.

I thought about the extravagant love verse in Ephesians and how the passage said to "learn a life of love." Loving God and loving people don't come naturally to any of us. We all have to be taught to value others and to learn a life of love.

Just then Jill entered the parlor and apologized for taking so long. I made the introductions, and Jill asked if I'd found a map yet. She asked how we could rent a boat to take down the Avon River.

Hika rose, reached for another brochure, and handed it to me. This one was of Christchurch with a clear map on the back.

"Thanks. I appreciate the information. Not only the map but also everything you said. Thank you."

Jill and I stepped out onto the porch. We were equipped with everything we needed for our journey into the fresh autumn afternoon. Meandering down the charming streets of Christchurch, we followed the map to the river Avon.

I thought of how different everything had been for me a

few short weeks ago when I was sitting around in sweats or pj's all day, closed up in the garage apartment. If someone had asked me then if I loved God, I would have said yes, of course. I never stopped loving God just because life had taken such a flip.

But I was in hiding. I wasn't around people, people, people.

Meeting Jill, kneeling beside Mr. Barry in the garden, holding Dorothea's hand—these were the treasures of this place. Being in the midst of people was what brought life back to me.

Jill and I continued along the twisting river trail. Well-watered trees rose above us and shaded our path. One after another of the gentle giants stood guard on their thick trunks and stretched out long strings of quivering leaves that they dangled over our heads. Every time the wind blew, a few more glittering gold coin leaves showered over us and tumbled down to the green earth. I selected a collection of them for Dorothea.

"I feel like I'm in Narnia," Jill said.

"I know. This is a fabulous place, isn't it?"

"You know what's amazing to me?" Jill stopped to snap a picture. "Do you remember my saying that Christchurch is the launching point for journeys to Antarctica, because this is the closest major city to the bottom of the world?"

"Yes, I remember your saying that."

"Well, you would think that for being so close to all that ice and all those penguins it would be much colder here. This is a place of surprises."

I agreed with her as we strolled past a large arch labeled the "Bridge of Remembrance." The inscription commemorated the gunners from that region who had served in World Wars I and II.

"Have you noticed a lot of war memorials since you've been in New Zealand?" Jill asked.

"Not particularly."

"You'll probably start to notice them now. If I remember correctly, over one hundred thousand troops from New Zealand fought in World War I, and over half of the soldiers were killed or wounded. For a small nation, it was devastating. Everyone knew someone who lost someone. I think it affected that entire generation in a deep way."

"I never thought of New Zealanders being involved in either of the world wars."

"That's because you and I grew up only hearing about America's part in fighting for world peace during the past century. It's a little stunning, isn't it, when you slip into a place like this and realize that we're not really the center of the universe after all?"

I stopped walking along the river trail and looked at Jill.

"Are you okay?"

"What you just said got to me. It's true. We're not the center of the universe, are we?"

"Certainly not the way we think we are."

I felt as if all kinds of new ideas were coming at me today. Jill's and Hika's comments weren't earthshaking, but they prompted me to think beyond myself. Both of them presented thoughts that were larger than the small, familiar world I'd lived in for so long. I decided I liked being shaken out of my comfort zone every now and then.

We picked up the pace and found the Antigua Boat Sheds without any trouble. Next to the rental stall was a waterfront café. The handwritten sign on the front offered pumpkin basil soup with bacon as the special of the day.

"What do you think? Should we eat first?" Jill asked.

I didn't have to be invited twice to try the local special of the day. We slid onto the bench of a picnic table on the patio and watched dozens of ducks as they paddled up to the riverbank's edge. They looked up to us, waiting for a snack to be sent their way. Once Jill's sandwich was served, she shared more than half her bread with them. We laughed as their bobbing white tails wiggled every time they ducked under for the next bite.

Several refined swans arrived, turning their long necks to gaze up at us. Their elegant forms alongside the pale pink roses that had climbed over the wall and lined the railing between us and the water set the perfect fairy-tale scene. The river was as blue as the sky and was all lit up with the sparkling reflection of diamond-cut sunshine. I couldn't wait to get in a canoe and paddle along with the ducks and swans.

A cocky young man at the boat rental stall greeted us with a tip of his straw hat. He seemed to think it humorous that the two of us "older" women wanted to rent a canoe and take it out by ourselves. He tried to convince us to wait half an hour until Evan, the boatman, returned with the fancy flatboat that most tourists "our age" preferred to take. Evan was, after all, an excellent punter.

Jill and I exchanged glances, and I knew we were of one mind.

"No thank you," we both said.

"We'd prefer to take out a canoe on our own," Jill added.

"All right then. You can have the red one there at the dock."

We paid with cash, picked up our paddles and life vests, and clambered into the canoe while the young man at the boat stall watched.

Not being particularly experienced at canoeing, Jill and I got in facing each other instead of both facing the same direction.

"That's not the way you should be seated," the young man said with a snicker.

"This is the way we seat," I said.

"Seat?"

"Sit," I declared, settling in with as much dignity as I could at that point. "This is the way we sit."

Jill was no help. She was laughing, and that made me want to laugh. But the situation wasn't as funny as she may have thought because the challenge of swinging my legs around without unbalancing the canoe was more of a risk than I was willing to take.

"Do you want to turn the other way?" I asked Jill quietly.

"No, we can make this work. Come on, I'll paddle us out of here."

I am happy to report that we pulled off the procedure as graceful as swans and floated with the current into the center of the shallow river.

But once we moved away from the dock, our challenges came to the forefront. That's when I put my paddle in the water, and Jill and I couldn't synchronize our paddling. Every stroke I made seemed to cancel hers.

"Right side," Jill called out.

I paddled vigorously.

"Your other right side!" she said, laughing. "We're headed for the tules!"

I never was good at determining my right from my left when in a pinch. With four bold strokes, I managed to ram us right into the tall grasses along the riverbank.

"Let me try to back us up," Jill said. "Don't paddle."

I realized then that the current was more of a problem than we had anticipated. In the deeper water toward the center of the river, the current appeared to gently flow back toward the boathouse. Along the side, where we were now wedged, a different, swirling current was at play.

Jill single-handedly maneuvered us out of the reeds and back into the calmer current, which, unfortunately, carried us right back to the dock at the boathouse before she and I had a chance to regroup and coordinate our paddling efforts.

"Hallo!" the smarty boat-boy greeted us from the launching dock where he had no doubt seen our entire escapade. "Does this mean we can sign you up then for the punting tour?"

"Just ignore him," Jill said under her breath, as if we were two girls at summer camp and the older boys from the neighboring camp had invaded our lake.

I thought she was hilarious to say we should ignore him, but I couldn't do it. I had to smart off. After all, he was wearing a straw hat and a bow tie like a missing member of a barbershop quartet. He was begging for sassy comments from the tourists.

"We're not sissies in this scenario."

"That's right. We are managing just fine, thank you," Jill added politely.

"Yeah. Save your punting tickets for some other old ladies."

"Kathy!" Jill flipped a sprinkling of water on me with her paddle. "Who are you calling an old lady?"

"Not us!"

"Exactly," she agreed. "Not us."

We managed to paddle from the boathouse and successfully move up the lazy river. The secret was for me to paddle backwards from how Jill was paddling, as well as on the opposite side. Somehow this procedure seemed fitting in light of everything else that felt upside down and backwards in this place.

The farther we paddled up the river, the more peaceful and shadowed the river became. On both sides of the water were long stretches of green grass with trees, benches, and concrete bike trails. Women pushing baby strollers smiled at us. Little children waved at us. A man on a bike took such a long look at our unorthodox seating position and paddling that his front tire went off the trail. He wobbled himself back on course and kept going, still casting glances at us over his shoulder.

"It's nice to have all the boys around here looking at us, isn't it?" Jill asked with a giggle. It seemed to me she was feeling the lightness of being adorable for the first time in a long time.

I considered reminding her why all the boys were paying attention to us middle-aged mamas. We weren't a couple of cute, young cheerleaders; we were inexperienced tourists, demonstrating our strange canoe-maneuvering techniques. I thought we resembled Dr. Dolittle's pushmi-pullyu creature, that endearing, two-headed alpaca that was joined in the middle. But if Jill was feeling young and flirty and having a great time, I wasn't going to be the one to spoil her fun.

Nine

Our canoe slid underneath a charming arched walking bridge as Jill chattered enthusiastically. "Don't you love the colors on the trees? They are so gorgeous. And that green area on the right must be Hagley Park. I read about it. When the city fathers built Christchurch, they set aside almost a square mile for a public park. A restaurant is at the edge of the herb garden. We might have to include a visit there on our pressing itinerary."

"Oh, yes, our pressing itinerary. I like the way you think. Eat a little, float a little. Eat a little, walk a little. My idea of a true vacation."

The river took a turn and came into a sunny area where more bobbing ducks peeked underwater for treats. They seemed to be on the same schedule as we were: eat a little, quack a little. Eat a little, paddle a little.

Floating toward us was a beautifully painted flatboat with a young man standing in the back, wearing a straw hat, white shirt, and bow tie. He was using a long pole to punt his passengers down the river.

"Look, Jill! It's Evan the punter we heard so much about. Should we wave?"

"We can do better than that." Jill paddled faster. "Come on."

She maneuvered our canoe within six feet of the sedate, "older" tourists who were sitting back with terry cloth hats on their heads and cameras around their necks.

"Hi, Evan," Jill called out.

"Hi, Evan," I echoed.

We were the two most popular girls on the lake at summer camp all over again.

"You're doing a great job, Evan," Jill said coyly.

"You're the best punter on the river, Evan," I added.

The tourists were all looking at us, startled at such enthusiasm in the middle of their placid float.

"Would you sing for us, Evan? Please?" Jill was pushing it now, but I remained her faithful sidekick.

"Yeah, Evan. We love it when you sing."

With one motion all Evan's passengers turned their heads and looked at him. He had gone red faced under his straw hat.

Evan kept punting, ignoring us and our request for a song. With a few significant strokes of the long punting pole, he was out of range from us and heading around a bend.

"Oh, Evan," Jill called after him, "you're breaking my heart!"

"Just one song!" I pleaded in a shout that echoed off the riverbank.

Evan was too far around the bend by then to glare at us. Jill and I leaned toward the center of our canoe and burst into laughter.

"Did you see the look on his face?" Jill said. "It was like his mother had come to check up on him his first day on the job!"

"I know. Poor kid. Too bad we aren't seventeen anymore. I think we could have talked him into taking us to the movies tonight."

"I never would have imagined you to be such a big flirt," Jill said. "You must have had all the guys wrapped around your little finger in high school."

"No, never. I would never have tried to pull a stunt like that in high school."

"I would have." Jill flipped her hair behind her ear.

"I can believe that. It's just one more reason I'm glad you and I met now instead of then."

"It's much more fun being flirty now. Trust me, you saved the best for the second half of life."

With more skill than either of us realized we could manage, we turned our little red convertible around and headed down the Avon River with the current speeding our journey. It seemed a symbol of how my life had been filled with so many years of paddling upstream, and now the current was hastening me forward into the fast-approaching second half of life. I knew I was going to be a different person. I already was.

"Look." Jill giggled.

Evan was waiting for us on the dock.

"Hello," Jill said calmly. All the silliness had subsided.

"I wanted to thank the two of you." Evan reached out a hand to help us from the canoe.

"Why?" Jill asked, as if by playing coy she could deny that we were the sassy canoers at the bend in the river.

"They liked your girly stunt back there."

I hid a smile. Those other "older" women who were punting with Evan were as young at heart as Jill and me. No doubt they wished they had rented the red canoe instead.

"They wouldn't stop badgering me about the song."

"Did you sing for them?" I asked.

"Yes, I did." His wide grin revealed a crooked front tooth and a light heart. "They liked the song so much I was given the most tips I've ever received from a tour group. So thanks. Thanks a lot."

We shook hands with grinning Evan. Generous Jill pulled out some money from her pocket and stuffed it in his hand. "Thanks for being such a good sport."

"No, thank you, really."

"You know what this means, don't you?" I asked. "Those people are going to tell their friends about Evan the Singing Punter, and you are going to get more special requests from tour groups than you can handle."

"All right by me!"

We had left Evan and were back on the river walkway when Jill said with great satisfaction, "The dynamic duo strikes again! We may very well have changed the course of history for all the punters in New Zealand."

"Not to mention setting an example of a stylish new mode for seating oneself in a canoe."

"Our way worked just fine," Jill said. "We didn't tip over or anything."

We topped off the waning afternoon with a little shopping and a lot more walking and followed it up with a wonderful night's sleep at our B&B.

In the morning, Hika and his wife served breakfast in the sunroom, complete with homemade fig jam and scones. We took our time getting out to see what we could see. We were moving at a much more leisurely pace than how things moved when Tony and I traveled together.

The most comfortable part of the trip for me was the way I felt the freedom to be alone with my thoughts when I wanted to. I didn't feel obligated to fill the space between Jill and me with words every moment we were together. That was refreshing, and I was processing a lot.

Jill seemed to be doing the same.

Our first stop was the town square only three blocks away.

"I love this Gothic Revival architecture." Jill stood in front of the cathedral and took it all in. "Don't you?"

I didn't want to tell her, but my eye had wandered from the architecture and was on the familiar coffeehouse logo on a building in the opposite corner of the square. We had been served tea for breakfast, and coffee was sounding pretty good.

"Yes, wonderful architecture," I said halfheartedly. "Are you by any chance interested in a little latte? A mocha, maybe? Or an iced tea?"

"It sounds good, but I'm actually more interested in exploring the insides of this church. Is that okay with you?"

"Yes, of course." I felt frivolous for being more excited about standing in the presence of an American coffee chain store than I was about entering a historical landmark.

Inside, the cathedral was dark and calm. Several people were sitting in the pews, quietly observing or perhaps meditating. The deep black wood of the pews fascinated Jill; she kept running her hand over the smooth corners.

"It says here," Jill whispered, reading to me from the tour book we were handed when we entered, "that the wood is from native trees called matai, and the rocks used to build the cathedral were from local quarries. It's beautiful, isn't it?"

I was beginning to grasp the allure of this old church and agreed with Jill. It was a beautiful place. I followed her to the front pew where we sat quietly together. Jill bowed her head and folded her hands.

"I am so thankful for you," Jill said a moment later, leaning close and whispering to me. "You have brought so much life back into my world, Kathy."

"Jill, I feel the same way. If I hadn't met you, I'd probably still be hiding out in our apartment. I am so thankful for the way you've included me in your life."

We both got a little teary as we exchanged a hug around the neck. Standing together, we slowly walked around the rest of the sanctuary and then climbed the 133 steps to the top of the cathedral. I was thankful for my few trots down to the Chocolate Fish and back during the past weeks. Otherwise, I would have been huffing and puffing much more than I was. At the top we took in an amazing view of the small city and the horizon.

"Look how blue the sky is. What shade would you call that?"

Jill looked and said, "New Zealand autumn. Has it been a while since you've seen a blue sky?"

"You remember how it is in Orange County. Lots of haze and smog. The sky is rarely a clear, deep shade of blue like this."

"There's Hagley Park." Jill pointed to a green area accented by lots of huge trees. "Are you interested in walking back over there? Or does a visit to one of the museums sound good?"

"Either one, as long as we fuel ourselves with a latte." I pointed to the coffee shop in the square that I'd noticed on our way into the cathedral. "Come on, my treat."

Jill was still teasing me the next morning about my affection for what she called "popular coffee." Our train to Picton left at 7:30 AM. That meant we were up at 5:30, packed and waiting outside for our cab ride to the train station before the day had barely opened its eyes.

I had barely opened my eyes as well and was lamenting that if we had the time I'd zoom over to the town square and see about getting us two ventis to "take away."

"I'm sure they have some sort of coffee on the train," Jill assured me. "It won't be popular coffee, but it should help us wake up all the same."

I gave an involuntary shiver in the early morning mist and tried not to think about a double espresso, or better yet, an Americano with half-and-half.

Closing my eyes, I saw a row of dancing paper coffee cups with skinny little arms sticking out above the recyclable brown sleeves. They were dancing to a Ray Charles tune. That's when I knew I was: a) overly tired; b) overly creative when it came to diverting my taste buds; or c) in need of a support group for California Coffee Withdrawal Therapy.

Once we were on the train, I asked about coffee and was told to listen for an announcement about when the tea car would open.

"'Tea car,'" I muttered. "That doesn't sound too promising for coffee."

"You know how they say *tea* here, but it can mean lunch or a snack. I think that's all it means. I'd be surprised if they didn't have coffee."

I settled back, watching the scenery roll by outside the large window. Our train seats faced each other with a table in between us. Jill recorded her thoughts and some doodles in her journal. I started to enjoy the brilliant green foliage; the narrow, twisting streams; and the distant hills. The rolling terrain was dotted with white, woolly sheep and pockets of wildflowers.

As we traveled north, the sun came at us in the train car at such an angle we couldn't see much of anything outside. The light seemed to expand and radiate in a wide burst. I felt as if we were traveling back in time to a place of ancient ferns and simple stone walls.

"What are those called, do you know?" I pointed to a clump of fern plants as we rolled past them.

"Those are *pongas*. The shape of the curly fronds out of the top is called *koru*. You'll see that shape a lot in New Zealand art and designs."

"I have noticed it a lot of places," I said. "And what's the story on the kiwi? Which came first? The bird or the fruit?"

"The bird. Definitely the bird came first. The kiwi birds don't fly. Did you know that?"

"No. I don't know anything about them."

"They're nocturnal and are nearly extinct, because they became such easy prey when settlers came with their domestic animals. The kiwi fruit is from China. The Chinese settlers brought vines to New Zealand that they called Chinese gooseberries. When the fruit did well here, they decided to export it and changed the name to kiwi fruit to identify it with New Zealand rather than China."

We talked about the plight of the poor kiwi bird, and I began to understand why many New Zealanders referred to themselves as Kiwis in a sort of compassionate alignment with their dear bird.

As the train rolled into our first stop, a buttonhole called Rangiora, I said, "I feel sorry for any bird that can't fly."

The next thought that popped in my head was, *Even midlife mama birds?*

My immediate mental answer was, *Especially midlife mama birds.*

It was crazy enough that I was asking myself questions like a Maori proverb, but even worse was that I was answering. Besides, if the thought was supposed to be directed toward me, I was already flying. I was soaring.

A mellow voice came on over the speaker announcing that the tea car was now open for service. Passengers were encouraged to "purchase food, which may then be taken with you back to your allocated seats."

Jill and I chuckled at the lengthy explanation.

"Would you like something?" I asked.

"Sure. I wouldn't mind a cup of tea. With cream."

I walked carefully down the slightly rolling floor toward the tea car and was the first passenger to step up to what looked like an ordinary counter at a deli or coffee shop. A clear case displayed wrapped sandwiches. A wire basket by the register offered individually wrapped oatmeal cookies. Behind the young woman who manned the counter was a large sign listing all the food options and prices. She didn't look as if she was quite awake yet.

I smiled at the not-too-cheery blonde and said, "One coffee with cream and—"

"Milk?" she asked.

"No, coffee."

"Coffee with milk," she corrected me.

"Yes."

"White coffee, then."

"Okay. White coffee. And one tea with cream."

"Devonshire tea?"

"No, just tea."

"Not with scones and cream?"

"Just cream, please."

"Right. The Devonshire cream tea, then. Scone or roll with the Devonshire?"

"No…"

"We only have the breakfast roll," she said.

"Yes, I understand. It's just that, all I want is—"

"I've got it. A breakfast roll and one Devonshire tea."

"No." I could feel the impatience of the waiting passengers behind me.

"And the white coffee," she added.

I leaned forward and patiently said, "I would like one white coffee and just one cup of hot tea."

"Of course it comes hot. We don't expect you to have a personal microwave at your seat."

I had no response to her snappy comment. Was she being funny? Was she insulting me? Was I on a hidden camera somewhere?

When I didn't respond, she punched some buttons on the computerized cash register. "Sixteen fifty, then."

"Sixteen dollars and fifty cents for what?"

"Devonshire tea, breakfast roll, and a white coffee."

At a loss for words, I surrendered and handed over a twenty-dollar bill. Stepping to the side, I heard the next customer order with a New Zealand accent and all the right phrases what he wanted.

Another young girl who was behind the barrier to the tiny onboard kitchen reached around the side and handed me a large paper bag, telling me to hold it steady.

Returning to my allocated seat, I placed the large bag on the table.

"What did you get?" Jill asked.

"I have no idea."

Ten

Jill laughed at my flustered response and opened the paper sack I'd brought back from the tea car. "Let's see what they gave you."

"I was trying to buy a single cup of tea for you, but I think I ended up with an entire tea party."

Coffee and tea were in reinforced paper cups with lids. The package also held two large scones, a container with cream as thick as fresh butter, two squares of butter, four packets of raspberry jam, and a plastic knife. The breakfast roll was a long deli roll sprinkled with sesame seeds and packed with fried egg; round, Canadian-style bacon; sliced, grilled tomatoes; and something that looked like flattened hash browns.

Neither of us had any complaints once we started our small feast. Even the coffee was drinkable.

"Our sugar just started to come in elongated packages like this at Riverview, the retirement community where I work," I said. "It's been so confusing for the residents because they're used to sugar in little rectangular packets."

"What do you do at Riverview? You said it's a retirement community, but what's your position there?"

"It's not very glamorous. My title is assistant, and that's what I do. I assist. Some days I organize group trips to the Bowers Museum or to lunch at Mimi's Café. Other days I change the bulletin boards in all the halls or help Mrs. Swensen carry her laundry basket back to her apartment."

"Or give a manicure every now and then?" Jill asked.

"I've given a few. I like visiting the residents who have been there a long time. Some of them move over to the assisted living section of our campus, and I love it when I go to see them and they remember me."

"What's your favorite part of your job?"

I leaned back and wondered if anyone had ever asked me that. "The hours have always been great. I started part-time when Skyler was in elementary school, and I could always adjust my hours to fit around my family. That was a huge bonus."

"But what do you enjoy the most when you're at work?"

"I don't know."

"Sure you do. Just off the top of your head, what's your favorite part of a workday?"

I said the first thing that came to mind. "I love being with stroke patients when they meet with their speech therapists."

"Why?"

I didn't feel as if Jill was putting me on the spot like a lawyer trying to uncover facts. Instead, she seemed to be turning over the soil of my heart like a tender gardener. She was preparing me for new bulbs that would burrow inside my thoughts and bloom in another season.

"I guess I like being around the speech therapists so much

because I see how they give the patients hope. When you've spent your whole life depending on talking as your way to get your thoughts across, it's horrible to have your voice taken from you."

I was on my soapbox now and sat up straighter. "Most people think the worst part of a stroke is losing the use of an arm or not being able to walk without assistance. What no one understands is how debilitating it is to lose your words. If you can't talk, people ignore you. They don't try to interact with you. Your needs and your opinions go unnoticed and unheeded.

"Whenever a speech therapist breaks through with a patient, that's when I say, 'This has been a good day.' Those are my favorite days. It doesn't mean every patient has the ability to train his throat and mouth to form words again. Some of them learn sign language or learn to write short thoughts on a pad. One therapist designed a special board for Mr. Harris that had big colored dots. Red for no, green for yes, yellow for hungry...it was so great. I loved seeing Mr. Harris's face light up when he discovered he could communicate again."

I paused to take a breath, and with a shrug I added, "I get a little passionate about this, I guess."

Jill grinned. "So, why aren't you a speech therapist?"

"Because I only went to community college for three semesters."

"So?"

"So, it takes a little more education than that to work as a speech therapist."

"So why don't you go back to school?"

"Because..."

I didn't finish the sentence because I didn't have a good reason. I hadn't seriously thought through the option in a long time. So much of my life had been about helping out with Tony's mom while she was still alive and then getting Skyler to college. Tony and I had worked hard to make sure she had the chance to go all the way through college and receive her BA. The past six months I had been focused on working as many extra hours as I could to pay for remodeling the kitchen. I hadn't spent any time thinking about the remodeling I could do in my life.

"I don't know; I don't know why I can't go back to school."

"I think you should," Jill said.

We left the topic out on the table, as the train rolled through a series of tunnels. My thoughts were experiencing the same light sensory changes of rushing through darkness into light and then back into darkness. First light, then dark. Light, dark.

Maybe I could go back to school...No, that's crazy. I can't do it...Yes, I can...No, I can't...Why not?

We rolled through a long tunnel and emerged with the shimmering South Pacific Ocean on the right. The sand that lined the shore was dark as obsidian and littered with kelp. Not a person was in sight.

The train slowed, and we could see from our observation car that we were coming into a town along the dark sand of Kaikoura Peninsula.

"Look!" Jill pointed to the ocean. "Dolphins!"

A dozen of the gray creatures were leaping in the blue water less than a quarter of a mile from the train.

"Wow! Did you see that one jump? It looked like it spun around in the air."

The train came to a stop, and the mellow-voiced conductor let us know we were taking a five-minute respite, in which we were allowed to get off the train and stretch our legs.

"Let's get off," Jill said. "We can take a closer look at those dolphins."

We exited the train, aided by the kind hand of a uniformed railroad assistant. Stepping through the small train station that doubled as a souvenir and snack shop, we walked out onto a broad cement patio. Below us, down the stairs, was the dark sand and pebble beach and beyond the sand were the rolling waves and playful dolphins.

"Look at them!" Jill pointed to the ocean. "They are having so much fun out there."

As the next large wave curled, we could see more dolphins rising in the surf.

"They are so sleek," she said. "I think dolphins are amazing, don't you? Look at how happy they are."

"They are."

Jill turned to me. "Come on! Quick! Let's run through the sand and touch the water."

Suddenly Jill was the land dolphin, dashing down the stairs, ready to play. "I'll race you," she called over her shoulder as soon as her feet hit the sand.

I rushed down the stairs and fiddled with my shoes and socks until my feet were naked.

Just then the train whistle sounded. Our five-minute respite already was over. The train was ready to leave.

Jill was at the water's edge, waving with big arm motions for me to join her. I pointed back at the tracks and yelled, "The train is leaving!"

She motioned again for me to come, her feet playfully kicking a spray of salt water in my direction. In a split second, I made my decision and ran to the water. One of us had to be the designated driver when Jill went into her intoxicating flirt mode. This time she was flirting with nature. I barely touched my toe to the wet sand and hollered over the roar of the surf, "We have to go!"

"Wait! Just look!"

A nearly translucent wave was cresting so close to shore that we could have swum out to meet it, if we were strong enough. In the curl of the wave we saw two dolphins, their noses jutting forward like the balancing arm of a surfer. The dolphins were riding the wave together.

Jill and I turned to each other with expressions of wide-eyed, open-mouthed wonder. We tilted our heads back, shooting our full-hearted laughter into the air the way the care-free dolphins were shooting the curl.

Over the blend of joyous sounds we heard the faint train whistle one more time. Jill blew a kiss to the dolphins and the sea. I grabbed her by the wrist, and together we dashed bare-footed through the sand, up the cement steps, and through the gift shop. The conductor was just lifting the footstool and giving the all-clear sign when Jill and I blasted out on the landing and cried out, "Wait!"

"Almost missed the train, ladies," the conductor said.

"No, we almost missed the moment," Jill said with her fabulous, free-spirited laugh following me into the train compartment.

We bustled our way back to our seats as the chugging motion of the train began. Our faces were bright as sunbeams. Our hair was wild and crazy from the sprint in the wind. The sedate passengers in our car gave us strange looks.

Jill didn't seem to mind them a bit as she took her seat. "That was awesome," she said, alive with glee. "How incredible! Wow!"

I nodded, still catching my breath. My heart continued to

race. We twisted in our seats as the train pulled away from the Kaikoura station, and we strained to see another glimpse of the surfers.

On the table, invisible, but definitely left there from before the train had stopped, was the possibility of my going back to school. The possibility of my becoming a speech therapist.

At that moment, anything seemed possible.

Two days later, I confided in Tony all the thoughts I'd pondered during the last part of the train ride. The morning was crisp, and I'd joined him on his walk to work so we would have a chance to talk. The last two days he had been working extra hours, and I wasn't ready to present the topic of going back to school until I had his complete attention.

"What do you think?" I asked after I'd spilled out all my ideas for school options.

"Go for it." Tony leaned over and planted a kiss on the crown of my head. My husband is gifted at seeing the big picture and editing it down to its most concise form. I knew I had his blessing, and it was up to me to think it through from there.

Later that day I sat with Dorothea for four hours and told her everything about the trip. This time, Mr. Barry didn't hide discreetly in the kitchen. He pulled up a chair and listened to my stories about Evan, the singing punter; Hika, the descendant of a Maori warrior; and Jill, the dolphin chaser.

I stopped in the middle of my description of the calm-water crossing we had on the ferry and realized that what I enjoyed about the getaway hadn't been the sights we had seen or the foods we had tried. The experience was rich because of the people.

He tangata, he tangata, he tangata.
It's the people, it's the people, it's the people.

I spent the next few days thinking a lot. When the rain kept me inside on Thursday, I sat in our one comfortable chair for many hours listening to the pings on the garage's roof. I had two medical books Mr. Barry had loaned me when I told him I was eager to learn more about what happens when a person has a stroke. When Tony came home, I summarized for him everything I'd learned. I couldn't believe how energized I felt.

The next morning, I toted my umbrella and took off on the slick sidewalk to meet Jill at the Chocolate Fish. I anticipated a long, leisurely, all-morning conversation, but Jill started off with a question that redirected everything.

"I have a huge favor to ask," she said as soon as we took our places at what had become "our" table by the window.

"Whatever it is, the answer is yes."

"You better wait until you hear what I'm asking."

Before Jill could say anything else, Tracey came over to our table with grand "hallos!" and lots of hugs. Pulling up a chair, she looked at us and said, "Do tell all. I've been dying to hear about your trip."

Jill and I took turns with the highlights, as Tracey listened intently.

"You girls have it made," she said brightly. "Where are you off to on your next lark?"

"We don't have any plans," I answered for both of us. "But wherever it might be, you'll have to come with us."

"Right!" Tracey paused before adding, "Or we could just drive around town and see how many lawn ornaments we can run over."

The three of us shared a great laugh.

Tracey stood and pushed in her chair. "The kitchen calls!"

With a more serious expression she added, "This is my place for now. My time will come to flit around like you two, but for now I belong here. For you two, this is the time of your lives to have the time of your lives."

Tracey left Jill and me at our window table with a flippant, "Ta!"

I looked back at Jill. She was biting her thumbnail.

"So, what were you going to ask me before Tracey came over?"

She took a sip of her mocha latte. "I had such a great time in Christchurch."

"I did, too."

"So much has changed for me since you showed up here, Kathy. And that's part of why I want to ask this favor of you. I was going to ask on our way home on the train, but I didn't want to sound like I was imposing."

"You? Imposing? Never." I knew what it was like to suddenly feel flustered when everything was going great. Apparently neither of us was willing to push too far in one direction or another and risk upsetting the balance that had come to us so easily at the beginning of our relationship.

"Okay, here it is. My niece is getting married next weekend. I told my brother-in-law I would come, and I know they're counting on me, but ever since I mailed back the RSVP card, I've been trying to think of how to decline."

"You don't want to go?"

Jill closed her lips, hesitating before quietly saying, "I want to go. I just don't want to go by myself."

"I'd be glad to go with you."

"Well, there's another little detail you should know before you agree. The wedding is in Sydney."

Eleven

"Australia?" I asked. "The wedding is in Sydney, Australia?"

Jill nodded. "James was planning to go with me, but now he's pulling back because of exams."

I'd met Jill's youngest son, James, the day I went to her home to book our on-line tickets for Christchurch. He was a tall, good-looking young man with dark, expressive eyes. He seemed intently interested in everything his mother had to say, which I thought was amazing and admirable.

Then I realized that James probably had been trying to fill the void his father had left and was trying to be responsive to his mom's concerns.

"I told James I'm fine going to the wedding by myself. It's a very small family affair, which is why my brother-in-law was so persuasive about James and me being there. We're the closest relatives on his side in this hemisphere, and there's no reason for me not to go."

"But…" I tried to draw out of Jill what she was thinking but not saying.

"But I don't think I want to go to Australia by myself. Traveling is the last 'alone' thing I've had to tackle. I didn't think anything of the trip when James was planning to go, but now…"

"Jill, you don't have to say anything else. I would love to go with you."

"Really?"

"Yes, really. I'm sure Tony will be all for it."

"It's such short notice."

"That's okay. I don't have anything on my calendar I need to cancel."

Jill still looked hesitant, as if she were asking too much of me.

"Hey." I reached across the table and gave her hand a squeeze. "Relax, it's dolphin time. The sun is shining; the surf is up. Let's ride the wave together. What did Tracey just tell us? This is the time of our lives to have the time of our lives. We're going to Sydney!"

A smile came to Jill's face.

I told her about one of my longtime friends in California who had been sending e-mails to me via Tony's work e-mail. "Last time she wrote, she said that I'm supposed to have an extra adventure for her. See? I have to go to Australia with you so she can vicariously experience the adventure."

"Well, then, since she's counting on it, I guess we can't let her down. You won't have to go to the wedding, if you don't want, and we can stay several extra days to play."

As I predicted, Tony was all for the excursion. He drove Jill and me to the airport the next Friday and added his encouragement for us to have the time of our lives.

I kissed him good under Gollum's gruesome gaze, grabbed

my gear, and followed Jill into the Wellington airport for the second time that month.

The clerk at the flight desk asked to see my visa. I pulled out my credit card and handed it to him.

"No, your visa, if you don't mind," he said in a weary voice, as if one too many travelers had pulled the same prank on him. I wasn't trying to pull a prank. I only had one credit card, and it was the Visa I held out to him.

Jill leaned closer. "He means your visitor's visa for Australia."

"We can buy our visitors' visas here, can't we?" she asked the clerk.

"Yes, of course. And how would you like to pay for that?"

I held out my credit card for the second time. "May I pay for my visa with my Visa?"

Jill stifled a giggle by coughing to cover it up. The clerk took my credit card without comment. Some sort of giggle enzyme must have kicked in at that point. I tried to swallow the impulse to burst out laughing and kept my mouth shut, as Jill and I purchased our visas with our Visas.

From then on, everything seemed funny to me. Maybe it was like a nervous tick. Or perhaps that's what happens when two mama chicks start flapping their wings. All the feather fluttering turns into a merciless tickling of each other's funny bones.

Once we were on the plane with seat belts fastened, Jill adjusted the magazines in the pocket in front of her to make more room to cross her legs. A bag fell out of the cloth pocket and landed on my foot. I leaned over to pick up what I assumed was the airsick bag and was surprised to see it was a mailer to send in film for developing.

The top of the bag had two statements in bold red and

orange letters. The first statement read, "Introductory Photo Offer Only $5.99." The second announcement was, "If affected by motion sickness, please use this bag."

I laughed and showed the bag to Jill. "Talk about making practical use of a bag! You can either use it to get sick, or you can use it to mail in your film."

"But it probably shouldn't be used for both," Jill said. "Oh, look at this line: 'Please take this bag with you and pass on to family or friends.'"

I looked closer and read the rest of the sentence for her. "'...pass on to family or friends if you are unable to use.' That's a very important phrase: *if* you are unable to use, then you should pass it on."

"Right, because if you did use the bag, not for the film developing option but for the *other* option, you might not want to pass it on to your family or friends."

We laughed so hard neither of us could stop. It was silly. I didn't care if people were staring at us. Jill and I were off on a lark, and this was only the warm-up.

The giggle enzymes were at peak effervescence as we tried not to laugh at the flight attendant who pointed out the emergency exits with the routine dignified pose of her two fingers stuck together.

I asked Jill for a tissue to wipe my dripping nose, and she offered me the photo developing bag, which we tore in half and shared in the absence of tissue.

"I don't think any of my family or friends would like me to pass this on to them now." Jill folded up her bit of damp paper sack. "I'm not sure what to do with it."

I rifled through my magazine pocket, pulled out my photo bag and turned it into a trash receptacle.

"Yet another use for the amazing, multipurpose, mail-in-your-film-developing-slash-motion-sickness bag." Jill said.

Giggles spent, we settled in like more respectable adults, as the pilot announced that this would be a three-hour and forty-minute flight.

"You know, I always pictured Australia and New Zealand right next to each other," I said. "I didn't realize they were so far apart."

"When you meet my brother-in-law, don't tell him that's what you think of Australia. He's lived there for thirty years and considers himself an Aussie."

I noticed that Jill said the word *Aussie* the same way I would say *Ozzie,* as in *Ozzie and Harriet.*

"They really are two different countries on two different continents," Jill said. "Kiwis and Aussies don't link themselves together."

"Well, that's good to know before I try out my New Zealand slang in Sydney."

"And exactly what New Zealand slang were you thinking of trying out?" Jill had lived in Wellington for six years and still sounded like an American. I'd been there two weeks, yet I was the one collecting slang terms.

"Okay, test me on this. See if you understand my use of Kiwi terms." I cleared my throat and pieced phrases together. "Last week I went to the chemist next to the dairy and was so buggered I got the colly wobbles and had to use the dunny before I could buy my cotton buds and sticking plaster."

Jill cracked up.

"Don't laugh," I said. "Translate for me."

"Okay, let's see. Last week you went to the drugstore next to the 7-Eleven, or corner market. You were so tired that you got that nervous, queasy feeling in your stomach and had to use the restroom. Then what did you buy? Oh, wait, I remember. Q-Tips and something else."

"Plasters."

"That's right, plasters. Band-Aids. I must say, Kathy, that's pretty impressive."

"We all have our hidden talents, don't we?"

"I'm not sure that *sass* is a God-given gift, but if it is, you are doubly blessed with it."

Our flight ended with a steep landing. Since our seats were in the middle section, we couldn't see out the windows and compare the view of Sydney from the air with the view of Wellington. The little snatches of color and light I did catch from the window seemed to be lots of blue water and red-roofed houses dotted everywhere.

Jill led the way through customs where a trained dog sniffed every bag that came off the luggage carousel. We turned in our paperwork, answered questions about whether we had food, plants, or animals we were bringing into the country, and made it to the car rental booth before most of the crowd.

With a distinctly different accent from the one I'd been adjusting to in New Zealand, the rental agent asked, "Will both of you be driving, then?"

I may have jumped at the chance to drive Beatrice on an isolated, two-lane road in Wellington, but being cleared to drive on a motorway in Sydney in a rental car was too intimidating at the moment. At the risk of losing all my newly acquired "cool" status, I turned down the offer.

"No worries," the clerk said. "We'll just process this for you now."

"I'm a little nervous," Jill said to me once we were in our

small silver rental car. "I'm used to driving in Wellington, but this might be different. You keep an eye out for me, okay?"

We went slowly at first, merging into the traffic and heading for the motorway.

"Do you know where you're going?" I asked.

"Downtown. Start watching for the signs that say Sydney."

I fiddled with the map, turning it upside down and right side up until I finally found the airport and traced the route to downtown Sydney.

Looking up at the next street sign, I said, "I think we're going the wrong direction."

"Are you sure?"

"Pretty sure. See if you can exit and turn around."

I continued to track our route on the map, as Jill exited and tried to point the car in the correct direction. Due to road construction, we had to take an unexpected turn, and neither of us could figure out how to get back on the right road.

"This is a nightmare," Jill said, as we inched along through another construction zone. After fifteen minutes in the thickening traffic, she said, "It looks like we can cut over onto another highway. Can you see the name? Is it one that will take us downtown?"

"I'm not sure. Can you pull into that hotel driveway for a minute so we can look at this map together? I'm completely turned around."

The only place for our car was in front of the hotel entrance. A valet came over and opened my door.

"Oh, no. Sorry," I said. "We're not staying. Just trying to find our way."

"California girls, huh?" the young Aussie said with a tease

in his voice. He probably made that comment to all American women.

"Yes, as a matter of fact, we're two born-and-raised southern California girls." Jill reached for a pinch of that cheerleader charm. "And we're lost. Can you show us how to get back on the motorway? We want to go to the Vacation Inn at the Quay."

"No worries. That happens to be one of our hotels." He launched into a fast-paced set of directions complete with hand motions and a wink for each of us before he said, "G'day" and sent us on our way.

"Okay, we turn right here." Jill put on her blinker. "Then what?"

"I don't know. I couldn't understand him. I thought you understood him."

"I thought you were listening."

"I was listening." The enzyme giggles were returning. "But I didn't understand a word he said."

"Okay. You know what?" Jill checked her watch. "I'm going to return this car."

"I don't think the car is the problem."

"Very funny. I still think we should return this car."

"At the airport?"

"Yes. Look at the sign. We're right back by the airport. I'm terrible at directions, and getting lost all the time is going to ruin this trip for us. I'd rather spend the money on public transportation or a taxi and not have to worry about driving everywhere."

I appreciated Jill's candid evaluation of her weakness. Had it been me, for the sake of the money already spent, I probably would have gutted it out, gotten thoroughly frustrated, and spent the rest of the trip stressed out.

"What time is the wedding?" I checked my watch.

"At five o'clock."

"Jill, it's already four-thirty. Are you going to make it?"

"It's four-thirty in Wellington, but here it's only two-thirty because of the time change. I still have time."

I reset my watch. "Five o'clock seems like an odd time for a wedding."

"It's a short ceremony followed by a sit-down dinner. This will work out fine. We'll return the car to the rental lot, grab a cab to our hotel; I'll change and then take a cab to the wedding. It makes it easier all around."

Jill's evaluation of our car situation felt as if she were offering me freedom to change my mind about something if the situation arose. She just said things as they were and moved on. She didn't need to be right; she just needed to try possible solutions until she found the one that fit.

I liked that approach to life.

We returned our rental car to an amused rental agent and hauled our luggage around to the taxi stand.

Our driver greeted us with, "G'day!"

"Not so far," I quipped.

"No worries," he said, as Jill showed him a printout from her computer with the name and address of our hotel. Off we went, sitting in the backseat and smiling contentedly. We were prepared for a much better start to our adventure now.

Less than ten minutes later, the driver pulled up in front of a hotel and hopped out to unload our luggage for us.

"We can't be downtown at the harbor already," Jill said, looking at the reservation. Then she added a humble sounding, "Oh."

I looked at the reservation with her.

She pointed to the full name of the hotel on the computer printout. "I reserved the wrong hotel."

"It's okay," I said quickly. "It doesn't matter. We're here. We can stay at least for tonight. Otherwise you'll be late for the wedding, and that was the main reason we came."

"You're right."

Just then the hotel valet opened the back door of the cab. "Hey, the California girls are back! Coming in style this time."

Jill and I busted up.

"And this time we're staying," I said, exiting the car to show I meant it.

Jill followed me to the check-in desk and explained her reservation mistake. She asked if we could stay there one night and switch to the Vacation Inn at the Quay for the remaining three nights.

After much tapping on the computer keyboard, the young woman at the desk told us that since our reservation had been prepaid on-line through a discount site, we were unable to make any changes.

Jill's brow furrowed, but I said, "That's fine. We're here. Let's stay here."

I knew that, if I were back in the U.S., I probably would have asked to see the manager. I would have pushed for what I wanted.

But I was changing. This trip was changing me. We were, after all, in the place of "no worries," right?

When Jill whooshed out the door forty minutes later in a gorgeous blue outfit and with a whiff of gardenia-scented perfume, I walked into the bathroom and smiled at the bathtub, my favorite "no worries" machine.

Twelve

The bathtub in our Sydney hotel room was longer and higher than the standard-sized tub—and it had whirlpool jets. Having a bathtub in our hotel room was a treat for me, but having one with whirlpool jets was a double delight. I ran the water and rummaged around for something to use as bubble bath. The hotel provided shampoo, shower gel, and mouthwash in small bottles but no bubble bath.

In my cosmetic bag I carried a variety of sample-sized bath oils. Don't ask me why I brought them all the way from California. I guess I thought I'd save money when we got here by using up all the little samples.

I pulled out my collection of bottles and set them on the tub's rim. They made a nice collection. Seven different sizes, colors, shapes, and fragrances.

Checking to make sure the hotel room's door was locked, I slipped out of my clothes and put my foot in the tub to test the three inches of water. It was taking a long time to fill, but the water was just the right temperature. So I settled in and did an "eenie meenie miney mo" with the bath oils.

The purple vial won. It was lavender scented. As I poured the entire contents into the water, the purple gel sank to the bottom and sat there like a sleeping jellyfish. I broke it up with my toe, coaching it to foam up, but all it did was break into smaller jellyfish that hunkered in the tub's depths.

"Okay, so much for lavender. I'm sure the water will smell nice, but I want bubbles."

Trying bottle number two, I released a clear liquid into the water, and nothing happened. The oil floated on top of the clear water.

I went for sample number three, an amber-shaded gel that had a wonderful vanilla scent. The bubble factor was still disappointing, so I dumped in the rest of the gels. An ambrosia of bath-oil fragrances filled the air. I was pleasantly pleased with the way the green apple scent blended with the cherry almond. It would be like bathing in hot fruit punch.

As soon as the water level seemed high enough to turn on the jets, I followed the directions on the timer, set the dials, and pushed the button to make the whirlpool do its whirling wonders.

Settling into the tub, I felt the bubbles begin to rise.

Those bath gels just needed a little more agitation. I'm glad I used all of them. They were all so small. This is dreamy!

I closed my eyes and hummed to the sound of the whirlpool jets while the growing effervescence surrounded me like bubble wrap. It was a lovely, lightweight, floating sensation. I could feel airy kisses on my earlobes as runaway, tiny bubbles bid me farewell on their way to outer space. I felt as if I were being massaged by hundreds of BB-sized bubbles as they rose with the force of the jets and ever so minutely tapped my shoulders and neck.

Oh, this is nice.

The water temperature, the tub's size and shape, the wonderful fragrance that encased me, and the energetic bubbles that were filling the tub and...I felt bubbles rising to my chin and then to my mouth. Lots of bubbles.

I opened my eyes and sat up. The bubbles had gone berserk! They had formed a chain gang and were escaping the tub's high walls at an unstoppable speed. I stood in an effort to make them sink back down into the tub and not spill over onto the bathroom rug. I was fast, but they were faster. The bubbles were mutating and multiplying at a freakish rate.

Stepping out of the tub, I scooped up a handful of runaways and deposited them in the sink. Another wave came over the wall with greater speed. I scooped them up, lifted the lid to the toilet, and tried to dispose of them.

When I turned around, a league of invading bubbles had breached the tub and was coming at me across the tile floor.

Turn off the jets! Turn off the jets!

I pushed one button, then another button. Nothing happened. I tried to reset the timer. It wouldn't budge. Plunging my arm into a three-foot-deep drift of bubbles, I fished around until I found the plug and gave it a tug.

The water drained from the tub, but the bubbles had no intention of following. I noted that part of the plumbing system in this Australian bathroom was the drain in the tile floor under the sink. As the bathwater went out, I could hear it going down the drain in the tub as well as down the larger drain under the sink.

Then two things happened at once. The whirlpool jets,

which were still running because I couldn't figure out how to turn them off, were beginning to sound like they were wheezing, gasping for water. All the jets had to siphon were the bubbles.

The second thing that happened was the lavender bath gel, which had lurked on the tub's bottom, must have been among the first to go down the drain. When the purple jellyfish reached the larger drain under the sink, instead of finding their way out to sea, they decided to do what they were originally created to do. They burst into a bazillion lavender-scented bubbles and rose from the floor drain under the sink, coming at me like a fierce army of awakened sea creatures.

This is not good! Not good at all!

I stuck the plug back into the tub and turned on the water so that the whirlpool jets would have something other than bubbles to drink. As soon as the water level rose to meet the jets' begging open mouths, the newly activated layer of mighty bubbles billowed over the side of the tub like Rapunzel letting down her golden mane.

Frantically scooping up the weightless enemy by the armsful, I deposited them in the toilet until they overflowed there as well. And then I flushed. Another mistake. Any motion only made more bubbles.

Grabbing the metal wastebasket, I shoveled the bubbles that now covered the floor up to my bare ankles. When the trash can was full, I tried to empty it in the only open cavern—the bathroom sink.

That's when I caught my reflection in the bathroom mirror. I had a floof of bubbles on my head and another outcropping coming out of my shoulder that looked like an elf's cap with a bent point. The expression on my face was one of panic. I never would have recognized myself, even in a police lineup. I should have been wearing a number around my neck to match the guilt I felt for the crime of setting off a bubble bomb and endangering the life expectancy of a formerly healthy whirlpool system.

Just then the phone rang, and I nearly jumped out of my skin. That would have been a sight, because all I was wearing was my fruit punch–scented skin and an assortment of bubble patches.

Wrapping a towel around me, I quickly exited the bathroom, closing the door securely behind me.

"Hello?" My heart was pounding. I was sure the hotel manager was calling to ask why the entire sewer system was being attacked by millions of bulbous jellyfish that strangely smelled of lavender.

"Room service calling. Will you be desiring turn-down service this evening?"

"Um, no. I mean yes. Actually, I could use some more towels." I tried to calm my voice. "If that would be convenient."

"Certainly. How many would you like?"

"Oh, I don't know. How about…"

My eyes were fixed on the closed bathroom door. I couldn't finish my sentence because the worst I'd feared was happening. The bubbles were oozing out from under the door and creeping across the carpet like thousands of minuscule Navy SEALs.

"Two towels?" the woman on the other end of the phone asked.

"Actually, four would be good. No, on second thought, how about if you double that."

"Eight towels?"

"Sure, why not." It was becoming more difficult to sound

nonchalant as the bubbles inched their way toward me. "Eight towels would be fine. And you don't have to come in to turn down the beds, but if the turn-down service includes chocolates for our pillows, I'm sure we'll make use of those."

The hotel employee obviously had been trained to remain polite in all circumstances. "And would you be wanting eight chocolates as well?"

"Sure, that would be lovely. Thank you." I hung up before she asked any more questions.

Grabbing the wastebasket under the desk, I placed it on its side in front of the bathroom door. The bubbles blithely stumbled into the trap set for them.

Then the sweetest sound fell on my ears. It was the sound of the whirlpool jets stopping. I hoped it was because their timer had gone off and not because they had been strangled by ropes of bubbles.

Standing beside the closed bathroom door, I leaned over and listened. I'm not sure what I expected to hear. Was that the sound of thousands of bubbles bursting? Or did I only wish that bubble bursting was what was happening on the other side of the closed door? I was afraid to open the door in case the bubbles had managed to form themselves into the boogieman. If I opened the door, he might come out, arms waving over his bubble head as he chased me around the room.

I told myself I should let the remaining bubbles calm themselves before I opened the door for inspection. I also told myself it might be good to put on more than a bath towel in case room service was speedy in delivering those towels.

As soon as I was dressed, I put the towel I'd been wearing to work, sopping up the escaped bubbles. The prisoners that had walked into my trash can trap had nearly all popped themselves. I wondered if the same phenomenon had happened behind the closed door.

It's now or never!

Turning the handle slowly, I entered the inner sanctum where everything—the tub, the floor, the toilet bowl—had a slick, glimmering sheen. If a bathroom could be glazed the way a donut is glazed, this is what it would look like.

It wasn't hard to clean up. I used every towel we had and wiped off the afterglow of the bubbles. It's possible this bathroom had never been so clean. Certainly it had never been so fragrant. I told myself I had done this hotel a favor in cleaning their bathroom so thoroughly.

Just then a knock sounded at the door. I took one last look around for unpopped bubbles before opening the door. The young woman holding the stack of towels inhaled with a look of surprise. "Mmm. It smells good in here. Like a tropical beverage."

I sniffed the air, as if I hadn't noticed. "Does it really?"

Thirteen

Jill returned to the room close to ten o'clock. I'd fallen asleep watching television but instantly revived when she stepped in. The first thing she said was, "Smells scrumptious in here. Did you have a fruit salad for dinner?"

"No, I had a fruit bath."

"What's a fruit bath?"

I told Jill the whole story, complete with all the bubbly details. She started to laugh when I described how I'd scooped the bubbles into the toilet. She kept on laughing, holding her sides, as I concluded with the comment the housekeeper made when she brought the fresh towels.

"Oh, Kathy, you're making me laugh so hard I have to go use the fruit bowl. I mean the..." she kept laughing and said, "Do you think it's safe to go in there?"

"All the bubbles are gone, if that's what you're asking. I don't think any commandos will be lurking in the corners."

Jill went in the bathroom and closed the door, but I could

still hear her laughing. When she came out she said, "The funniest sight in there is all your empty bubble bath bottles lined up on the counter. Definitely evidence that a wild party went on in there. And here I was worried that you would be bored, staying in the room by yourself. Did you order anything to eat?"

"I had a chicken sandwich from room service about an hour ago. And I ate half of our chocolate mints. The other half are for you, on your pillow. So how was the wedding?"

Jill changed into yellow pajamas sprinkled with a variety of what looked like paper-doll cutouts of shoes, purses, and hats.

"The wedding was lovely. Lovely in every way. The bride was a blushing beauty, and the groom couldn't take his eyes off her. I was happy for them. Young love. There's nothing like it."

"Were you okay being there by yourself?"

"It was pretty good, actually. I thought I'd be lost at dinner, when everyone was seated as couples, but I ended up sitting beside the officiating pastor and his wife, and guess what? She was from California! Escondido. The pastor grew up here in Australia, but he and his wife live in Oregon now. Gordon and Teri were their names. They were so fun to talk with."

"I'm glad they sat with you."

"Me, too. Gordon and Teri brought me back to the hotel. I'm sure it was out of their way. I almost invited them to come up so you could meet them. I didn't because I thought you would be in bed, but here you were, having a fruit fest without me."

"Not on purpose, believe me. So how did it go with your brother-in-law?"

"Okay. Not great." Jill settled under the covers and twitched her mouth right and left before finishing her thought. "He came on pretty strong about James and me moving here."

"Here? To Sydney? You don't want to move to Sydney, do you?"

"No, I don't think so."

"Why does he think you should move here?"

"After Ray died, a lot of my family and a few close friends invited James and me to live with them. I know they meant well, but I couldn't leave Wellington right away because, well…there were some unfinished complications."

Jill paused. I waited for her to go on.

"Even after I was free to go, I didn't want to leave Wellington. I didn't want to be taken in by someone who felt sorry for us. Besides, James was already at the university. I'm sure I could leave him and he'd be fine, but I'm settled in Wellington. At least for now."

"I'm sure you've thought about going back to California."

"Lots of times. I don't know if that's what I'm supposed to do. I have this small feeling that I'm not done with Wellington yet. I think my brother-in-law feels responsible to do something for me. He and his wife are great people, but I don't want them to be my umbrella. Does that make sense?"

I nodded. "You want to be under your own parasol."

Jill nibbled on her thumbnail and then she got the correlation. "Like the parasol light at the B&B. Yes, that's a good way of saying it. For now, I feel like I need to be under my own parasol."

I tried to imagine what it must be like to be a widow at such a young age. One of my friends in California who had divorced recently told me she hadn't counted on the loneliness. I couldn't imagine my life without Tony. I knew I didn't appreciate him enough.

"Jill, may I ask you something?" I wasn't sure if the time was right, but I asked anyway. "When you want to tell me, I want to hear the whole story."

"The whole story?"

"Yes, the whole story about how Ray died."

Jill didn't look at me. She kept biting her thumbnail.

"I'm not saying you need to tell me now. Just whenever you want to. And if you don't want to, that's fine, too."

"Hasn't Tony said anything about it?"

"No."

She looked surprised.

"And I won't ask him, either." I looked directly at her. "Even if he does know, I'd rather hear everything from you. If and when you want to talk about it."

"I don't think I'm ready to do that tonight," she said in a small voice.

"That's okay. This is an open invitation. Definitely a come-as-you-are sort of invitation. No obligations attached."

I expected Jill to cry as we talked about Ray, but she didn't. Her smooth, fair skin took on a glow, and her expression was one of gratitude. "Thank you, Kathy. I will tell you sometime. Just not tonight."

"No worries," I said, trying to sound lighthearted.

We settled in for a cozy night's sleep. I felt as if an invisible sweetness had strung itself like a clothesline between Jill and me in our twin beds. When laundry day came, I had no doubt Jill would hang up the personal unmentionables of her life story. And I would be there to hold the line for her.

In the morning we opted for breakfast in the hotel restaurant instead of room service. We thought that route would prompt us to get up and dressed and out the door instead of lounging in our pj's and eating breakfast in bed.

The restaurant offered a buffet breakfast, and we filled our plates with many of the foods we would find at home in California. I had scrambled eggs, toast, and bacon that was flat and thick and not very crinkled or crispy. Stopping at the juice and condiment table, we reached for plastic, individual-sized tubs of butter and jelly.

"What's this?" I asked Jill, holding up a tiny tub of something called Vegemite.

"You should try it."

"But what is it?"

"I can't tell you."

"What do you mean you can't tell me? Don't you know what it is?"

"Oh, I know all right. In New Zealand our brand is Marmite."

"Your brand of what?"

"Just try it."

I followed Jill back to our table and kept pestering her. "Is it like peanut butter?"

"No."

"Honey?"

"What, dear?" Her expression let me know that my goofy wit was beginning to rub off on her.

"Just answer me this, Miss Smarty Party. What are you supposed to do with Vegemite?"

"Well, different people have different opinions of what should be done with Vegemite." Her poker face was starting to crack at the corners of her mouth. "I will simply tell you that you should try it and see what you think. I will also tell you that it's considered a comfort food."

"Like chocolate?"

"I can't really answer that."

"So do I spoon it on my eggs or what?"

"Try it on your toast," Jill suggested.

Eager to get this silly game over with, I peeled back the top and spread all of the dark molasses-colored Vegemite on half a slice of toast. It had the consistency of jellified honey and smelled like Worcestershire sauce.

"Are you sure people eat this? I mean, it's safe for ingestion, right?"

"Yes. Just try a bite."

I did. Never in my life had I experienced such a disagreeable explosion of confused tastes on my poor tongue. It was a challenge to make myself swallow the whole bite.

"I don't care for it." I politely put the slice of toast to the side of my plate and made a face.

Jill was laughing now. This had been good fun for her.

"I'm sure you were making up the part about its being comfort food. What is it, really? Condensed sushi? Purse-sized shoe polish?"

"No, it's really, truly a type of spread for bread or whatever, and it's really, truly considered comfort food."

I shook my head, refusing to believe her. "Then my taste buds have not yet flipped down under because I…" instead of finishing my sentence, I demonstrated my shoulder-shaking dislike of the goo and downed my orange juice in one gulp.

Jill bowed her head to pray over our breakfast. "Lord, for what Kathy is about to swallow, may she be truly grateful. Amen."

"That was rude!" I teased her.

"I know. I was just giving you a hard time. I'll really pray now."

I bowed with her while my tongue made a clean sweep of the inside of my mouth. This time when Jill said, "Amen," I had no problem agreeing with her and adding my amen as well.

Enjoying the rest of my breakfast, I picked up the Vegemite wrapper and said, "You know what this reminds me of?"

"I don't think I want to know."

"No, I mean the name. Remember the *I Love Lucy* episode where she's trying to do a commercial for some elixir she keeps drinking until it makes her tipsy?"

"Oh, yeah. Vetavitavegamita."

"No," I said. "It was Meatavitavegamin."

"No, Vitametavegamite."

"No, I think it was Vegamitavitamita."

"That's not it. All I remember was Lucy's line, 'It's so tasty, too!'" Jill laughed. "I'm guessing you wouldn't apply that same line to this sample of Vegemite."

"Vitameatavegamin!" I said with the snap of my fingers. "That's it!"

"If you say so. Come on, Lucy. We have some sights to see."

The concierge provided us with a map along with several brochures containing details on what to do in Sydney. He greeted us with, "G'day," and said, "No worries" twice before showing us how to get to the train station, which was the closest form of public transportation and only two blocks away.

Bright autumn sun laced with a soft breeze greeted us as Jill and I walked in step. The temperature felt warmer than when we had left Wellington. A tall palm tree shaded the small train station where we bought two tickets to the Quay, which the map indicated was the main harbor area. I was eager to see the famous Sydney Opera House. Jill had some definite opinions about the art museum.

"I'm glad we're not driving," she said, as the two of us boarded the quaint train. The seating area we settled in felt similar to a subway. Across from us a little boy with a gleeful Australian accent was trying to snatch a piece of candy out of his grandpa's hand. Three teenage girls in belly button–revealing T-shirts were discussing what they should buy for another girl's birthday gift. I agreed with Jill about not having a car. I liked getting a touch of Aussie Saturday life on the public transportation.

The train rolled into the station near the Quay. Jill and I followed the crowd off the train, past some tourist shops, and into an open area bustling with movement. Visitors and locals strolled in the sunshine and dined at the open-air cafés. Others rushed to get on one of the many ferries and other touring boats that docked in the long harbor at what was labeled the Circular Quay.

We turned to the right, and there stood the Opera House, white and elegant against the seamless blue sky at the end of Sydney Harbor. The sight took my breath away.

"I've seen pictures of this landmark for years." I flipped up my sunglasses to get a better look as we walked toward it. "But this is really something. It reminds me of a huge ship with its sails at full mast."

"And the bridge." Jill pointed to the left. "Do you recognize that? Think of how many times we've seen fireworks being launched from that bridge. And there it is!"

I was glad that Jill didn't feel embarrassed to play tourist with me. I wanted to see everything.

"Let's see if we can buy tickets for whatever performance is playing at the Opera House," Jill suggested.

We headed for the great alabaster structure, and I commented that the area we were walking through had a southern California feel to it. I smiled when I heard the familiar ring of a cell phone nearby. It even sounded like the personalized tune on my phone.

That's when I realized it was my phone. Skyler was calling from college to tell me she had landed the summer job she had hoped for on campus in the admissions office.

"I'm thrilled for you, Sky! That's great news!"

"Thanks, Mom. So, what are you doing? Washing Dad's jeans and hanging them outside in the rain again?"

"No, as a matter of fact, I'm walking up the steps toward the entrance of the Sydney Opera House."

Skyler didn't respond.

"Are you still there?"

"You can't be serious," she said. "You're in Sydney? Australia? *The* Australia that I've wanted to go to since I was, like, seven?"

"Yes, that very same Australia. I came over here yesterday with Jill. She had to go to a wedding, and we thought we'd have a little getaway. Dad said he was going to send you an e-mail. Didn't you get it?"

"No, my computer isn't working. But don't worry. I have a guy who's working on it for me and..." with a giggle she added, "he's really cute!"

It felt good to hear my daughter's voice and her giggle. Before we hung up she begged me to buy certain Australian souvenirs for her—and, oh yes, she promised to pay me back. She ended with, "Mom, did you know that you are the coolest?"

"Coolest what?"

"You are the coolest world-traveling, God-loving, adventure-taking mother on this planet. When I grow up I want to be exactly like you!"

I closed my cell phone with my head in the clouds. Skyler's words across the miles and across the continents made up for all the times in high school that she had rolled her eyes and given me that get-a-life look.

The truth was, I *had* gotten a life, and suddenly I was cool. My life was flipped. Flipped completely down under. And I wasn't sure I ever wanted it to flop back to the way it had been.

Fourteen

What surprised me the most about the Sydney Opera House was the immensity of the building. I felt as if a great fish were swallowing us when we went inside. Jill read to me from the tour brochure that the building was finished in 1973 and had gone ninety-five million dollars over budget. Neither of us, even with our familiarity with the film industry, could imagine a project going so far over budget.

The part that surprised us the most was that the building wasn't a single, huge concert hall but rather a complex with several performing arenas. We found that we could buy tickets on the spot and go to an opera that evening, a jazz concert later in the afternoon, or a Shakespearean performance at seven. The system was much less formal than anything I'd experienced in the U.S.

We both agreed on tickets for the opera, even though we knew nothing about the performance being presented that evening. It just seemed that, when at the Opera House, go to the opera.

"What would you think about going to the art museum now?" Jill asked, unfolding the map the concierge had given us. "I read in the tour brochure that it has some extraordinary Aboriginal art. It's not far from here. We could walk through the botanical gardens."

"Sure!" I was still euphoric about being "cool," according to Skyler. Jill could have asked if I wanted to walk across the top of the harbor bridge attached to nothing but a bungee cord, and I would have done it.

The botanical gardens were brimming with autumn flowers still in bloom and a wealth of imposing old trees. The sun was warm enough to prompt us to peel off our sweaters. Jill pulled up her hair in a ponytail, and we talked about how much we loved the weather.

At a split in the trail, we stopped where half a dozen people were standing and staring up into a huge tree. The tree was thick with what looked like black pods the size of kittens hanging from the branches.

"What are you looking at?" Jill came alongside an older man who had a pair of binoculars.

"Bats." He handed her the binoculars. "Fruit bats. Curious creatures."

I immediately took several steps backward as a shiver ran up my spine. Jill peered through the binoculars and made appreciative comments about how clearly she could make out the details of the bats' folded-up wings.

From where I stood, I could easily see that this horde of nocturnal creatures was hanging upside down. There had to be hundreds of them. A young man with a backpack picked up a stone and threw it up into the tree. A great fluttering sound followed.

Jill and I instinctively grabbed each other by the arm and took off running away from the disturbed bats. Behind us we heard the older man yelling at the rock thrower.

"Are they following us?" I squealed. I couldn't bring myself to turn around and look.

"No, they're going back to the tree."

We slowed our pace to a walk and joined in a burst of nervous laughter.

"That was too creepy," I said with a shiver. "I'm going to have nightmares about bats chasing me."

Jill playfully reached over and fluttered the back of my hair with her hand, as if imitating the sensation of a bat hiding in my tresses.

"Not funny! Not funny! Not funny!" I spouted, pulling away.

"You're not fond of bats, I take it."

"You're quick!" I teased her back.

Jill chuckled and pointed to where we exited the botanical gardens to connect with the art museum. "How did you handle Batman while you were growing up?"

"Never watched it. Never went to see the Batman movies. Wouldn't let my daughter keep any Batman-related miniature action figures that came with her kid's meal. Bats are awful. Bats are evil. Bats should never be made into toys for children to play with or appreciated in any way, shape, or form!"

Jill laughed.

"Why are you laughing? Bats are not funny. They are wicked."

"Okay! Well, it's unfortunate you don't feel the freedom to express your *true* opinion on the topic."

We walked another few yards before I turned the tables. "So, what are you afraid of?"

"Nothing," Jill said with an all-too-cocky kick in her step, as we entered the stately art museum. While we rode the escalator to the lower level to view the Yiribana Gallery, I told Jill she couldn't get off that easily. There had to be something she was afraid of.

"Hobbits." She winked.

"That joke doesn't work here. We're done with the hobbit jokes. I'll find out what you're frightened of one of these days, and then I'll demonstrate how an understanding friend should treat another friend's phobias."

Jill took off a few steps ahead of me with a carefree flip of her hand, as if she didn't have a fright in the world. I knew it was only a matter of time.

Taking one look at the art in front of us, I thought we were in the wrong wing. Jill, however, offered low, appreciative humming sounds and drew closer to the pictures.

"These are exceptional," she murmured, gazing at one of the many walls lined with large canvases. Each of the paintings was made up of thousands and thousands of perfectly round dots all placed so as to form a pattern. The colors were earth colors: sand, green, blue, black.

"Don't you love this? It's like a bird's eye view on an ancient world but with so much energy that it seems to move."

I had to do a double take to make sure Jill wasn't joking. Trying to sound as polite as possible, I said, "I don't think I'm seeing what you're seeing."

Jill did a double take on me to make sure I wasn't joking. "It's all about the balance. That's the beauty of how the Aborigines view the world. Look at this one."

Jill explained the way the dots lined up to form shapes and impressions of shape. She gave me a crash course on how

Aboriginal art compared with the European Impressionists, including a side note on how Monet captured light and time of day with his many water lily paintings. Jill saw much more in these paintings than I did and kept talking about the balance.

When she finally used the word *geometry,* I confessed that I didn't like math. I'd never liked math.

Jill lifted an eyebrow in disbelief. "Without math, how would we have art?"

She lost me on that one. I saw art as a free expression of color and shape, and as something I definitely wasn't gifted in. Words came easier to me. Tony used to say that one-liners were my art form.

It wasn't as if having sassy one-liners on the tip of my tongue was necessarily a gift, but for some reason as we strolled past another row of Aboriginal art, I felt compelled to think about how to make use of my own strange art.

"What does this art say to you?" Jill asked.

"I don't know if it says anything specific. It reminds me of pottery."

"Pottery," Jill repeated. Obviously the comparison had never entered her mind. "What kind of pottery?"

"Navajo."

We rounded a corner and came into a room with an umbrella-style clothesline set up against the back wall. Jill burst out laughing, but I didn't.

From the clothesline hung a hundred papier-mâché bats, all linked to the clothesline wire with their toes, and all of them cocooned by their wings. The wings were delicately painted the same way the pictures had been with various rows of colorful dots. Each bat was different.

Or so Jill said.

I stayed far away from the clothesline bats, even though I knew they were too colorful to be real. They still spooked me. I already was fighting with my sense of being watched every time I hung our clothes outside on the line. I didn't want to entertain even the slightest thought that a bat, decorative or real, might appear one day, hanging from the clothesline when I walked outside with a basket of laundry.

"Come on." Jill cheerfully tugged on my sleeve. "You might enjoy some of the paintings upstairs a little more."

We wandered through the high-ceilinged rooms, admiring what I referred to as masterpieces. Many of the huge, detailed paintings that lined the walls were originals by artists whose names I recognized like Dante Gabriel Rossetti. The Victorian women these artists painted were round and fair skinned with diaphanous gowns and flowers in their flowing blond hair. They represented the idealized, romanticized woman and were everything I had grown up wishing I could be.

We strolled through more rooms where I saw a picture of a landscape with creamy-colored sheep. Jill saw a harmony of sky and earth in a sixty-forty ratio. I saw a picture of a woman darning socks. Jill saw a median line that intersected at the woman's eyes and not her hands.

Somewhere between a dark and mystical oil of St. Francis of Assisi and a colorful rendition of the Parable of the Ten Virgins, I started to glimpse what Jill saw. What made the art beautiful wasn't so much the subject of the painting but rather the balance of lines and color used to present the subject.

"It's not so much what happens inside the frame," Jill said in a final explanation of how math defines art. "But how balanced the subject is. That's what makes the scene beautiful to our way of viewing it."

I was enjoying the tour with my own personal art appreciation instructor, but I was slow to let Jill know how cool I thought she and her insights were. After all, she kept using math terms to make her point.

One scene of a Victorian woman bending to pick up a seashell caught our attention and caused both of us to stop and appreciate it for our own separate reasons. The image inside the round center of the gold frame was dressed in a creamy, loose-fitting dress that was accented with blue embroidery around the hem and flouncy sleeves. Her feet were covered with delicate sandals. In the distance all that could be seen was a faint peninsula that shaped the boundary of the calm bay.

"What do you see?" Jill asked.

"An elegant woman standing on a deserted beach. I love her dress and the serenity of her posture. She gives the appearance of having all the time in the world to stroll along the beach and examine shells."

"It's definitely a beach from this side of the world," Jill said. "You can tell by the color of the sand, the water, and the cliffs in the background. Those are down under shades. That woman belongs there. That's her beach. She's not just visiting. She walks that sand daily looking for treasures."

Apparently Jill was getting a personal message from the painting. I sat down on the wide bench in the middle of the gallery for those wanting to contemplate a painting. I chose, instead, to contemplate Jill.

"What do you see in this picture?" I asked.

Jill tilted her head.

"All the lines in the picture direct us to whatever she's holding in her hand. And that treasure is kept hidden from our view because she hasn't opened her hand all the way."

Turning to face me, Jill said in clear, precise words, "I hold a treasure in my hand. But I don't know what it is."

"A talent, maybe? A gift? A passion for something?" I wasn't sure I knew her well enough to guess what that hidden passion might be. However, I knew whatever it was, she was closer to discovering it now than she had been for many months. Perhaps many years. She had changed so much in the few weeks I'd known her.

We continued to gaze at the picture. I was beginning to see the lines, the symmetry, and the median angles. Those lines didn't ruin my appreciation for the subject but rather made me aware of how right Jill was about the necessity of geometry.

Jill had said something earlier about how art is most beautiful when it's balanced. Dark and light. Intense and subtle. I wondered if she saw the same balance in life. The heaviness she had carried the past two years was now giving way to a lightness in her spirit.

"Do you mind if we stop by the gift shop?" Jill asked, when we started to leave the museum a short time later.

I never objected to shopping. I bought a poster-sized copy of the Victorian woman on the beach while Jill bought a postcard of the same print along with a dozen postcards of the Aboriginal art.

"Do you think you might frame that?" Jill asked.

"Yes, I was thinking of hanging it over our bed. You've seen the picture Mr. Barry has there now. It's a big bunch of tropical flowers. Ever since I took the obnoxious bedspread off the bed, the picture feels out of place."

What I didn't tell Jill and knew I would never tell Tony was that in a peculiar way I missed the old bedspread. The one I had bought on a shopping trip with Jill was similar to the one I had at home. The muted tones of the new, pale yellow bed-spread would go nicely with the colors in the picture. But once I'd gotten the quieter colors on our bed, the garage seemed smaller. Duller. The bright bedspread had been the inescapable focal point of the room, but at least it gave the room a focal point. I knew that after Jill's art lesson, I'd be sizing up our apartment with a new eye for balance and looking for "inter-sections of repeated colors." I doubted that any of my decorating attempts from here on out would be easy unless I gave consideration to the importance of geometry.

"Remind me to give you a lesson in something later," I said, as we left the gift shop.

"Okay. A lesson in what?"

"I don't know yet. Something that will make you feel more informed yet leave you with the feeling that your life was less complex before you learned that lesson."

"Okay," Jill said hesitantly. "And before you decide what torturous lesson you're going to teach me, are you in the mood for more shopping?"

"Sure. Shopping I can do painlessly."

"Or are you hungry? Because if you want to eat, according to this map, I think we could walk to a place called Woolloomooloo and go to a place that serves *pie floaters.*"

"And exactly what is a pie floater?"

"It says here it's a meat pie swimming in a bowl of pea soup."

Jill and I exchanged grimaces.

She looked back at the tour book and added, "Served with a kangaroo tail as a spoon."

Fifteen

I *was only kidding* about the kangaroo tail spoons." Jill laughed at the shocked expression on my face. "But the rest of the description is what it says right here."

I grabbed the book out of her hand. "Do they have any recommendations for one of those cafés by the water we passed earlier? Not that I'm against meat pies swimming in pea soup or anything, but the Vegemite was enough of a stretch for my taste buds this morning."

"Let's walk back to the harbor and see what strikes our fancy." Jill snatched the map back from me. "I think it's shorter if we go this way."

As we walked, I playfully asked, "Should I be questioning your sense of direction after the way we drove around in the rental car?"

"No. I'm much better on foot than I am behind the wheel. And before you say anything, Miss Kathy Girl, I happen to know how safe you are behind the wheel as well!"

We only made it two blocks before seeing a store with out-back gear in the window.

"Wait, Jill. Skyler wanted a hat. An outback hat. Do you mind if we stop in here?"

Jill didn't seem to mind stopping to shop anytime, anywhere.

When we first entered the store, I was distracted from looking for a hat because the first thing I saw was a case of Australian opals in a variety of jewelry settings. A pair of light blue opal earrings in a silver setting looked like something Skyler might like, even if it wasn't something she had asked me to buy for her. I tried to figure out the price in U.S. dollars while Jill shopped for hats.

"What do you think of this one?" Jill tried on a khaki green hat that flipped up on the side and had a tie that hung far below her chin.

"It's a little manly, don't you think? Maybe something smaller."

"Actually, this one is the Manly hat." The clerk stepped closer and handed Jill a wide-brimmed hat made from neutral canvas.

"It looks like a beach hat," I said, wondering what the joke was since my husband wouldn't consider anything "manly" about such a hat.

"Exactly," the clerk agreed. "A Manly Beach hat."

We looked around at a few other items and then exited without buying anything, feeling a bit worn down from the confusing exchange.

"Have no fear," Jill said. "I can see another shop less than a block from here. We'll find a hat for Skyler before the sun goes down."

We made our way back to the harbor—one gift shop at a time. I was relieved that Jill enjoyed shopping as much as I did.

For me, half the fun was trying on every hat and comparing prices on all the opals. I always felt better about a purchase when I knew I'd gotten a good deal.

"Look at these little kangaroos!" Jill said, as we entered one of the gift shops near the Quay. "They even squeak! I'm buying this one with the Australian flag."

She picked up a stuffed mama kangaroo with a joey peeping out of her pouch. "Oh, and this one has to come home with me. My granddaughter needs it."

Between the two of us, we snatched up all nine of the little kangaroos and started trying on more hats. I'd plopped at least a dozen on my head, but all the outback ones were pretty large and heavy.

"What do you think of this hat?" Jill put on one that looked more feminine than the others.

"That's cute. If Skyler doesn't like it, I'd wear it." I took the hat from Jill and tried it on.

"Sold," I said without even looking at myself in a mirror. This was the first hat of the day that wasn't too big for a woman-sized head.

I took the hat and stuffed kangaroos to the counter and noticed another shopper browsing by the jewelry case. She was comparing her opal necklace with a silver one on display.

"That's very pretty." I nodded at her necklace.

"Oh, thanks." Her accent sounded southern. "I just bought it at the Rock. They only had gold over there. I like this silver one better. Have you been to the Rock yet?"

"No, where is that?"

"Other side of the harbor. Darling shops. And they have a flea market going on. My husband bought himself a pair of leather boots. You should go over there."

"You called it the Rock?"

"That's right. Isn't that right, honey?"

Her husband stepped in and said, "It's the Rocks, not the Rock. It's the oldest part of Sydney, right off the harbor, where the convicts landed in colonial times. The store we liked was on Lower Fort Street."

"Thanks. We'll go there next."

Leaving the store with Skyler's girlish outback hat and a bagful of kangaroos, we hailed a cab and asked to be taken to the Rocks. We were still in a shopping mood, and time was of the essence. When we reached Lower Fort Street, we did a little opal jewelry browsing before making our way down the uneven brick streets to the Saturday market.

The brick buildings around us seemed to hold in their secrets of rowdier times in this square. Today, artisans—not Great Britain's undesirables—filled the Rocks.

I bought a Christmas ornament at the first stall we passed and paused to try some organic hand lotion. The woman who created the lotion showed me her line of soaps, shampoos, and bath oils.

"Step away from the bubble bath." Jill teased, as she came up from behind and pretended to be on patrol. "You know what happened the last time you had several bottles within reach. Just put down the bath oil, and nobody gets hurt."

I chortled and said I was sampling the lotion. I held out my hand for Jill to sniff the sweet fragrance.

"Nice. Plumeria," Jill said.

"We call it frangipani," said the clerk.

"We'd like two bottles," I told the woman.

"I should get one, too," Jill said.

"No, that's why I'm buying two. One is for you."

Jill put her wallet back in her purse and gave me a tender look. "Thank you, Kathy."

"You're welcome."

Jill looked as if it had been a long time since anyone had surprised her with a little gift.

We headed toward another stall where a man was playing what the sign called a didjeridoo. He blew into the end of a long, hollow tube, and the vibrating sound that came from the primitive instrument filled the area with a rounded sort of hum.

As we watched him play, we noticed three women who had to be at least our age, dressed like underwater ballet swimmers but with some comic twists. They wore brightly-colored swim caps that had plastic flowers attached to their sides, orange swimmer's goggles, one-piece bathing suits in matching blue with yellow and pink polka dots, matching blue tights on their legs, and pink jelly sandals. Their waists were decked out with inflatable kiddy inner tubes that had yellow duckies on the blue circles. The women's arms were adorned with blown-up, bright yellow floaties.

One woman had a snorkel in her mouth and was making exaggerated gurgling noises. The other two women were calling out the strokes, "And one, two, turn to the side, three, arms up, and four."

Jill and I, along with a dozen others, stopped to stare at the bizarre street theater company. The three women, in perfectly synchronized motions, treated the open air as their practice swimming pool and moved through the crowd performing their routine as smoothly as any dance ensemble. Trailing behind them was another woman in a gray shark costume, blowing bubbles through the shark's wide-open mouth. They were having a ball.

Jill and I laughed even though none of the other spectators seemed to know how to react.

"Chilly, this water today, don't you think, girls?" one of the swimmers said.

"Brisk!" said the other.

"Gurffple!" said the one with the snorkel.

"Lovely day, no less. Again, ladies, from the top. Push to the surface and down…"

Off they went. Arms up, then bending at the waist, all in unison.

The gathering of curious viewers was now laughing with Jill and me. "Well, that's one way to get your exercise!" a woman said.

"Where do we sign up?" Jill asked me, as we watched the blue-legged ballerinas waddle and wiggle away from us. "That was daring and darling. I loved it!"

"Should we see about starting up our own routine and try it out in front of the Chocolate Fish?" I asked.

"I'm sure Tracey would be all for it."

"Come on, Jill! You could put those old cheerleading skills back into use."

"Thanks for the encouragement, but I don't think out-of-water ballet is the hidden treasure I hold in my hand."

We chuckled and continued our trek through the open market. We could still feel the low vibrations of the didjeridoo instrument, as it released more vibrating sounds into the air and into the earth beneath our feet.

This is a strange and wonderful place.

That same thought repeated itself throughout the afternoon. We bought a variety of fun souvenirs at the outdoor market, including a boomerang and a wooden bowl made from the burl of an aged eucalyptus tree. Jill wanted the bowl for her coffee table and was enthralled with the various lines and squiggles that showed through the sides of the polished wood. Her appreciation for the symmetry of the lines didn't bother me so much anymore. I wondered if I was beginning to make peace with math.

We found great prices on opal jewelry, and I splurged on a blue opal necklace with matching earrings for myself. The shade of blue in the stones reminded me of the blue sky over Christchurch and the inviting blue of the water in front of the Chocolate Fish. I knew that whenever I looked at the necklace, it would make me feel happy.

By four-thirty we were more than ready for something to eat and were thrilled to find an outdoor café right on the harbor that had a table open for us next to the water. Our prime seats gave us a perfect view of the bridge, the Opera House, and the ferries that came and went at a quick pace from the Quay.

"This couldn't be better!" Jill motioned to the panorama before us. "What a beautiful afternoon; the air is so warm and nice. We'll have to take a ferry ride tomorrow."

I took a drink of my iced tea. "I just thought of something. We aren't exactly dressed for the opera, and I don't think we'll have enough time to go back to the hotel to change."

"Well," Jill said, reaching into one of our shopping bags. "I think you should jazz up your outfit with this hat." She popped the outback hat on my head. "What do you think?"

"Hey, be nice. I like this hat!"

"I do, too. It looks great on you. I think Skyler may have to come here herself and pick out her own hat."

Reaching into one of my shopping bags, I pulled out several of the stuffed kangaroos. "We could skin these little critters and quickly make evening gowns for ourselves out of their fur. We certainly have enough pelts to make two floor-length gowns."

Jill laughed.

At that moment I noticed a tattered white feather that had floated from one of the many birds dipping in and out of the café area. They were hopping around looking for a leftover crust or a bit of forgotten French fry. The feather landed on our table. I snatched it up and slipped it into the inside pocket of my purse.

"Grabbing a feather for the final touch on our evening wear?" Jill asked.

"I'm starting a collection," I said, reminding Jill about the two feathers that were in my hair the day we met at the Chocolate Fish. I didn't tell her that my plan was to create a greeting card with the feathers.

We clinked the rims of our iced tea glasses as the waitress stepped up to take the rest of our order. We talked her into snapping our picture, and I knew this would be the picture I would frame. I would long remember the sensations of this place and the lightness of this day.

"I heard you talking about the dress code for the opera," the waitress said when she delivered our Thai salads. "Some people dress up, but there's no dress code, so you'll be fine in what you're wearing."

"Too bad," Jill said, surprising the waitress and me. "I was hoping for an excuse to shop for something really extravagant."

"We can still do that, if we eat quickly."

"Who can eat quickly in a setting like this? I'm going to savor each bite."

I felt the same way. We watched sailboats in the harbor,

took small bites of our delicious salads, and savored each moment of the balmy Sydney evening.

Since we were so close to the Opera House, we took our time strolling over there. As we walked up the steep stairs, we saw people dressed in formal attire as well as others who were in shorts and T-shirts. This definitely was a gathering place for everyone.

Our seats were terrific. The entire theater filled with eagerly chatting guests. All around us in our section were school children that Jill and I guessed to be about eighth- or ninth-graders. All of them wore school uniforms. The boys were from one school, and the girls were from another. Both of us loved listening to the conversations and innocent flirting that was going on between the two groups. Jill and I kept exchanging grins and eyebrow-raised expressions.

The musicians took their places. The lights dimmed. The students' politeness was impressive as the room quieted, and the curtain went up.

The program called this performance "Opera Favorites," and the first song was "Nessun Dorma" from an opera called *Turandot*. A stout man delivered the song, and I knew I'd heard it before. I didn't know where, but part of the melody was familiar. On the forceful notes, the singer's voice reverberated in the rounded auditorium. When his tones grew softer, the room seemed to shrink with his voice.

I was amazed that one man's voice could fill the space so powerfully. I was also astounded that such a large group of students would be held in respectful silence as he sang. I knew very little about opera, so I'm sure I didn't appreciate the performance as much as I might have. But I doubted that a roomful of California students the same age would have given the performance the same kind of attention and appreciation.

The applause rose heartily from the crowd, as the performer took his bow. Next came an aria from *Madame Butterfly,* and again, when the woman sang, I knew I'd heard the song before. Maybe I knew a little more about opera than I'd realized.

Intermission came sooner than I expected. Most of the audience cleared out of the auditorium. Jill and I followed and found ourselves on the open deck of the lower level of the Opera House facing the harbor. When we had entered the Opera House, the evening sky was dressed in twilight. We had missed the sunset, but now, in front of this magical opening to another world, we looked out on Sydney Harbor with all the twinkle lights winking back at us.

"Everyone is so chatty!" Jill looked around.

Some of the audience were waiting in line to buy beverages. Others were leaning against the railing, pointing up at the stars that were doing their twinkling best to match the lights reflected in the harbor waters.

A lit-up ship puttered past us, with music loud enough for us to hear. We could see couples dancing on the top level. It was a splendidly romantic sight, one that would have made a fabulous subject for a beautiful photograph or, better yet, an oil painting.

Jill's profile dipped slightly. Her shoulders dropped. I saw a tear dance alone down her cheek.

"Are you okay?"

"I miss Ray," she whispered.

The only thing I knew to do was to stand with her. So I did. Shoulder to shoulder, leaning with our arms on the railing, watching the romantic scene float past us.

Sixteen

The second half of the "Opera Favorites" performance put both Jill and me in a weepy mood, and we used up all the tissues that we had between us. I didn't sense any self-pity from Jill. This was a peaceful sadness.

With few words, we took a cab back to our hotel. If there is such thing as a beautiful sorrow, that was the sensation Jill and I shared under the stars that night.

We carried our shopping bags to the elevator and arrived back at our hotel room a full fifteen hours after we had left. Unlocking the door, we both sniffed when we entered. Not from tears but because the room still smelled like a big fruit ambrosia.

The message light was blinking on our phone. Jill listened and said, "One message. From my brother-in-law. He invited us to his house for lunch tomorrow. What do you think?"

"It's up to you."

"Let's decide in the morning," Jill suggested. "It's too late to call him now anyway."

Jill decided the next morning not to see her brother-in-law. I would have been fine either way, but she told him we were going to visit a nearby church and then do some more sightseeing.

The closest church was a small community church where we were welcomed as special visitors from America and invited to stand and say a few words. Jill said a few, and I said even fewer. It turned out that even the pastor that day was visiting. His message was from a familiar passage in the Gospel of John.

After attending the same church for so many years, I enjoyed the freshness of being with this group of eighty or so faithful believers. It was a personal time of worship with nothing about the service that resembled a corporate production. This church in Sydney was similar in many ways to Jill's church in Wellington that Tony and I had visited the week before.

As Jill and I boarded the bus that stopped a few blocks from the church, I mentioned how much I enjoyed being at a small church.

"It's interesting that you would say that because I was just thinking how much I miss the megachurch we used to belong to in California. Grass is always greener on the other side of the world, isn't it?"

We headed for the harbor without a set plan of what we were going to do with the rest of the gloriously sunny day that stretched out before us. I looked through a couple of pamphlets on Sydney that I'd picked up in a rack at the hotel.

"What about going to the beach?" I asked. "We can take a ferry to a couple of different beaches, or we can take a bus to Bondi Beach."

"Sure." Jill looked over my shoulder at the map. "I don't believe it."

"What?"

"Do you remember that clerk in the first shop we went to yesterday and how he was trying to convince us that the hat he was showing us was a Manly Beach hat?"

"Yes."

"Well, look on the map. Manly Beach." Jill chuckled. "He wasn't teasing us or making it up. There really is a Manly Beach, and that was a Manly Beach hat!"

"Then that's the beach we're going to."

We got off the bus at the Quay and found the right dock for the ferry to Manly Beach. I stopped in front of the sign that read, "Manly Ferries," and wondered if anyone else thought that sounded funny.

"Come on." Jill ignored the sign. "This is the one we want. They're boarding now."

We packed into what felt like a floating, wide-bodied bus with more than a hundred other eager weekend beachgoers. The seats outside on the deck in the delicious fresh air were all taken, so Jill and I went inside and sat at the end of a long row. It felt like sitting in a movie theater except the show was all around us outside the windows.

With smooth maneuvering, the ferry pulled out of the busy dock and headed for the open bay. On both sides we could see dozens of sailboats of all sizes with passengers seizing the gorgeous day. The tall buildings that lined the harbor area began to diminish as we motored past some of the many bays and inlets of the wide, deep blue harbor.

Flipping through the tour pamphlet, I found a map and saw that we would soon be on a beach that faced east, and the water would be the Pacific Ocean. The South Pacific, to be exact. I was amazed that, after so many years of facing west to put my feet into the Pacific Ocean, I was now on the other side of that vast expanse of water. It was one of those moments in which my mind tapped into the amazement of where I was.

When we docked in Manly Cove, all the other travelers seemed to know where to go to cross the peninsula to Manly Beach. A loud, chirping sound accompanied the green crosswalk sign. We moved like an army of ants through a long outdoor mall of shops and came out at a wide, sandy beach teeming with Sunday swimmers of all ages.

Jill tapped my arm and pointed to a young man who stood a few feet away with his arms crossed and his back to us, gazing out at the water. He had on a broad-rimmed khaki beach hat like we had seen in the store yesterday. He wore red swim trunks and a tank top. On the back of the tank top, in bold letters, were the words, "Manly Lifeguard."

Jill whispered, "I wonder if that helps bolster his self-image."

Now she was ready to start with the Manly jokes. "Do you think it's a joke T-shirt, or is it real?"

"Oh, it's real," Jill said. "There's another one." She pointed to another "Manly Lifeguard" positioned in a lookout stance in the sand.

"It's good to be under the watchful eye of so many Manly Lifeguards," I said.

"I know. Especially with their Manly shoulders bulging out of their Manly tank tops."

We shared a giggle and found an open space where we could sit in the sand. Both of us had worn summer skirts and cotton blouses to church that morning. Since we didn't know we were coming to the beach on this trip, we hadn't packed our swimsuits. Not that I would have gone swimming, if I had my suit. But I could have waded in up to my knees, just for the experience of being in the Pacific on this side of the globe.

Jill sat demurely in the sand while I ventured out to the water. I thought of the Victorian woman in the painting who strolled along the beach in a cotton gown that fell to her ankles. I imagined I was she and stooped to pick up a broken shell.

The warm salt water rushed over my bare feet, as a wave tumbled to shore. I waded out a little deeper and wedged my feet into the sand. Hundreds of swimmers and splashers, along with a few body surfers, frolicked in the sparkling surf, their voices mixing with the crashing sounds of the waves. At the spot where the long sidewalk edged the sandy beach, dozens of tall star pine trees anchored themselves into the sand the way I planned to anchor myself into the sand.

This might be "Manly" beach, but I'm having a very "womanly" moment right now. I smiled at the beauty all around me and twisted my feet deeper into the soft sand.

Just then a loud siren sounded from the shore. Everyone looked around to see what was going on. A voice boomed over the loudspeaker. "Everyone out of the water. We've had a shark sighting. This is not a drill!"

I never knew I could run so fast in sand.

I wasn't the only one who kicked into high gear. The water emptied in seconds. Everyone stood and stared out to sea. Three of the Manly lifeguards jumped in a motorized raft and entered the water. As the crowd of stunned beachgoers watched, the raft headed out to where several surfers had been paddling on their boards, waiting for the waves to pick up.

"I saw it," a woman next to us said. "Did you see? The fin was sticking out of the water."

We all squinted and tried to make out what was going on as the lifeguards motored in a wide circle. One of them motioned to shore, and another raft was launched with three more lifeguards.

"Something is definitely out there," a guy said, moving closer to the shore.

"It's no small wonder, really," said a short woman who stepped up next to us. She was smoking a cigarette with quick, short puffs and wore a bikini even though she had to be at least sixty. "You know they keep sharks in the Oceanworld aquarium just the other side of the wharf in Manly Cove."

"Really?" Jill said, as if trying to make polite conversation yet keeping her eyes glued on the water.

"That's right. You can get in the tank and swim with the sharks, if you like. But swimming out here, in the ocean, you don't know what you might meet up with."

As one great audience we all were standing, inching closer to the water to see what was going on. Everyone spouted opinions and impressions of what was seen out there.

With both rafts motoring in a circle, we watched while one of the lifeguards threw a rope into the water the way a cowboy would toss a lasso.

"They're not going to catch it like that!" someone exclaimed. "That shark will eat them alive."

"It's not a shark," another viewer said. "It's a person."

Everyone in earshot of that observation gasped and strained even harder to see what the lifeguards were now pulling to shore.

"They wouldn't haul a body in like that," someone said. "It has to be a fish. Dolphin, maybe. It's big, whatever it is. Look, isn't that a fin sticking up? Could be a shark, after all. Wouldn't be the first time here. Ah, wait. No worries. It's a log!"

A collective sigh rippled along the shoreline as everyone saw that the Manly lifeguards had bravely lassoed a log with a finlike branch sticking out the topside. Some people laughed; some just looked relieved. A few joked loudly enough so the rest of us could hear.

"They better throw it back in where they got it!" the woman next to us said, rubbing her cigarette stub into the sand. "Otherwise the Greenies will be all over them for disrupting the natural habitat of floating logs."

I was amazed how everyone entered into the conversation and joked around, as if we had all come to the beach that day as one big group. No one seemed to be taking himself or the situation too seriously. I felt like we were at a grand neighborhood picnic.

When people returned to the water, Jill joined them. I watched her step right in, kicking playfully at the waves. I pulled out my camera and took a couple of pictures of her.

Beyond Jill rolled blue, blue ocean for thousands of miles. I thought of my home at the other end of that blue. I missed Skyler; she would love this beach. She would love the "everybody's on vacation" feel of this town and these people. Tony would love it here, too. I wondered if the three of us would ever visit a place like this together, or were our family travel days over?

Using my sweater as a pillow, I lay back and felt the powerful sun on my face. This was a good day. This was a good place to be. I thought of the hundreds of trips to the beach I'd taken at home in California. Those treks always meant packing an ice chest, towels, blankets, and umbrellas. Today we had taken a bus and a ferry to the beach, and here I was in my "Sunday clothes" enjoying the beach with nothing more than a sweater for a pillow. My life definitely had become simplified since we moved here.

A contented smile traipsed across my lips. I wondered if moving into the minimalist apartment had been the first step in learning how to live comfortably with less.

"You look relaxed." Jill stood next to me and playfully sprinkled the last of the salt water that clung to her fingers.

"I am. Hey, is it raining?"

"Just sprinkling."

"How was the water?"

"Shark free and log free. Very nice. Wish we had brought our togs."

"Our what?"

"That's what they call swimsuits here. Our bathing togs."

"I'm sure you could go buy a new one in any of those surf shops we walked past."

"Yeah, I saw a lime green bikini in the window of one shop that I thought might work for me."

I sat up. "Let's do it, Jill. Let's buy a couple of bikinis. Lime green ones. Who cares? Nobody knows us here. When are we ever going to be on this beach again?"

Jill laughed. "My bikini days ended after my third child."

"Who cares? You saw that woman who was standing with us during the shark roundup. And look at that lady over there." I nodded toward a woman who was larger than either Jill or I was. She had on a bikini top and a pair of shorts that covered most of her large rear but didn't stop her belly from hanging over.

"Oh, the peer pressure of it all!" Jill pretended to bite her thumbnail.

"We'll buy cover-ups and stay covered up except when we're in the water. What do you think?"

"You're serious."

"Yes, of course I'm serious. Come on, we'll never be eighteen again, but we can pretend we are for one afternoon while we swim at Manly Beach. What do you say? We might even get a second look from one of those Manly lifeguards."

"Oh, we'll get a second look, all right," Jill said under her breath. "I can almost guarantee you that."

Breezing through several surf shops near the shore, we quickly found that the sizes they carried in swimwear catered to a crowd that was at least thirty years our junior. The first store we went into looked promising because they had such a wide selection on a rack in the back. A sale clerk asked if she could help, and we guessed at the sizes we each needed. She pulled a pink bikini off the rack and handed it to Jill. It was at least two sizes smaller than what Jill needed and three sizes smaller than what I estimated I needed.

"So sorry," the salesclerk said. "That's the largest size we carry."

"Come on." I pulled Jill out of the store. "Shopping for bathing suits is rarely a good idea. In a beach town like this with a strip of fashionable shops, it's a really bad idea."

"They have no idea, do they?" she said, fanning herself. "She had to be all of what? Nineteen, maybe? I doubt she's ever weighed more than a hundred pounds in her life. Young and thin and beautiful. They think they rule the world."

"I know. She's probably a cheerleader, too."

Jill paused and then gave me a glinty-eyed look. "Oh, that was low, Salerno!"

That's when I remembered that Jill had been a cheerleader.

183

I wasn't referring to her; the words had just bumbled out of my mouth.

"Sorry!" I pinched my fingers together and pretended to zip my mouth closed.

"You don't have to zip it, Kathy. I'm way beyond being offended. Let's go do something else." Jill pushed back her hair and flapped the collar of her blouse in an effort to cool off.

"We can still go back and enjoy the beach. Or if you want, we can shop like we did yesterday. That was fun. They have a lot of souvenir shops around here with cute stuff other than clothes."

Jill fanned her rosy face. "I have to stick with my own rule on this one."

"What's that?"

"Shop till you drop or a hot flash makes you stop."

Seventeen

I laughed at Jill's hot flash joke as we walked back toward Manly Beach, where more balmy hours of the day awaited us.

Looking over her shoulder, Jill said, "Is that an ice cream shop?"

"Comfort food?"

"You know it."

I led the way. "American comfort food beats Vegemite any day."

We bought waffle cones with single scoops and strolled along the extended walkway that lined the immense stretch of beach.

"We could be skinny again if we wanted to be," Jill said.

"Speak for yourself. I never was skinny."

"I'm more concerned about staying healthy than getting skinny."

We agreed and reviewed all the reasons healthy was better

than skinny. Then we compared our health problems, scar tissue, and choices of vitamins and agreed that, when it came to stretch marks, we were powerless.

"Mine are all on my thighs," I said.

"My belly is atrocious," Jill said. "I can't believe you almost talked me into putting on a bikini and exposing my stomach to the public. The notion was liberating for a few minutes, but maybe that little princess was right; bikinis shouldn't be sold in mama-sizes."

We spent the rest of the afternoon enjoying the sand, sun, and soft ocean breeze. For dinner we bought fish and chips at a take-away place across from the beach and ate on the cement sea wall with our feet hanging over the edge.

"Before we board the ferry," I said. "I have to buy one thing, if you don't mind shopping with me for this souvenir."

"Sure," Jill said. "Are you going to buy one of those Manly Beach hats after all?"

"No." I opened the door for her to a small shop. "I think you and I need matching Manly Beach towels."

I got mine in yellow. Jill picked blue. We also bought some postcards and floaty pens that showed a Manly ferry rolling back and forth in the harbor every time the pen was tilted.

Then Jill found the best souvenir of the trip. It was a long stick with a trigger handle. On the top of the stick was a plastic shark. Every time the trigger was activated, the shark opened its mouth and snapped its plastic teeth. We bought matching sharks, too.

"So, what do you want to do tomorrow?" Jill asked while we waited in line to board our return ferry. "We don't have all day since our flight goes out at seven that night. I wish now we had arranged to stay longer. There's so much more to see here."

"I know. I'd like to go to the Blue Mountains. Did you see that brochure?"

"Is that where the Three Sisters are? Those three big rock formations?"

"That's right," said an older man standing near us. His Australian accent sounded as if he had been gargling with gravel. "The Blue Mountains are two hours from here. You should see some of the outback while you're here. Cleve's Bush Walkers put on a fine tour. It's an all-day tour, though."

"Thanks," Jill said. "I don't think we'll have enough time on this trip."

"Well, you remember Cleve's Bush Walkers then for your next visit. They'll show you the sights and fix you up with some lizard for lunch."

"Lizard?" Jill repeated.

"Goanna lizards are 'bout this long. Skewer it right on a stick over an open fire, and you've got yourself a meal. Cleve catches 'em and cooks up enough for the entire tour group."

"And tourists actually eat… " Jill could barely say the word, "…lizard?"

"Aww, no worries. Goanna lizard's not so bad. The way Cleve sautés it, you'll say it tastes like chicken."

I noticed that Jill had moved away from the helpful man.

"What's wrong, Jill? Are you not fond of lizards?"

She lowered her chin and looked at me hard without answering. That's when I knew I had her.

"So, would you say that you're not fond of lizards, or would you say the way you feel about lizards is similar to the way I feel about bats?"

"Kathy, please." She turned away from the guy in line and lowered her voice. "I beg you. Grace me on this one, will you?

I'll let you slide with the nasty cheerleader comment, but I can't talk about lizards." Her voice was so low she only mouthed the last two words.

"No worries." I grinned. "Your secret is safe with me."

Our source of outback lore had taken up with some Asian tourists, leaving Jill and me to make a dash for it once the next ferry started to board passengers. We scrambled up to the top deck so we could have prime seats to watch the dramatic approach into Sydney Harbor. The sun was beginning its fading act, slipping behind the landscape of tall buildings as the city lights were coming on. I thought it strange to watch a sunset that wasn't dipping into the Pacific. Here, the sun rose out of the ocean.

"Look." Jill pointed to the star-studded sky. "The Southern Cross. Did you recognize it?"

I'd never seen the Southern Cross. I stared at the night sky. Even the stars looked different in the lower half of the hemisphere.

Down under. Backwards. Upside down. Everything is different in this place.

"What a gorgeous night," Jill said.

We wrapped our new beach towels around our shoulders for warmth and watched the harbor bridge come into view. The bridge's lights, along with the lights coming from the Opera House on the far left, sparkled dramatically over the calm, teal waters that were fading to black.

"So, what are we going to do tomorrow?" Jill asked.

"Can it involve an animal?"

Jill didn't look amused. "What kind of animal?"

Imitating the voice of the man in line, I said, "No worries, mate. I'm not talking about seeing a…" I mouthed the word *lizard.* "How about finding us a real, live kangaroo?"

"Yes, great idea," Jill said. "We have to pet a koala bear while we're here, too. I know they have a wildlife park somewhere, and a zoo."

We settled back in our Manly Beach towels as the ferry approached the dock. This had been a fine day.

To make our fine day complete, upon returning to the hotel, we ordered room service and checked out a video from the hotel collection of Australian films. I was all set for *Crocodile Dundee,* but keeping Jill's lizard and possible additional reptile phobias in mind, I agreed to a documentary on Ayers Rock.

However, as soon as we ate, we fell asleep. So much for showing documentaries at a slumber party.

When the phone rang at seven with our morning wake-up call, we both rolled over and moaned that we wanted to sleep some more.

Jill got up before I did. Her turn in the shower gave me a chance to wake slowly. As I did, I thought of how, for so many years, my morning prayer had been along the lines of, "Please let my day go smoothly." It struck me that such a prayer always came with the assumption that the day was "my" day, and the schedule was "my" schedule. All I was asking for was God's nod of approval on my agenda, as if He were my supervisor. Figuring out life was up to me. I never invited His rearranging. Rarely did I enter into the ebb and flow of speaking and listening, which I knew was essential for any relationship, if it was to grow.

Reaching for the devotional I'd brought with me, I read the verse for that day. I was hoping the verse would speak to me the same way the Ephesians verse had started me thinking about extravagant love.

Today the verses were from Lamentations 3. It wasn't a book of the Bible I'd turned to often, but I recognized the passage. "The unfailing love of the LORD never ends!... Great is his faithfulness; his mercies begin afresh each day."

Sitting up in bed, I whispered humbly to the Great God of this universe, the God who rules all that is visible and invisible, upside-down and right side up, that I'd rather experience His extravagant love and mercy every day than to receive the check-off mark I'd been asking for all these years. I pictured myself laying aside my day and waiting for Him to offer His day to me as a gift.

When Jill stepped out of the bathroom I smiled. "Do you want to hear a great verse for us for today?" She sat on the edge of her bed towel drying her hair while I read the Lamentations verse to her.

Stopping abruptly, Jill looked at me. "There's more to that chapter, you know." She pulled out her journal and flipped to one of the pages in the middle. "These verses were sent to me in a card right after Ray died, and they hit me so hard it was as if I couldn't swallow them. I wrote them here because I knew that one day I'd be able to read them, and they wouldn't make me choke."

She looked down at her journal and then back at me, as if she was looking for encouragement before taking a leap.

"Would you like me to read it?"

"No, I can do this." Jill's voice was tight as she read. "'I will never forget this awful time, as I grieve over my loss. Yet I still dare to hope when I remember this: The unfailing love of the LORD never ends! By his mercies we have been kept from complete destruction. Great is his faithfulness; his mercies begin afresh each day.... For the Lord does not abandon anyone forever. Though he brings grief, he also shows compassion according to the greatness of his unfailing love. For he does not enjoy hurting people or causing them sorrow.... Can anything happen without the Lord's permission?'"

I watched Jill's expression as she tried to swallow the strong words. She turned to me with a hopeful smile. "It's taken me two years to believe that God didn't utterly abandon me. He does show compassion. It's taken me this long to begin to believe that."

"I admire you so much, Jill."

"I don't know if I'm to be admired. I still have a hard time with the last part of that passage. If nothing happens without the Lord's permission, then why would such a compassionate God give permission for Ray to die? It doesn't make sense to me. I keep looking for a reason, but there isn't any."

I still didn't know how Ray had died, so I felt inadequate to offer any suggestions. Over the years I'd heard plenty of answers to that question from friends at church, but here, in this place of upside down, none of those reasons seemed to fit.

"Do you think God is fair?" Jill asked.

I wasn't sure how to answer that. What came out of my mouth was, "He must not be."

Jill looked surprised.

"I mean, I've never done anything to deserve the love and mercy He gives me each day. If He were fair, I'd be condemned."

Jill looked down at her hands for a long pause. "I guess it does work both ways, doesn't it? That is, if there's a balance in life the same way there is in art, we don't deserve all the good things He gives us, do we?"

"I know I don't."

"And His love is pretty generous, when you think of all the things that could go wrong every day."

"I happen to have a verse about that." I turned to the Ephesians passage I liked so much. "Tell me what you think of this. 'Mostly what God does is love you. Keep company with him and learn a life of love. Observe how Christ loved us. His love was not cautious but extravagant. He didn't love in order to get something from us but to give everything of himself to us. Love like that.'"

"'Not cautious but extravagant,'" Jill repeated. "That's hard to do after you've been hurt deeply."

I nodded even though I knew I'd never experienced the same deep wound that Jill had.

"Would it be okay if I copied that verse?"

"Sure." I handed her the devotional book and headed for the shower. Turning at the bathroom door, I said, "I still believe what I said to you the day we had tea at my house. You are not invisible. To other people or to God. You are very much alive, Jill."

Her smile broke the somber cloud she had been sitting under. "Thanks, Kathy."

While I showered and finished dressing and packing up, Jill went to gather information from the concierge about where we could find a "real, live kangaroo." The option she chose was a wildlife park outside the city, not far from the Olympic stadium.

Jill and I rented a car, this time directly from the hotel. The vehicle was equipped with a satellite navigational system that saved us from getting lost and driving around in circles.

The automated voice on the directional system said, "Turn right five hundred meters ahead," and we turned right. It was a wonderful thing.

We pulled into the Olympic Park and drove around looking at the arenas. Jill found a parking place, and we walked to the main square. Seeing the structure where the Olympic torch for the 2000 games had burned so brightly choked me up. The huge Olympic "cauldron," as they called it, was now a spectacular fountain at the center of a park surrounded by leafy fig trees. What got to me was the awareness that I was standing in a place where history had been made.

Jill was even more affected by the fountain. When I looked at her, tears were streaming down her cheeks.

"I'm sorry I keep crying all the time."

"That's okay."

"It's just that Ray came here. For the 2000 games. He and I were supposed to come for four days, but I had a sinus infection that went into my ears. I was afraid if I got on a plane my eardrums would burst. So Ray came by himself and had a wonderful time without me."

She drew in a wobbly breath. "I never knew I'd regret losing four days with him out of the thousands we spent together. If I had it to do over, I would have chanced the burst eardrums."

I paused a moment. "No, you probably wouldn't have."

Jill looked at me, surprised for the second time that morning by my quiet irreverence to her lament.

"I mean, maybe you would have done things differently, if given the chance. But, really, Jill, you made the best decision at that time based on the circumstances."

She adjusted her sunglasses. "You're right. When you think you have all the time in the world with someone, you focus more on yourself than on him."

We walked around the fountain in silence, reading the names of the athletes who had received medals at the 2000 games etched in the pavement.

"Thank you," Jill said as we got back in the car.

"For what?"

"For telling me what I needed to hear. It's as if all these small doors in my heart keep opening and the closed-up hurt and tears come pouring out. You must be sick of this by now."

"Not yet."

"The only good is that each time one of those doors opens, I feel as if I'm healing. You keep giving me truth, Kathy, and I need that. When I'm left to my own imagination, I tell myself all kinds of things. Not everything I tell myself is true."

"We all do that. More than once you've given me truth, you know."

"All I know is that having you here, right now during this time in my life, feels like God sent an extravagant gift to me. I mean, when I think about it, he brought you here all the way from my grandpa's orange grove!"

"So what you're saying is that you see me as a big fruit, is that it?"

Jill chuckled.

I tried to honor the seriousness of her observation. What I intended to say was, "I've benefited greatly from your friendship, too, you know." But what came out was, "I've bene-fruited from your friendship, too, you know."

That's when we both cracked up.

"We make quite a pear," Jill said between her laughter bubbles. "Get it? Pair? Pear?"

It took a few minutes for us to compose ourselves before Jill started the engine. I punched in the wildlife park's address on the keyboard for the directional system, and a map with a red line showed up on the screen. We dabbed away our giggle-tears, and before long found ourselves winding through a hilly canyon that we both said reminded us of Trabuco Canyon in California. The eucalyptus trees were what made the connection for me.

The park wasn't large, and only a few visitors strolled around. But our timing was perfect because we arrived five minutes before the feeding of the koalas. The fuzzy, gray fur balls draped themselves in the most humorous poses over a dozen tree stands. We stood only a few feet away from the open area and watched the sluggish snuggle bears while they did absolutely nothing but try to keep from falling off their posts.

A park guide entered the center area with switches of fresh eucalyptus. One of the eight koala bears opened his eyes long enough to pay attention to what was happening.

"Come here, then, Victor." She reached for the koala by the arms and pulled him toward her the way I'd seen a chimpanzee reach for a long-armed baby chimp. The guide positioned Victor on the railing, handed him a sprig of eucalyptus leaves, and filled the visitors in on the facts about koalas. The one bit of information that everyone laughed at was how the average koala sleeps for eighteen hours a day.

"Think about that the next time your teenager doesn't want to get out of bed on a Saturday."

We were invited to come close and have our pictures taken with Victor. Jill pulled out her camera and snapped a shot of me with my arm around the oblivious fellow while he munched on leaves with his eyes half shut. I couldn't believe how soft he was. I'd heard a mom call her little girl a "cuddly koala" on one of our earlier bus rides, and now that phrase had more meaning. This little guy was irresistibly snuggly.

Jill took her turn for the picture. I snapped three from different angles. A startling sound made us stop and look around.

"What was that?" I asked.

"Kookaburra," the park guide said. "It's a bird with a loud call."

"Sounds like a donkey," Jill said.

"You'll find the kookaburras in the aviary by going left on the trail through the park."

"What about the kangaroos?" I asked.

"Keep to the right on the trail."

We set off and found a sign at the trails' intersection. Arrows pointed to our options of animals to visit. I read the list aloud. "Wallabies, dingoes, emus, wallaroos, wombats…here we are. Grey kangaroos. This direction."

"This seems unreal, doesn't it?" Jill asked.

"What do you mean?"

"All these animals! It's hard to believe they're real."

"You just touched a koala bear," I said.

"I know. But the sign could point us to the unicorn pen, and I'd believe there was such a thing as a unicorn."

I knew I'd feel the same way the moment I saw a real, live kangaroo up close. Kangaroos always seemed mythical to me. I didn't know if it was the concept of the built-in front pocket, which any mother could make good use of, or if it was the way they hopped. All I knew was that, according to the sign, if we stayed on this path, we would come face-to-face with a real, live kangaroo.

Eighteen

A fence and a low gate with a simple latch enclosed the kangaroo area at the wildlife park. Jill lifted the latch, and we entered a dirt area that was partially shaded. To my delight, a kangaroo about two feet tall came hopping over.

I chortled. "It's a kangaroo!"

"What were you expecting?"

"It's hopping! Look! It's a hopping kangaroo."

"That's what they do, Kathy."

"I know, but this is my unicorn, like you were just saying. I can't believe it's real and that they let us come into this area with them. Hello, little guy. You are so cute. You know I have food, don't you?"

When we bought our entry tickets to the park, we had also purchased two bags labeled "kangaroo food." I opened my bag and looked inside to see what kangaroos liked to eat.

"Cheerios? Jill, look! The kangaroo food is Cheerios! Do you know how much I've missed Cheerios since we left California? I can't believe the kangaroos get to eat Cheerios!"

"Maybe it isn't really Cheerios." Jill sniffed the contents of her kangaroo food bag. "Maybe it just looks like Cheerios."

"It smells like Cheerios." I held a small amount in my hand and smelled the round o's.

"Kathy, you're not going to eat them, are you?"

"Why not? They're Cheerios."

"You don't know that. Not for sure."

My mouth was just an inch from my handful of Cheerios. My tongue slid over my lower lip, oh so willing to connect with one of the tiny o's.

"Kathy, don't do it!" Jill squealed. "You should see yourself! You look so funny. Even if those are Cheerios, you don't know where those little o's have been."

I pulled back my tongue. "You're right."

While we carried on our Cheerios debate, the kangaroos in the open area were slowly hopping toward us. I looked down, and one fellow was checking around my feet for any dropped treats.

"Put some in your hand, and see if he'll eat out of your palm." Jill reached for the camera.

"What if he bites the hand that feeds him?"

"Then I'll take a nice close-up shot for the insurance claim."

"I don't see you sticking your hand out here."

"Somebody has to take the pictures."

The patient little kangaroo looked up at me with the most adorable doe eyes I'd ever seen. The long, innocent lashes seemed to be batting at me, pleading for me to share my precious Cheerios.

"Hello," I said to the unafraid kangaroo. "Or should I say, g'day?"

He rose to his full height and came up to my hip.

"Are you hungry? These are Cheerios, you know. Do you like Cheerios?"

"They're not Cheerios," Jill said.

"Don't listen to her. I know Cheerios when I see them. And you are so cute I'm going to share my Cheerios with you. Here."

He put out his small paws so that they held steady my hand. With a flick of his long, dry tongue, this real, live kangaroo ate out of my hand.

I laughed with glee. "His tongue tickles! Look at him! He is so adorable! I want to take him home with me!"

Another kangaroo rose from the shade and hopped over on feet the size of baby-sized water skis. I laughed again. I couldn't help it. These guys were irresistible. Their ears stood straight up, flicking, listening, picking up every sound.

The other kangaroo joined the littler one, and the two of them peaceably ate together from my hand.

"Here you go. Hang on. Let me get some more. Jill, you have to feed one of them. They are so sweet."

"I'll feed this one," she said, as a larger kangaroo came bounding our way. It was about three feet away when Jill let out a soft squeal. "Kathy, look! This one has a baby. In her pocket!"

I thought I was going to cry, I was so happy. The image of that mama kangaroo hopping over to us and standing mere inches away with her little joey popping out of her pouch had to be one of the most amazing things I'd ever seen.

Jill giggled.

I was right with her. "I can't believe you're real," I said to the kangaroos. It was as if a fairy tale had come true before my eyes.

Jill's infectious laughter filled the air. The unafraid kangaroos came closer, their big eyes looking up at us with curious blinks. The joey stuck one arm out of his mama's pouch, then the other, and twisted around, as if trying to look up into our faces. The first kangaroo rested his tiny paw on my leg, the way a toddler reaches to feel the security of his mother beside him.

The delight of that moment imbedded itself in my mind as sweetly and as permanently as the memory of my first kiss.

I touched the soft fur of the steady fellow and whispered, "You're real."

Much later that same night when I arrived home, Tony said he wanted to hear all about our trip. My conversation kept returning to the kangaroos.

"You really liked those magical marsupials, didn't you? Or was it the Cheerios you were really crazy about?"

I threw a pillow at him. "You would have been proud of me. I didn't eat any of the kanga food. I thought about it, but I didn't snatch a single *o*. I couldn't once I saw those darling faces with those big eyes looking up at me." I demonstrated with my best kangaroo expression.

Tony smiled. "I love it when you're like this."

"Like what?"

"Full of life. Happy."

"Do you really want to see me full of life? Then let's go to Australia. You and me. What do you think?" I snuggled up to Tony.

"You just want to go back and see your kangaroo pals."

"Yes, and other parts of the country. The concierge at the hotel told us we needed to come back in the winter to go skiing in the south. He said the season opens in June. Isn't that crazy? Skiing in July? That's too late for us, though, because we'll be back in California by then."

"Maybe," Tony said.

"What do you mean *maybe*?" I watched his expression closely to make sure he wasn't joking around.

"I put my name in today for another project. It doesn't mean I'll get it, and it doesn't mean I'll take it if it's offered. We had a big meeting this morning. Walter announced his next production and gave all of us a chance to put in for specific positions before the studio goes public with the project."

"What's the film?"

Tony smiled but kept his lips sealed. I knew that meant that if he told me he would have to kill me. Insiders are very loyal in his industry when it comes to not releasing information on a film before the studio is ready to issue a press release. Anyone who slips and divulges information is treated like an infidel and is kept out of the loop on further industry disclosures.

"What do you think?" Tony asked.

"If you have the chance to take the job and you really want it, then take it, Tony."

"Are you sure?"

"Yes."

"I know it was hard for you when we first got here. You've done a great job of making the best of it. I don't want to put too much of a strain on you."

"You're not. I'm okay with staying. Really."

Tony scratched the back of his neck and looked at me as if to say, *"Who are you and what have you done with the wife I brought over here with me?"*

"I thought you wouldn't like the idea because it would

mean staying here longer, and if you're eager to go back to school, it could slow down that process."

"It might. Or I might be able to take classes here. I don't know. I'm not worried about that right now, Tony. What matters the most to me is that you have a chance to pursue some of your dreams. My turn will come."

Something inside of me felt that was true. That's the only way to describe what I was feeling. I didn't know how to express it. In my heart, I knew that God was extravagant with His love and His gifts to His children. I also knew that this was a time for me to be extravagant with my husband by giving him all the freedom he needed to pursue this next opportunity. It felt right.

Tony didn't seem to know what to say, but it didn't matter. What followed were lots of mushy kisses and not a lot of words.

On Wednesday, Jill and I met at the Chocolate Fish at our usual table. Tracey brought a whole plate of chocolate fish and pulled up a chair, eager to hear all our stories about Sydney. Jill presented Tracey with one of our little squeaking kangaroos. Tracey laughed and said she would let him ride around on the dashboard of Beatrice.

"Or better yet," Tracey said, "how about if I manage some sort of pouch on the front of Beatrice? We could tuck this little joey in the pocket on the grille."

I didn't doubt that Tracey might try such a setup just to watch our reactions.

"I'm so glad you're getting out and getting on with your life, Jill. It's a good thing. I'm sure you know that."

Jill nodded. "I know. I can't believe how much has changed for me in the past few weeks."

"It's ever since *she* showed up." Tracey grinned and pretended to shield her mouth, as if I couldn't hear her.

"I'm sitting right here, you know."

"I know. And I hope you know how great it is that you showed up when you did. Which reminds me, what are you two doing Friday night?"

Jill and I both said we had no plans.

"Then what do you think of the three of us having a girls' night out? I thought we could go to the movies."

"Sounds fun."

"Good. We have a plan. Now, I'd love to sit here another hour, but there's no telling what state the kitchen has gotten into while I've been chatting." Tracey started walking away and added, "I'll pick you up in Bea around six-thirty on Friday. And dress like you mean it."

Jill and I swapped glances that said we weren't sure what Tracey's last line meant. All I knew was that I had a ton of laundry to do. I told Jill, "I've been waiting for another sunny day, so I can hang the clothes outside instead of in the bathtub. I'm beginning to miss having a clothes dryer more than I thought I would."

"More than Cheerios?" Jill asked.

"Yes, more than Cheerios."

"What else do you miss?"

"A little bit of everything, but nothing so much that I can't wait to go back." I was about to tell Jill about the possibility of Tony's extended assignment, but for some reason it seemed better to wait until the possibility was stronger. I could see the two of us making plans to do something four months from now, and then, if Tony didn't get the job, it would feel like the disastrous bathing suit shopping experience. It seemed better to keep quiet until I could talk confidently about staying.

"You know what I realized the other day? I miss teaching," Jill said.

"You do?"

"I really do. I haven't taught for the past few years, but after you were so kind as to play the role of the interested student at the art museum in Sydney, I've been thinking about how much I love it."

"I wasn't playing the role of the interested student. I was interested. I'm sure I gave you a hard time about it, but, Jill, you're a great teacher. I learned so much. You have such a freshness and passion in the way you explain everything."

"I forgot I had that passion."

"Well, the passion is definitely back. You should do something about it."

Jill looked out the window at the water and drew in a deep breath, as if she were trying to breathe in the fresh, salty air. I realized this was the same profile I'd seen the day we met. But this time, instead of tears on her face, I saw a chin-up look of determination.

"Maybe this is the treasure you're holding in your hand," I suggested, thinking of the painting we had enjoyed together in Sydney.

Jill swished her lips back and forth the way she did when she was contemplating something. "No," she said after a moment. "This isn't it. Feeling the passion for teaching is a good thing, but this isn't the treasure I hold in my hand."

"Do you know what it is?"

"Not yet."

"I almost forgot." I reached into my purse and pulled out a card-sized envelope. "It's not exactly a treasure by any means, but I do have a little something for you. Here."

Jill looked at the envelope. "You're not going to believe this, but I have a card for you, too."

We exchanged envelopes, and I opened mine first. On the front of the homemade card Jill had doodled an adorable mama kangaroo. She had bright pink lips; long, flippy eyelashes; and a broad Manly Beach hat on her head. In her pouch was a box of tissues.

Inside Jill had written, "Thanks for showing up when you did, Kathy. You have no idea how much I appreciate you. I have thanked God a million times for you and the sunshine of your friendship. If you ever need me for anything, just say the word, and I'll be there in one big kangaroo hop."

"I love it, Jill. Thank you." I flipped back to the kangaroo doodle on the front and smiled. "This is so cute."

"I considered adding Cheerios," Jill said dryly. "But I was afraid you'd try to lick them off the paper."

"Very funny."

As Jill opened my envelope, I felt compelled to apologize. "Now remember, I'm not an artist like you."

"I'm not an artist," Jill said quickly.

"Yes, you are! Look at this. I could never draw like this."

"I'm a doodler, Kathy. Not an artist."

"Doodling is art."

She pulled my card out of the envelope. "And so is this! How fun! The feathers!"

"You recognize them?"

"Of course. Although they did look a little more artsy in your hair than here on paper."

"That's because I'm not an artist. Not even a doodler."

Jill opened the card and read my one-liner aloud. "'Sisterchicks of a feather sip lattes together!' How perfect!"

"I hope I managed to glue the two feathers at the right median and interpose the best ratio balance for the canvas."

Jill cracked up. "You were listening."

"Told you I was. If an art appreciation class doesn't open up for you to teach, I think you should consider leading art appreciation tours. I'd be the first to sign up."

"Now that sounds like fun. How about art tours to Paris? They have that big Louvre, you know." Her twinkling-eyed expression made it clear that she thought she was flinging out the wildest of all possibilities.

I wasn't ready to scale it down. "Why not? You have the time, the expertise, and you love to travel. There's no reason you shouldn't lead art appreciation tours to Paris."

Jill looked as if a whirlwind of possibilities was about to sweep her up and transport her to an exotic locale.

I knew that feeling.

Nineteen

Friday morning I asked Tony if he had heard anything new on the job opening. He said, "Mad Dog thinks they hit a judder bar with the finances. Nothing new. Happens all the time."

"Wait. What did you say? They hit a what?"

Tony thought back on what he had said. "Oh, a judder bar."

"And what is a judder bar?"

Tony smiled and wheeled his bike toward the door. "Haven't you heard that one around here yet? That's what the guys at work call a speed bump. I gotta go, Kath. I love you."

I kissed him as he flew out the door and called out, "Make sure you don't hit any judder bars!"

I had some wet laundry ready to hang on the line, and the morning sunshine motivated me to jump on the chore. The act of standing and stretching my arms over my head to fasten sheets and shirts and even my underwear to the clothesline had become a small act of worship. I loved the way the soft breezes would come and make the clothes move. My pj's danced without music. In a funny little way, I envied them.

Tony called my cell phone around four o'clock, and I reminded him that I'd made plans to go to the movies with Tracey and Jill that night.

"Maybe you and Mad Dog can do something after work," I suggested.

"No can do. Mad Dog has a blind date."

"A blind date? With whom?"

Tony paused. "If he knew, it wouldn't be a blind date, now would it?"

"Tell him I hope it goes well."

"Yeah, well, if it doesn't go well, I'm his out."

"What do you mean?"

"If he wants an excuse to leave, he's going to dial my cell and hang up. I'm supposed to call him back and make it sound like he has to come to the studio immediately."

"I can't believe you guys are doing that! How do you think the poor woman is going to feel?"

Tony hesitated again, as if I'd missed the obvious. "Have you forgotten who we're talking about here? This is Mad Dog. What woman wouldn't thank me for making the call?"

"Tony!"

"Don't worry. Mad Dog is standing right here. I'm just giving him a hard time. You should see the guy. He's as nervous as a cat. A Mad Cat."

In the background I heard a loud "meow!"

"What are you planning to do, then? Are you going to come home and wait for Mad Dog's call or stay there at work?"

"I think I'll stay here. Don't worry about me. I have plenty to do."

"Okay. I'll see you when I get back."

Tony's voice took on an ethereal quality as he added, "I hope you and your friends have the time of your life during this time of your life."

He was mocking Tracey's inspirational line, but I didn't care. I kind of liked being in his lineup of friends that he could tease. It was a good place for our marriage to be.

Beatrice, the Blazing Bumble Bee, pulled up in the gravel driveway at precisely 6:35, and I was ready to go. Jill and Tracey looked gorgeous. Both of them had done their hair and makeup with a little more pizzazz than usual. Jill had on a lime green sweater set with the sleeves pushed up and a row of beaded bracelets on her forearm. She looked fresh and cute.

"I don't think I dressed up enough." I looked at my knit shirt, jeans, and athletic shoes.

"We have time, if you want to make a quick change," Tracey said. "It's up to you."

"I'll be right back." Dashing inside, I remembered that Tracey had told us to dress like we meant it. I wasn't sure on Wednesday what that meant, and now I wasn't sure what combination in my wardrobe would fit that description. Going for a pair of sandals instead of the running shoes was a good first step. The jeans were okay, but I dressed them up with a crisp white blouse that I'd ironed for the trip to Sydney and then hadn't packed. One of the plusses of having dark hair and eyes was that anytime I wore white, I looked like I'd cleaned up. The opal earrings and necklace I bought in Sydney were a quick add-on, and I was out the door.

"Classy," Jill said, when I slid in the front seat next to her.

"That's a great look on you," Tracey agreed. "Love the earrings."

"Thanks. Sorry to keep you waiting."

"No worries. We have time." Tracey eased Bea out of the driveway and down the road.

We chatted like a box of budgies, which I'd learned meant we sounded like a bunch of cheerful, twittering birds. When Tracey approached the Embassy Theatre, I knew where we were. That was a Wellington first for me.

"Are you two popcorn eaters?" Tracey asked. "Or should we go out for Pavlova afterward?"

I didn't know what Pavlova was, but popcorn seemed mandatory for a girls' night out at the movies.

"We're getting it with extra butter, of course," Tracey said, as we stepped in line at the concession stand. "And three large diet soft drinks to cancel the effects of the extra butter."

The three of us were chuckling at the universal female dieting logic, when a man came up behind Jill and said, "If you're the lady in green, I'm the man in black."

We all turned and I nearly shrieked. "Mad Dog!"

He stumbled back half a step on the plush carpet. "Kathleen, what are you doing here?"

"Mad Dog?" Jill echoed.

"Hallo!" Tracey said.

I'd never seen Mad Dog look so stunned. He even took off his cap and greeted Jill with reverence.

Jill barely moved.

Mad Dog nervously glanced at me and then at Tracey. I saw the cell phone looped on his belt buckle, ready to draw.

Regaining his composure, Mad Dog said, "Ahh, just wanted to…yeah. Well. Have a nice evening. Hope you enjoy the show." He looked over the top of my head, and by his expression it was clear that another woman dressed in green had entered the building.

Mad Dog bolted across the lobby, and the three of us watched as a young-looking blonde in a tight emerald green sweater smiled and responded to his pickup line.

"Well, Bob's your uncle," Tracey said. "That was a bit on the awkward side, wasn't it?"

Jill still hadn't said anything.

It was our turn to order. Tracey stepped up to the counter and asked for a tub of buttered popcorn. "Jill, you want anything else?"

"No."

We found three seats near the front, and Jill settled in the middle between Tracey and me. I looked around the beautifully refurbished theater and felt as if we had stepped back in time to an era when viewing a film was a big event and everyone dressed up for the occasion.

I kept glancing at Jill to see if she had snapped out of the haze she slipped into after the less-than-suave encounter with Mad Dog. Obviously more happened in the concession line than Mad Dog mistaking his blind date's identity.

"You know, Jill." Tracey leaned over with the tub of popcorn on her lap. "If you think you might be interested in a blind date yourself one of these days, I have a possibility in mind for you."

"That's okay."

"No, really. This guy has a great personality."

Jill still wasn't smiling. I couldn't tell if Tracey was teasing or really trying to set up Jill.

"He has a great sense of humor, too."

"Not interested."

"His name is—"

"I don't want to know." Jill's freshly manicured fingers covered Tracey's mouth.

"But he has nothing to do with the film industry," Tracey said as the lights dimmed.

"Still not interested."

In one final attempt, Tracey leaned over and said, "He delivers our buns."

That one got Jill. A slight grin inched across her lips. She turned to me. "Will you trade places with me?"

I knew she wasn't serious about trading. I was beginning to catch on to the sarcastic twist in Kiwi humor.

"Come on, Kathy, trade places with me. Please?"

"He has really large buns," Tracey said in an exaggeratedly loud whisper.

Jill reached for a handful of popcorn and told Tracey to "shush" upon threat of being assaulted with the popcorn.

The three of us laughed a lot during the film. Not because the movie was hilarious, but because Tracey kept slipping in more strategic puns. Bun puns, to be precise.

We left the theater feeling euphoric.

"Pavlova anyone?" Tracey asked. "I thought we would go to Sophie's. Have you been there yet, Kathy?"

"No, I take all my dining business to the Chocolate Fish."

"Good answer," Tracey said. "Remind me to give you a chocolate fish next time you're in."

"I'm beginning to feel like a trained seal with all the little fish you keep tossing at me."

Tracey laughed and promised she would cut back on the fish treats. "Either that or you'll have to equip our table with a row of squeaky horns, so I can start entertaining the other guests."

Jill laughed that time, and I felt so happy.

There is nothing as fabulous as the feeling of belonging.

Sophie's turned out to be a small restaurant in the Lambton Quay area. As we entered, Tracey told us that Wellington had more restaurants and cafés per capita than New York City.

"I'm always ready to scout new places to eat," she said, as the three of us took our seats at a table in the corner. "Unless the restaurant is in the wop wops."

"Out in the boonies," Jill translated for me.

"A wop wop would be a great name for a kiddy treat," I said. "It's so fun to say. Wop wops. Wop wops. Try it. Wop wops."

Tracey looked at Jill. "Now I'm the one who wants to change seats. You can sit by the wop-wop woman."

The waitress stepped up to our table, and Tracey said, "Cappuccinos all around?"

"Decaf," I said.

Tracey turned to me as if I'd ordered denture cream. "Decaf? Oh, come on, Kathy, live a little!"

"Okay, regular."

We all laughed some more. The waitress walked away, not at all impressed with our humor.

"Jill," Tracey's expression turned earnest, "I'm glad you bounced back."

Jill nodded.

"It's a new day." Tracey continued her pep talk. I assumed they were talking about the awkward encounter with Mad Dog, but I didn't know if I should enter the conversation. It felt catty to say that I knew he was going on a blind date. What I didn't know was Jill's connection with Mad Dog or why seeing each other had affected them so intensely.

Our cappuccinos came, and we let Tracey order dessert for us since she kept saying Sophie's made the best Pavlova in town. Tracey said she was eager to hear my opinion of the dessert, as an unbiased American. I told her I had nothing to compare it to since, as far as I knew, I'd never had Pavlova.

"Have you told her the story behind it?" Tracey asked Jill.

Jill shook her head so Tracey jumped right in. "Supposedly when the Russian ballerina Anna Pavlova came to New Zealand, a chef created this airy dessert to keep the dancer light on her feet when she performed. The Australians say they created it, but the Kiwis know it came from one of their chefs first."

"So what's in a Pavlova?" I asked.

"It's made of egg whites," Jill said. "Sort of a sweet meringue. Sometimes it has fruit on top; other times it's drizzled with chocolate. I've never had one I didn't like."

The Pavlova looked like a slice of pie, cut in a triangle shape, covered with raspberries, chocolate sauce, and a fat dollop of whipping cream. The texture was light and airy, and the taste was sweet, but not too sugary sweet.

"Two thumbs up," I said after the first bite.

Tracey grinned. "We'll make a Kiwi out of you yet. We did a pretty good job with Jill, don't you think? Oh, there's Susanne! Hallo! Do you two know Susanne?"

"No." We smiled and politely nodded at the young woman who had just entered the restaurant.

"If you don't mind, I'm going to pop over and say hallo. I'll bring her back around to introduce you." Tracey slid out of her seat and met Susanne with Tracey's trademark bright greeting and cheery hug. Instead of returning to the table, the two of them began a head-tilting, much-nodding sort of conversation.

Jill looked down at her unfinished Pavlova and smoothed her finger over the handle of her cappuccino cup. She let out a long sigh and blinked, as if trying to keep back the tears.

"You okay?"

"Kathy, do you know how Ray died?"

"No."

"Do you mean Tony still hasn't said anything to you?"

"No."

"Or Mad Dog?"

"No. I never asked either of them. Like I told you that night in the hotel in Christchurch, if and when you want to tell me, I want to hear. But you don't have to tell me anything, if you don't want to. It won't change my relationship with you one way or the other."

Jill's expression was one of gratitude. "Jackamond is such a small studio. I thought for sure someone would have said something to you by now. I didn't want to be the one to bring it up."

"You don't have to say anything, if you don't want to."

"No, I want you to know. I want to be the one to tell you. I'm ready to talk about it now." Jill lifted her chin, her expression steady. "I was there the day Ray died."

She took a breath and added, "And so was Mad Dog."

Twenty

Jill adjusted her position in her chair so she could speak quietly. I leaned closer, knowing this was the final door in her heart to open.

"Ray was a location manager. He would go ahead of the production company and scout out locations for a shoot, but…I'm sorry—you know what a location manager is."

"That's okay. Just say whatever you want to say."

"I got so used to telling the story for the reporters and the lawyers. Let me start again." She took a tiny sip of her cappuccino to fuel her efforts.

"Ray had scouted a location for a Jackamond coproduction. It was at Oriental Bay, which isn't far from here. The site was an old warehouse on the wharf. Ray obtained all the clearances to use the warehouse, and it passed the safety inspection, so he went down with a small team to run some test shots. The editing department reviewed the shots and made some recommendations for the lighting."

Like Jill, I was familiar with the steps taken before the actual shooting. But I was feeling a lurch in my stomach. I knew about the warehouse accident. And not just because of Tony's job. The trade journals ran articles on it, pointing out the unnecessary risks taken in the increasingly competitive film industry. I didn't stop Jill to tell her that. I wanted her to have the freedom to say whatever she needed to.

"Ray took me with him that day. We planned to go to lunch after the test shots. Mad Dog met us there, and the three of us went into the building. The structure looked reliable; otherwise, we wouldn't have gone in. The rest of the crew hadn't shown up yet."

Jill swallowed. "The authorities think it might have been the strain from the camera crew and all their equipment in the warehouse a few days earlier, but no one knows exactly why the floor broke through. Ray and Mad Dog fell into the water. I was standing back and lost my balance, but I didn't fall in."

She blinked back the tears. "I thought it was going to be like in the movies. They would come bobbing up in the water, laughing like Mel Gibson and Danny Glover."

The first tear rolled over her cheek. "But when I moved closer to the edge, I could see that it was a mess under the wharf. Cement blocks were sticking up, and sharp boards floated on top of the dark water. Ray surfaced with blood on his forehead. He called out my name, and I yelled back that I was okay.

"Then he called out, 'Mad Dog,' and I screamed, 'Ray, don't go back under!' But he did. Mad Dog was unconscious, so Ray pushed him up to the surface and tried to get him balanced on one of the protruding blocks of cement. Then Ray just slipped back down under the water. We found out later he had broken his ankle and several ribs when he fell. One of the broken ribs punctured his right lung and…"

My hand closed around Jill's wrist. I gave her a comforting squeeze. "You don't need to say any more." I knew the story from there. Mad Dog had a broken arm and a concussion. The court case against the studio had become cumbersome because the wharf was part of a historical site, and a former studio employee testified that Mad Dog had a reputation for being reckless.

Reaching into my purse with my free hand, I offered Jill a tissue and kept one for my tears as well.

"You know what?" She dabbed her eyes. "It feels different telling this to you. I've told it so many times to so many people who wanted to pick apart the facts. I feel like I don't have to explain any of it with you. I can just put it out there and let it be what it is."

All kinds of thoughts raced though my mind as I fumbled to find something comforting to say. But I didn't let a single syllable slip from my lips. It was not my place to label this experience for Jill; my part in her life was to be her friend. Sometimes true friends say the most when they don't say anything.

Tracey returned to the table, introduced us to Susanne, and after a few moments of polite conversation, we ended our girls' night out with Tracey single-handedly carrying the conversation all the way home. Fortunately, this wasn't a challenge for dear Tracey.

Tony was waiting up. I told him everything.

"I never made the connection that Jill was Ray's wife," he said.

Tony told me that Mad Dog never had talked about the accident. Tony hadn't put the pieces together.

"I'm having a hard time finding a place to put these feelings. I mean, I like Mad Dog, of course. I'm glad he's still alive. But Ray sounds like he was an amazing man. If God was going to rescue one person from that fall, why did he choose Mad Dog?"

Tony looked stunned.

"What are you thinking?" I asked.

"You used the word *fall*," he said.

"Right. They fell through the floor."

"I know. I've heard the story a dozen times. I just never got it. It's a perfect picture."

Once again my husband had edited his thoughts so quickly I was lost. "A perfect picture of what?"

"Christ. Why did He rescue any of us after the fall? He gave up His life for us."

I didn't like Tony's edited version of the traumatic events one bit. For hours I lay awake rearranging all the information my brain had been given that night. The only settling thought I could manage was that I, too, had been rescued after the fall. It wasn't because of anything I had done, but God's extravagant love had reached down and rescued me, taking me from death to life.

I wanted my life to count for something. I wanted to live out the rest of my days expressing that same extravagant love to others. I didn't want to be cautious and live out a string of unfulfilled days, pitifully folded up into myself. I wanted full days and a full life.

It occurred to me, as dawn softly brought her warming glow through the curtains, that I had just been given the answer to my math equation. Forty-five years plus extravagant love would equal the kind of life I wanted to live, no matter how many days or years were left.

By noon I was done with all the pondering. I wanted to be with Jill. I called and asked if she wanted to meet for a latte.

"Would you mind coming to my house instead? I'm not dressed for going out, but you're welcome to come over."

All the way to Jill's I wondered if the events of last night had sent her into a slump. I expected to find her in her pajamas when she opened the door, but instead, she was wearing tattered painting clothes.

"Come see what I've done."

Jill led me to her bedroom and opened the door to show me the half-finished paint job. All her furniture was covered with plastic tarps; she had taped the edging of the baseboards. The color was a rich shade of pumpkin orange.

"Wow!" I said.

"I've had the paint for a couple of years. Ray and I were always going to do this when we had time, but you know what? We never had time. I have time. I woke up at 4 AM and decided I had time to do this. What do you think of the color?"

"I love it."

"Really?"

"Reminds me of an orange grove," I said with a warm smile.

"That's what I thought, too."

"Do you want some help?"

"You're dressed too nicely," Jill said.

"No, I'm not. Give me an old shirt like you're wearing, and I'll be fine. I don't care about these jeans."

Jill looked at the shirt she had on. It hung off her shoulders and almost to her knees. "This was one of Ray's," she said with the corners of her lips upturned.

"He was a big man!" I wished the words hadn't flipped out of my mouth the way they had.

"Yes, he was," Jill said proudly. "He was an awesome man. A very big man." She tilted her head. "Do you want to see our wedding pictures?"

"What about painting the room?"

"I need a break," she said. "I want you to see our pictures."

For the next two hours, Jill took me to visit her life when Ray ruled the world. She likened it to when dinosaurs ruled the planet, because he was larger than life. I loved hearing the stories and watching her face light up with each page she turned. I was still processing the details of Ray's death, as if it had just happened the night before. Jill was moving forward. She undoubtedly had relived the experience a thousand times. Now she was thinking about other things. She was in such a different place from the person I had met less than two months earlier.

"I've been thinking about what you said about going to Paris," Jill said.

"Paris?"

"Giving the art tours," Jill said.

"You were the one who brought up Paris," I reminded her with a tease in my voice. "Something about art museums and your friends Mona and Monet."

"Mona?"

"Lisa." The way I said it sounded as if I were trying to play a swimming pool game of Marco Polo.

Jill laughed. "I'm considering leading art tours to Paris. So what do you think of that?"

"I think Bob's your uncle, and the world is waiting for all you have to offer."

Jill filled her quiet home with the sweetest, most endearing laughter. "It's more like, God's my Father, and He has a handful of mercies He's been waiting to give me."

On that note, Jill and I turned our attention to her paint job. We came up with all kinds of new decorating ideas, including the upside-down parasol as a light fixture.

"All we have to do now," I said, "is go shopping for a parasol."

"Oh, isn't that too bad; we have to go shopping."

"And get someone from the studio to come over and rewire the light. I'll ask Tony to have one of the lighting guys over."

"Make sure he doesn't ask anyone in special effects. When we first moved in, Ray had a special effects guy wire our front patio for us."

"What happened? I would think he'd do an extremely good job."

"*Extreme* is the key word in that sentence. I had a laser show on my front deck every time I turned on the lights. If we had music going while we were out there, the lights pulsed with the music. The neighbors thought the wacky Americans were trying to host an outdoor disco."

"Is it still hooked up?"

"No, I dismantled the system."

"By yourself?"

"Never underestimate the power of a woman with a pair of wire cutters."

It seemed Jill was about to surpass me as the queen of one-liners the way she was going.

During the next week we shopped till we dropped or one of Jill's hot flashes made us stop. We found the perfect parasol along with an assortment of must-haves such as nightstands, a shower curtain, a waffle maker, and eight CDs with fun music that got Jill's head and shoulders bobbing whenever she put one on.

I told Tony it was like having a baby shower, the way we were buying everything Jill needed to prepare for her new life. She said she was making up for not buying anything other than food the past two years.

Ten days after starting the renovation, Jill's home felt new. She and I had painted three more rooms, hung new curtains, and had one of the living room chairs reupholstered. Her beautiful wooden bowl from the Saturday market in Sydney sat in a prominent place on the coffee table. In the bowl she cradled a handful of postcards from the locales she and I had been.

We were rearranging the furniture when, out of thin air, Jill said, "There's one thing I didn't tell you about Ray, and I think I need to tell you now."

I found it hard to believe there was any detail about Ray I didn't know. While we had been working side by side for the past week and a half, Jill had reminisced about Ray as a sort of final cleansing. With each story from their years together, she seemed to find a place to put that experience in the new structure of her future. I was there mostly to listen and wield a steady paintbrush.

I leaned against the edge of the couch. "What's that?"

"It's actually more about Mad Dog than it is about Ray." Jill brushed the bangs out of her eyes with the back of her wrist. "For the last few weeks, of all the things I've thought through hundreds of times, this is the part that has bothered me the most."

"Do you mean since you saw Mad Dog at the Embassy Theatre?"

Jill nodded. "You saw the look on his face. All that shame and regret is still there. I never told you, but Mad Dog came to my house after the settlements were finalized. I was still so raw inside. I remember opening the door that day, seeing Mad Dog, and feeling like I wanted to hurt him."

"You weren't ready to face him, I'm sure."

Jill seemed to have made so much progress in finding peace. I didn't want her to digress now. Especially for an un-settled feeling she had about Mad Dog.

"It was more than that. I..." She folded herself into the cor-ner easy chair. "I hated him. There, that's the truth; I've said it aloud. Finally. I hated him. Mad Dog lived, and Ray died, and I hated him for that."

I pulled up a chair and sat across from Jill.

"When Mad Dog came to me, he tried to apologize. He said he knew Ray was a good man, and Ray should have been the one who lived and not him. I just stood there. I didn't say anything. I think he was looking to me for a release of some sort." Jill started to cry. I hadn't seen her cry for days.

"And what did you say to him?"

"I told him..." Jill swallowed and cried some more. "I told him I had nothing to say to him. I said he would have to live with what happened the same way I had to live with it."

She wiped her tears on her sleeve. "You know what? I'm embarrassed to admit this, but I was okay with that until the day I met you."

"The day you met me?"

She nodded. "It was something you said. You said that you

were the one who has enjoyed the reward of my husband's zeal because he saved those crazy orange trees."

For an instant I was really worried about Jill. I wasn't tracking with her logic. Maybe she was tipping off-center emotionally because of all the processing she'd been through during the past few weeks.

"When you said that, Kathy, I immediately thought of Mad Dog. I didn't want to think of him, but his face was right there in front of me. And as clear as we're talking now, I thought, 'Mad Dog's life is also the reward of my husband's zeal, and a human life matters more than a couple of trees.'"

I didn't know how to respond.

Jill drew in a deep breath. "At Ray's funeral the pastor read a verse from John in which Jesus said there's no greater love than for a man to lay down his life for his friend. When the pastor read that, everyone looked at Mad Dog, but I couldn't look at him. I still can't look at him. I don't hate him anymore. I feel something different for him, but it's not hate."

I blinked back the tears that had been brimming my eyelids and looked at the postcards fanned out inside the wooden bowl on the coffee table. The card on top was the picture of the Victorian woman from the museum in Sydney. She now stood in the center of Jill's living room, cradled by the bowl and holding a treasure in her hand.

"I don't know what to do," Jill said.

"Open your hand." I didn't know why I said that or what it meant.

"What?"

I tipped my head toward the postcard. "What do you have in your hand?"

Jill looked at her palm. "Nothing. Except a small callus

under my wedding band. That's all. Are you saying it's time for me to remove my wedding band?"

"No. I mean, I don't know. I was looking at the postcard, and that thought just popped into my head. I don't know what it's supposed to mean. I don't know what you're supposed to do."

I felt so foolish. *Why did I say that? Just because I inadvertently said something meaningful without knowing it the day I met Jill doesn't mean I'm a fountain of wisdom. But she's waiting for me to spout the next life-changing one-liner.*

"Jill, how about if we finish moving the furniture around, and then we can talk some more about this."

"I don't have anything else to say. I know it's awkward because Tony works for Mad Dog and you've known him all these years. That's why I kept this to myself for so long."

"I'm glad you got everything you're feeling out in the open. I just don't know what to do with it."

Jill rose, and with a slight shrug, she said, "Neither do I."

Twenty-one

On our final day of touch-ups to complete Jill's renovations, we talked Mr. Barry into bringing Dorothea over to see the changes I'd been telling her about. He pushed her wheelchair up the steps to the deck and into the living room.

From Dorothea's position in the middle of the room at renovation central, she used her pointer finger on her left hand to direct the final-day operations. I saw what Mr. Barry meant about the red nails. Those baby fireballs could grab your attention from all the way across the room. All it took was one wag of her index finger, and I hopped up to move a lamp or a chair a few inches to the right or left to satisfy our sweetest critic. Dorothea was a happy woman that day.

So was Jill.

Mr. Barry took Dorothea home in the late afternoon. We invited them to stay for dinner, but Dorothea had worn herself out giving directions. Tony had agreed to come over to Jill's with the lighting guy since the parasol light was the final detail that needed to be put in place. Jill offered to prepare dinner for the lighting guy in return and opened the invitation to Tony and me as well.

She and I went to work in her newly spruced-up kitchen. Jill had promised me she would make her favorite New Zealand lamb dish with her version of Pavlova if I'd make something American.

A few days earlier, Skyler had sent me a box of Cheerios as a joke. I brought the box with me to Jill's that day, but I hadn't shown it to her. All I said was that I had the first course covered. I also brought all the ingredients to make chocolate chip cookies from a recipe I knew by heart.

The weather was nice enough for us to have dinner on the front deck so, as soon as the cookies were in the oven with the timer set, I volunteered to set the patio table.

"Do you need salad plates?" Jill asked, trying to guess what I'd brought for the first course.

"No, soup bowls. And some milk. And maybe some sugar."

Jill grinned. If she had guessed my surprise, she was being gracious enough not to spoil my fun. Giving me what I needed, she sent me to the deck where I poured the happy treat into the bowls. Then, because no one was watching, I picked up one of the golden rings, held it between my fingers, and murmured, "My precious!"

Then I popped it in my mouth.

I would have performed my tribute at dinner, but I didn't know whom Tony was bringing from the studio with him. If it was a true Middle-earth kind of guy, I might be putting Tony's job in jeopardy. And that would not be good, since Tony still hadn't heard if he'd gotten the position on the next project.

I lit all the candles in the whimsical holder that circled the center of the patio table. That's when I noticed the wire that led up the center of the umbrella pole and spread out along the spokes with hundreds of twinkle lights.

Ten minutes later, I opened the front door. "Jill, can you come out here a minute?"

Jill arrived, drying her hands with a dishtowel. I plugged in a cord, and the twinkle lights inside the umbrella lit up—along with the blue and green laserlike light show.

"What did you do?"

I held up my two tools. "Never underestimate the power of a woman with a pair of wire cutters *and* a roll of duct tape!"

The studio van stopped at the bottom of the driveway.

"Good. The lighting guy and Tony should be able to fix this." Jill reached over to pull the plug before it started an electrical fire.

Lifting my head, I saw Tony coming up the driveway. Next to him was Mad Dog.

"Tony!"

Of all the people you could have chosen, why did you choose Mad Dog?

"It's okay." Jill stopped me before I pulled out a one-liner that I wouldn't be able to swallow later. "I asked Tony to bring him."

"You did?"

"Yes."

Jill looked calm, but I felt rattled. Mad Dog was the last person I thought she would ever want to see. Especially in her own home.

Mad Dog came up the steps and walked toward us on the deck. At first his head was down, but as he came closer, he cautiously glanced up at Jill. She met his gaze, and the two of them looked at each other. Not the way they had awkwardly glanced back and forth at the Embassy Theatre. This time they met each other eye to eye.

Jill took two steps toward Mad Dog. "The last time you stood here at my door, I told you I had nothing to say to you. I do have something to say to you now."

She lifted her chin and held out her open palms, as if offering the invisible treasure Mad Dog had once come seeking. Her voice was a whisper. "It's okay, Marcus. Really. I don't hold anything against you. Not anymore. I want you to have your life back. All of it."

Apparently while Jill and I had been renovating her home, God had been doing some renovating inside the home of her heart. Tonight was open house.

Mad Dog just nodded, but I saw a light in his eyes that I hadn't realized had gone out until it came back on.

With few words, the four of sat down to our bowls of Cheerios. I looked out at the sea and watched as the Southern Cross began to traverse the evening sky. God was filling His treasure chest with extravagant mercies; somewhere, on the other side of this planet, it was a new day.

Epilogue

Tony didn't get the position at Jackamond Studios, so we didn't stay for another three months. He actually finished his project ten days ahead of schedule. It was his gift to me, he said, so we could see more of Australia and New Zealand together before we had to fly back to California.

At first I took it hard that he didn't get the job extension. I had come to love New Zealand so much that I didn't want to leave. I told Tony that, and he asked me, "What do you love about New Zealand?"

I only had to think for a moment before I gave him the answer. "It's the people, it's the people, it's the people."

Dorothea cried when I kissed her good-bye. Her great big, blobby tears and all those deep-throated guttural sounds didn't scare me one bit when she tried to communicate. I told her I was going home so I could attend school to learn how to become a speech therapist for stroke victims. That's when Mr. Barry got blinky-eyed, too.

Tracey filled every empty corner of my packed luggage with bags of chocolate fish. "For all the times you need to reward yourself for doing a little sumthin' good," she said.

Mad Dog is back here in Los Angeles. He and Tony have worked together on two projects since their New Zealand days. Their most recent project won an Oscar. It wasn't the first Oscar won by a film Mad Dog worked on. But it was the first one he had worked on since he had become an unshakable God-follower.

In a concise manner, Tony said Mad Dog trusted Christ the night we stood on Jill's front deck. My husband had gotten into a complicated discussion with Mad Dog earlier that week at the studio about why God's Son had to come in after us because of our fall into sin. Mad Dog and Tony held opposite views until that moment when Jill stepped forward and gave Mad Dog the treasure she held in her hand. Then Mad Dog understood about extravagant sacrifices and the love attached to them.

Jill and I decided a week before Tony and I left that we didn't believe in saying good-bye to each other. She suggested we say *au revoir* instead. That's because she was listening to a French language program and ordering French movies to watch. We both knew that Paris would become a reality for her.

"And depending on which way around the globe this little free bird flies," Jill said, "I would estimate that a certain house next to two old orange trees is exactly halfway between here and Paris."

That was three years ago. Jill has been to Tustin to see me five times already. She's been to Paris three times and has two more grandbabies.

Her most recent visit was last month, and I think that's

what prompted me to write down our story. That and the fact that to celebrate Jill's visit, Tony strung a big hammock for us between the orange trees. "Ray's orange trees" we now call them.

Jill and I tottered out to the hammock the night she arrived, armed with a mound of comforters. We got ourselves balanced—a very important aspect of any form of art, including verbal scrapbooking. There, beneath a canopy of orange blossoms, we cut and pasted our favorite shared memories such as sipping mocha lattes at the Chocolate Fish, painting Jill's walls and Dorothea's red fingernails, the fallen lawn hobbit, the above-water ballet troupe, feeding the kangaroos, the lights on Sydney Harbor, and Evan the singing punter.

Then, because I'd waited a long time to do this, I sat up straight and said, "Jill, don't move! There's a lizard—"

I didn't have a chance to finish my joke before Jill turned the prank on me. In one motion the two of us were tumbled down under once more. This time it was only down under the emptied hammock, where we landed together on soft California orange grove soil.

We laughed until the neighbor's dog started to bark. Then, with all the comforters tucked around us, we settled into the best years of our friendship like two sassy mama birds swaying back and forth in a big, fluffy nest. We were at home with each other. No matter what side of the globe we were on. We both knew it would be that way the rest of our lives. And forever.

Discussion Questions

1. When she arrives in New Zealand, Kathleen finds herself without a close circle of friends for the first time in her life. Have you ever found yourself in a season of life without a single close girlfriend to share the journey with you? Did you go looking for one, or did one find you?

2. Why do you think Kathleen never took on the nickname "Kathy" before? Do you think she went back to "Kathleen" when she returned to California? Have you ever had a nickname that marked a significant change in your life?

3. Do you think Kathy would have agreed to drive a vintage truck in California, or did she jump at the chance just because she was in New Zealand? Have you ever found it easier to try a new experience when you're in a brand-new place?

4. Did Kathy seem like the kind of woman who was given to extreme mood swings the way Tony observed after she knocked over the hobbit? Or were the emotional dips and highs all part of the adjustments she had to make in order to find her place in Wellington?

5. Have you ever felt like you were eighteen again? What experience prompted that feeling?

6. Why was it hard for Jill to talk about Ray with Kathy? Do you think Kathy did the right thing to simply listen, or should she have asked more questions about Ray earlier?

7. What did you observe about the ways Jill processed her grief? Have you experienced grief in your life? If so, how did you process it?

8. How do you feel when you are around people like Dorothea? Have you ever known someone like Mr. Barry?

9. Why do you think it was important for Jill and Kathy to get away and have a little adventure in Christchurch? How did that experience bond their friendship? How have adventures bonded some of your friendships?

10. Have you ever been amazed by an animal the way Kathy was enraptured by the kangaroo? What was it, and how did it affect you?

11. How would you have answered the question Jill asked Kathy: "Do you think God is fair?"

12. What did Jill mean when she told Mad Dog she wanted him to have all of his life back?

13. How did Jill and Kathy both receive and express "extravagant love"? How do you see that kind of extravagant love showing up in your life?

14. When they see the painting of the Victorian woman on the shore, Jill tells Kathy that she holds a treasure in her hand, although she doesn't yet know what it is. It later turns out to be forgiveness for Mad Dog. What unrecognized treasure do you hold in your hand?

More Sisterchick Adventures
by
ROBIN JONES GUNN

SISTERCHICK n.: a friend who shares the deepest
wonders of your heart, loves you like a sister, and
provides a reality check when you're being a brat.

SISTERCHICKS ON THE LOOSE

Zany antics abound when best friends Sharon and
Penny take off on a midlife adventure to Finland,
returning home with a new view of God and a new
zest for life.

1-59052-198-6

SISTERCHICKS DO THE HULA

It'll take more than an unexpected stowaway to keep
two middle-aged sisterchicks from reliving their college years with a little Waikiki wackiness—and learning to hula for the first time.

1-59052-226-5

SISTERCHICKS IN SOMBREROS

Two Canadian sisters embark on a journey to claim
their inheritance—beachfront property in Mexico—
not expecting so many bizarre, wacky problems! But
they're nothing a little coconut cake can't cure...

1-59052-229-X

a sisterchicks® novel

THE GLENBROOKE SERIES
by Robin Jones Gunn

Come to Glenbrooke…a quiet place where souls are refreshed.

SECRETS *Glenbrooke Series #1*
Beginning her new life in a small Oregon town, high school English teacher Jessica Morgan tries desperately to hide the details of her past.

1-59052-240-0

WHISPERS *Glenbrooke Series #2*
Teri went to Maui hoping to start a relationship with one special man. But romance becomes much more complicated when she finds herself pursued by three.

1-59052-192-7

ECHOES *Glenbrooke Series #3*
Lauren Phillips "connects" on the Internet with a man known only as "K.C." Is she willing to risk everything…including another broken heart?

1-59052-193-5

SUNSETS *Glenbrooke Series #4*
Alissa loves her new job as a Pasadena travel agent. Will an abrupt meeting with a stranger in an espresso shop leave her feeling that all men are like the one she's been hurt by recently?

1-59052-238-9

CLOUDS *Glenbrooke Series #5*
After Shelly Graham and her old boyfriend cross paths in Germany, both must face the truth about their feelings.

1-59052-230-3

WATERFALLS *Glenbrooke Series #6*
Meri thinks she's finally met the man of her dreams...until she finds out he's movie star Jacob Wilde, promptly puts her foot in her mouth, and ruins everything.

1-59052-231-1

WOODLANDS *Glenbrooke Series #7*
Leah Hudson has the gift of giving, but questions her own motives, and God's purposes, when she meets a man she prays will love her just for herself.

1-59052-237-0

WILDFLOWERS *Glenbrooke Series #8*
Genevieve Ahrens has invested lots of time and money in renovating the Wildflowers Café. Now her heart needs the same attention.

1-59052-239-7